D1213337

MATHEMATICAL TECHNIQUES OF OPERATIONAL RESEARCH

ADIWES INTERNATIONAL SERIES

MATHEMATICAL TECHNIQUES of OPERATIONAL RESEARCH

by

L. S. GODDARD

Professor of Mathematics in the University of Tasmania

1963

PERGAMON PRESS

OXFORD · LONDON · NEW YORK · PARIS

ADDISON-WESLEY PUBLISHING COMPANY, INC.

READING, MASSACHUSETTS · PALO ALTO · LONDON

U.S.A. Edition distributed by
ADDISON-WESLEY PUBLISHING COMPANY, INC.
READING, MASSACHUSETTS · PALO ALTO · LONDON

PERGAMON PRESS
International Series of Monographs on
PURE AND APPLIED MATHEMATICS
Volume 38

Library of Congress Card Number 62-11551

Set in Times New Roman 10 on 12 point and printed in Poland
PWN – DUAM

Z.G.M.K. – Poznań

CONTENTS

PREFACE

OPERATIONAL research has carved out a place for itself and become identified as a subject in its own right only in recent years. The impetus has been the need for improved industrial efficiency. Still more recently relatively advanced mathematical models and techniques have been introduced into the subject, and by now the mathematician contemplating entry into the O.R. field needs a somewhat formidable array of mathematical tools. This book is concerned with these tools and the reader will observe that a wide variety of branches of mathematics are drawn upon, such as analysis, linear algebra, special functions, the theory of probability and combinatorial analysis.

In Chapter I the basic mathematical ideas used in later chapters are summarized. It is not surprising, in view of practical applications in an uncertain world, that extensive use is made of the theory of probability. Hence a major part of the chapter is concerned with this subject.

Chapters II and III are given to accounts of linear programming, including the special cases of transportation and assignment. Various applications are discussed, including, for example, the Trim Problem, but no attempt is made to discuss problems of numerical analysis related to linear programming since this subject is too extensive for a general book of this kind.

In Chapters IV and V the theory of queues is presented. This, of course, is an extensive and rapidly growing theory, and there is no question of the account being complete. But the reader is introduced to the general stationary properties of the single-channel queue, and of simple queues in series and in parallel. Some transient properties of queues are also discussed.

Machine Interference, which is an aspect of queueing theory, is treated in Chapter VI, and Chapter VII deals with the important and mathematically rather difficult subject of Stock Control (or Inventory Theory). Here, for the most part, attention is concentrated on discrete rather than continuous problems, that is, situations where the demands made upon a stock are for discrete amounts (which may perhaps be made at discrete intervals of time). In such a case considerable use may be made of probability generating functions, and the resulting mathematical treatment is somewhat easier.

This book is designed for two classes of readers. It is primarily for the graduate mathematician contemplating a career in operational research, and although the mathematics is not "proved" at every stage (for example, König's theorem, used in the Hungarian method for solving the assignment problem, is only stated and then used) an attempt has been made to make the account sufficiently complete for the reader to be able to grasp the essential features of the tools which are introduced. It is hoped however that the book will also be consulted by managers and industrial leaders who want to learn something about what O.R. is and what it can do. For such readers the important feature upon which attention should be concentrated is not the mathematical detail but the types of models (of real situations) which lend themselves to a mathematical treatment.

I wish to thank Mr. A. M. Hasofer, Lecturer in Mathematics in the University of Tasmania, for valuable help in the preparation of Chapters I and VII and for considerable assistance in proof reading. I would also like to acknowledge my debt to the Operations Research Society of America, for permission to reproduce graphs from some of the papers published in the Journal of the Society during the years 1955–7.

L. S. GODDARD

CHAPTER I

MATHEMATICAL INTRODUCTION

A great deal of operational research has been successfully carried out with practically nothing beyond school arithmetic and algebra. The essence of the matter in the early days was the construction of models which involved only the simplest mathematics, and happily these were sufficiently robust to have some application to the practical problems at hand. But, with the first flush of success over, the model makers have become increasingly concerned with models which depend heavily upon mathematics. And one of the features of operational research to-day is that the mathematical methods employed belong to a surprisingly diverse range of ideas. Because of this an outline is given in this chapter of some of the methods to be used in later chapters. The material is presented under the three headings Algebra, Analysis and Probability. We lean heavily upon the methods of probability theory, but it is emphasized that we shall not be concerned with such topics as the statistical analysis of practical numerical data, nor with the statistical design of experiments. For these and related matters the reader is referred to some of the numerous books on industrial and applied statistics.

ALGEBRA

1. Matrices and vectors

In Chapters II and III use will be made of the concepts of vector and matrix. A *vector* is set a of numbers, $u_1, u_2, \ldots, u_n$, where n may be finite or infinite. It is supposed that the numbers are taken in a definite order, that is, u_1 first, u_2 second, and so on. The vector is then referred to as an *ordered* set; and the numbers u_1,

$u_2, ...,$ are called the *components* of the vector. In much of the theory and practical usage of vectors attention is concentrated on the notion of a vector as a single entity, that is, on the set of components, as a set, and for this reason it is necessary to have a symbol to denote the set. Also it is necessary to distinguish between the set, $u_1, u_2, ..., u_n$, written as a row, and the same set written as a column. Let $\mathbf{u}$ denote the vector, written as a column and let $\mathbf{u}'$ be the same vector written as a row ($\mathbf{u}'$ is called the transpose of $\mathbf{u}$). If we wish to indicate components we write $\mathbf{u} = \{u_1, ..., u_n\}$ and $\mathbf{u}' = (u_1, ..., u_n)$. We shall adopt this convention: a symbol, if it denotes a vector, means a column vector; if the corresponding row vector is intended then a prime (′) is attached to the symbol.

A *matrix*, A, is most conveniently introduced as an array of mn numbers, a_{ij}, called the *elements* of A, where m and n are given positive integers (with possibly m or n or both infinite). We write

$$A = \begin{pmatrix} a_{11}, & ..., & a_{1n} \\ \vdots & & \vdots \\ \vdots & & \vdots \\ \vdots & & \vdots \\ a_{m1}, & ..., & a_{mn} \end{pmatrix},$$

if we wish to display the elements of A. Note that the suffix i refers to a row and the suffix j to a column, so that a_{ij} is the element in the ith row and j^{th} column, where $i = 1, 2, ..., m$, and $j = 1, 2, ..., n$. It is clear that A may be regarded as an ordered set of n column vectors, or m row vectors, the jth column vector, for example, being $\{a_{1j}, a_{2j}, ..., a_{mj}\}$. We refer to A as an $m \times n$ matrix, and, in the case where $m = n$, A is said to be square and of order n. We shall normally only be concerned with square matrices.

Let A and B be square matrices, of the same order n, and let $A = (a_{ij})$, $B = (b_{ij})$. Addition, subtraction and multiplication are defined thus:

$$C = (c_{ij}) = A \pm B, \quad D = (d_{ij}) = AB,$$

where

$$c_{ij} = a_{ij} \pm b_{ij}, \quad d_{ij} = \sum_{k=1}^{n} a_{ik} b_{kj}.$$

It is to be noticed that the definition of the product AB involves the sum of the products of corresponding elements of a row vector and a column vector. This leads to a new definition.

Scalar product

The scalar product of two (column) vectors $\mathbf{u}$ and $\mathbf{v}$ of the same length is the sum

$$\mathbf{u}'\,\mathbf{v} = (u_1, ..., u_n)\,\{v_1, ..., v_n\} = \sum_{i=1}^{n} u_i v_i \,.$$

Note that $\mathbf{u}'\,\mathbf{v} = \mathbf{v}'\,\mathbf{u}$.

2. Systems of linear equations

In some problems, particularly those of linear programming, it is necessary to solve a system of linear equations in $x_1, ..., x_n$, say. A linear equation is one of the form

$$a_1x_1 + a_2x_2 + ... + a_nx_n = c\,,$$

where the $a_1, ..., a_n$ and c are given numbers. The equation may be written in the condensed form,

$$\mathbf{a}'\,\mathbf{x} = c\,,$$

where $\mathbf{a} = \{a_1, ..., a_n\}$, $\mathbf{x} = \{x_1, ..., x_n\}$, and likewise a system of m linear equations,

$$a_{11}x_1 + ... + a_{1n}x_n = c_1\,,$$
$$\cdots\cdots\cdots\cdots\cdots\cdots$$
$$a_{m1}x_1 + ... + a_{mn}x_n = c_n\,,$$

may be written in the form,

$$A\,\mathbf{x} = \mathbf{c}\,,$$

where A is the $m \times n$ matrix (a_{ij}), $x = \{x_1, ..., x_n\}$, $c = \{c_1, ..., c_n\}$. It may be shown that the system has a solution if $m < n$, but if $m \geqslant n$, there is a solution only if certain conditions are satisfied. These conditions may be expressed most conveniently in terms of the notion of linear dependence, which is now introduced.

Linear dependence of vectors

Let $\mathbf{u}_1, \mathbf{u}_2, ..., \mathbf{u}_r$ be a set of r (column) vectors, each of length n. The vectors are said to be linearly dependent if there exists a set of scalars, $c_1, ..., c_r$, not all zero, such that,

$$c_1\mathbf{u}_1 + ... + c_r\mathbf{u}_r = 0 .$$

Otherwise, the vectors are said to be *linearly independent*. It is to be noted that any $n + 1$ vectors of length n are linearly dependent, since the equations

$$\lambda_1\mathbf{u}_1 + ... + \lambda_{n+1}\mathbf{u}_{n+1} = 0 ,$$

form a system of n equations for the $n + 1$ unknowns $\lambda_1, ..., \lambda_{n+1}$, and there is always a solution since the number of equations is less than the number of unknowns.

To return to the system,

$$A\mathbf{x} = \mathbf{c} ,$$

of m equations in the n unknowns, $x_1, ..., x_n$ we shall state, but not prove, the following theorem on the condition for a solution.

THEOREM 1: The system $A\mathbf{x} = \mathbf{c}$ where A is $m \times n$, $m \geqslant n$, and $\mathbf{c} \neq 0$, has a solution if and only if the maximum number of linearly independent columns (or rows) of the matrices A and $[A, \mathbf{c}]$ are the same, where $[A, \mathbf{c}]$ is the matrix obtained from A by adjoining the column $\mathbf{c}$.

Regarding uniqueness of the solution we can state

THEOREM 2: The system $A\mathbf{x} = \mathbf{c}$, where $m = n$ (that is A is square of order n), and $\mathbf{c} \neq 0$, has a unique solution if and only if the columns (or rows) of A are linearly independent.

In the case where $m < n$, suppose that there are m columns of A which are linearly independent, and let the unknowns x_1, ..., x_n be so numbered that these m columns consist of the first m. The equations $A\mathbf{x} = \mathbf{c}$ may be written in the form

$$x_1P_1 + x_2P_2 + ... + x_nP_n = \mathbf{c} ,$$

where $P_1, P_2, ..., P_n$ are the columns of A, and $P_1, ..., P_m$ are then linearly independent. By writing the system in the form,

$$x_1P_1 + ... + x_mP_m = \mathbf{c} - x_{m+1}P_{m+1} - ... - x_nP_n ,$$

and using Theorem 2 we see that there is a family of solutions of the system $A\mathbf{x} = \mathbf{c}$, the family depending on $x_{m+1}, ..., x_n$ which, since they may take any values, are to be regarded as $n - m$ arbitrary parameters. Use will be made of this family of solutions in Chapter II, especially in the discussion of the Simplex Method of linear programming.

ANALYSIS

3. Introduction

It will be assumed that the reader is familiar with the notion of continuity of a function, $f(x)$, and with the ordinary (Riemann) definition of the integral of $f(x)$ over some given range (a, b) of x, throughout which $f(x)$ is continuous. However, in the theory of probability set out in the next section, it is necessary to extend the notion of a function to include the possibility of a number (possibly an infinite number) of discontinuities, with finite jumps in the value of the function at the points of discontinuity. Thus, suppose $f(x)$ is defined by

$$f(x) = \begin{cases} g(x) & (a < x < c) \\ h(x) & (c < x < b) \end{cases}$$

where $g(x)$ is continuous in (a, c) and $h(x)$ is continuous in (c, b), and

$$h(c) - g(c) = j > 0\,.$$

The graph of $f(x)$ then shows a jump of magnitude j at $x = c$ as shown in Fig. 1; $f(x)$ is said to display a finite discontinuity,

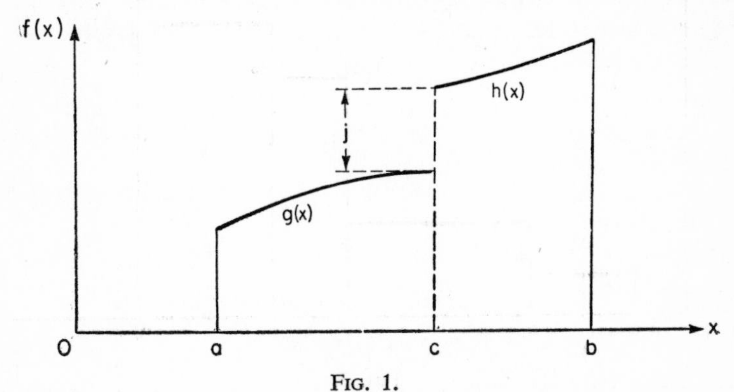

FIG. 1.

with a jump, j, in the value of $f(x)$, at $x = c$. In practice it is sufficient to confine attention to functions $f(x)$ which are never decreasing, that is, where $f(x_2) \geqslant f(x_1)$ if $x_2 > x_1$, and in this case it is clear that the graph of $f(x)$ consists of a number of continuous arcs, as for example in Fig. 2.

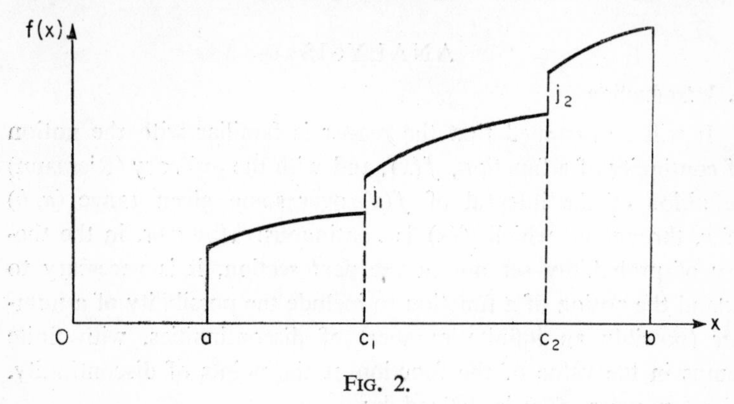

FIG. 2.

The extreme case occurs where these arcs are segments of straight lines parallel to the x-axis, as shown in Fig. 3, and in this case $f(x)$ is called a step-function. This case is particularly important since (see the next section) $f(x)$ may then be the distribution function of a discrete probability distribution.

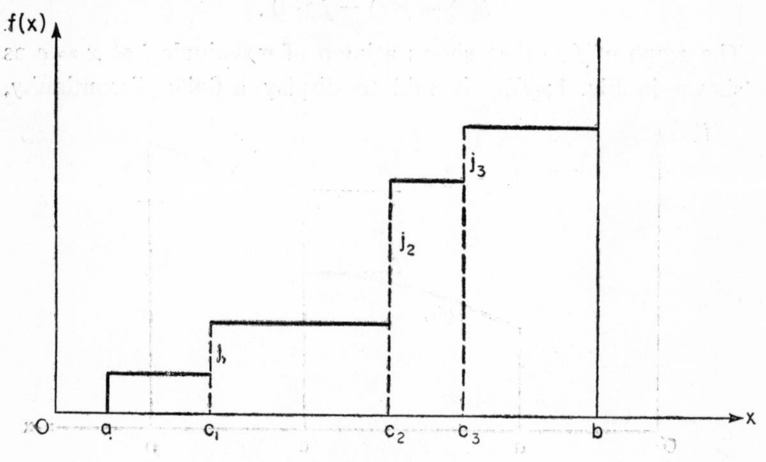

FIG. 3.

4. The Stieltjes' integral

Let $F(x)$ be a function which is never decreasing in the interval (a, b), and let $u(x)$ be continuous in this interval. Divide the interval by means of the points $x = x_i (i = 0, ..., n)$, where

$$a = x_0 < x_1 < x_2 < ... < x_{n-1} < x_n = b ,$$

into n intervals, and in each of these sub-intervals take an arbitrary point, $x = y_i$, so that

$$x_i < y_i < x_{i+1} .$$

Consider the sum,

$$\sum_{i=0}^{n-1} u(y_i) [F(x_{i+1}) - F(x_i)] .$$

It may be shown that, as $n \longrightarrow \infty$ in such a way that the length of each sub-interval tends to zero, this sum approaches a certain limit. We call this limit the Stieltjes' integral of $u(x)$ with respect to $F(x)$, and write it in the form J, where

$$J = \int_a^b u(x) \mathrm{d}F(x) .$$

Examples: (i) If $F(x)$ has discontinuities at $x = c_i (i = 1, ..., n)$, with a jump j_i at $x = c_i$, and if $F(x) = \varphi_i(x)$ in the interval (c_i, c_{i+1}), where $\varphi_i(x)$ is differentiable in this interval, then

$$J = \sum_{i=0}^{n} \int_{c_i}^{c_{i+1}} u(x) \varphi_i'(x) \, \mathrm{d}x + \sum_{i=1}^{n} g(c_i) j_i ,$$

where $c_0 = a$, $c_{n+1} = b$.

(ii) If $F(x)$ is a step function, defined on the interval $(0, \infty)$, with a jump p_i at $x = c_i$ $(i = 1, 2, ..., \infty)$, then

$$J = \int_0^\infty u(x) \mathrm{d}F(x) = \sum_{i=1}^{\infty} u(c_i) p_i ,$$

provided the series converges.

5. The Dirac delta function

Consider the function $F(x)$ defined by

$$F(x) = \begin{cases} 0 & (x < \mu) \\ 1 & (x > \mu) , \end{cases}$$

with a unit jump at $x = \mu$. Clearly, for any continuous function, $f(x)$,

$$J = \int_0^\infty f(x)\mathrm{d}F(x) = f(\mu)\,.$$

The function $F(x)$, because of the discontinuity, has no derivative at $x = \mu$. However, as Dirac found in the development of his theory of quantum mechanics (2), it is desirable to modify the function, so that a derivative does exist. Let us then, without paying attention to mathematical rigour, approximate $F(x)$ by a continuous function $F^*(x)$ which is very nearly zero for $x < \mu$, and very nearly 1 for $x > \mu$. Then $\mathrm{d}F^*(x)/\mathrm{d}x$ is very nearly zero for $x \neq \mu$ and has a very large value for $x = \mu$. It is the limit of this function, $\mathrm{d}F^*(x)/\mathrm{d}x$, as $F^*(x) \longrightarrow F(x)$, which is called the Dirac delta function, $\delta(x - \mu)$. Formally, $\delta(x - \mu)$ is defined by:

$$\delta(x - \mu) = \begin{cases} 0 \ (x \neq \mu) \\ \infty \ (x = \mu) \end{cases}$$

and

$$\int_0^\infty \delta(x - \mu)\,\mathrm{d}x = 1\,.$$

From the value of J above, it is clear that for any function $f(x)$, continuous at $x = \mu$,

$$\int_0^\infty f(x)\,\delta(x - \mu)\,\mathrm{d}x = f(\mu)\,.$$

6. Bessel functions

We shall only summarize here the definition and properties of Bessel functions which are required for this book. Consider the equation

$$x^2\mathrm{d}^2y/\mathrm{d}x^2 + x\mathrm{d}y/\mathrm{d}x + (x^2 - n^2)\,y = 0\,,$$

where n is a positive integer. It may easily be shown that one solution is $J_n(x)$, where

$$J_n(x) = \sum_{s=0}^{\infty} \frac{(-1)^s(\frac{1}{2}x)^{n+2s}}{s!\,(n+s)!}\,.$$

This function is called the *Bessel function of the first kind of order n.* By referring to one of the many books on Bessel Functions the reader will find that $J_n(x)$ is oscillatory and, for large x, approximates to a trigonometric function with zeros occurring at intervals of approximately π.

We shall not need $J_n(x)$ directly, but in Chapter IV on the theory of queueing, the following modification of $J_n(x)$ is used. Let

$$I_n(x) = J_n(ix)/i^n = \sum_{s=0}^{\infty} \frac{(\frac{1}{2}x)^{n+2s}}{s!(n+s)!},$$

where $i = \sqrt{(-1)}$. This function, $I_n(x)$, is called the *modified Bessel Function of the first kind of order n.* It differs from $J_n(x)$ in that it is not oscillatory, but is increasing everywhere with x, and $I_n(0) = 0$ if $n > 0$. It will be useful to have available the standard formula:

$$n \int_0^{\infty} e^{-vx} I_n(x) \frac{dx}{x} = \frac{1}{\{v + \sqrt{(v^2 - 1)}\}^n},$$

where n is a positive integer.

7. The incomplete gamma function

This is the function $I(u, k)$, defined by

$$I(u, k) = \frac{1}{k!} \int_0^{u\sqrt{(k+1)}} e^{-x} x^k \, dx,$$

where k is a positive integer and $u > 0$. It has been extensively tabulated by Pearson (6).

In Chapter VI, on Machine Interference, we shall have occasion to express in terms of $I(u, p)$ the polynomial, y_m, where

$$y_m = 1 + (m-1)p + (m-1)(m-2)p^2 + \ldots + (m-1)!\,p^{m-1},$$

m being a positive integer. It is easy to show that

$$y_m = e^{1/p}(m-1)!\,p^{m-1}\left[1 - e^{-1/p}\left(\frac{1}{m!\,p^m} + \frac{1}{(m+1)!\,p^{m+1}} + \ldots\right)\right],$$

and, by repeated integration by parts, that

$$\frac{1}{(m-1)!}\int_0^z e^{-x}\,x^{m-1}\,dx = e^{-z}\left(\frac{z^m}{m!}+\frac{z^{m+1}}{(m+1)!}+\dots\right).$$

Hence, putting $z = 1/p$, we have

$$y_m = e^{1/p}\,(m-1)!\,p^{m-1}\,[1 - I\{1/p\sqrt{m},\quad m-1\}].$$

8. Integral equations

An integral equation is one involving an unknown function under the integral sign. The only type which arises in this book is of the form,

$$f(x) = \int_0^\infty k(x-y)\,f(y)dy \qquad (0 < x < \infty)$$

which is said to be of the Wiener–Hopf type because of its discussion by Wiener and Hopf (8) in 1931. A general solution may be given (7), but we shall not make use of this. Instead, in Chapter IV, on the theory of queueing, use will be made of the solution by Lindley (4), for the equation

$$F(x) = \int_0^{x+1} k(x-y+1)\,F(y)\,dy\,.$$

By writing $x = z - 1$, $y = z - u$, this becomes

$$F(z-1) = \int_0^z k\,(u)\,F(z-u)\,du\,.$$

In the particular case where $k(u)$ is of the form,

$$k(u) = au^{n-1}\,e^{-bu}\,,$$

where a and b are positive constants and n is a positive integer, Lindley showed that there is a solution of the form,

$$F(z) = 1 + \sum_{i=1}^{n} c_i\,e^{\lambda_i z}\,,$$

where $\lambda_1, ..., \lambda_n$ are the (complex) roots of the transcendental equation, $(1 + b\lambda)^n = e^\lambda$, and $c_1, ..., c_n$ are constants (involving $\lambda_1, ..., \lambda_n$). For the details the reader is referred to Lindley's paper or to Chapter IV, p. 110.

9. The Laplace transform

Let t be a positive real variable, and s a complex variable with real part $R(s)$. For the function, $f(t)$, the *Laplace transform* of $f(t)$, is defined to be $F(s)$ where

$$F(s) = \int_0^\infty e^{-st} f(t) \, dt , \qquad R(s) > 0 .$$

If $F(s)$ is given, and it is desired to find $f(t)$, an inversion formula is available, namely,

$$f(t) = \frac{1}{2\pi i} \int_{c-i\infty}^{c+i\infty} e^{st} F(s) \, ds ,$$

where the line of integration is to the right of all singularities of $F(s)$. However, for the reader unacquainted with the theory of the functions of a complex variable, there are two consolations. Firstly, there exist several dictionaries of Laplace transforms, for use in any given case where the inverse is desired (see, for example, Refs. 3,5). Secondly, for the purposes of this book it is found that $f(t)$ is generally not required but instead the expansion of $F(s)$ as a power series in s. This will be discussed in the next section, on the theory of probability, where it frequently happens that it is easier to find the Laplace transform of a probability distribution rather than the distribution itself.

PROBABILITY

10. Introduction

The definition of probability has been set up on a mathematical basis in various ways, and there are philosophical difficulties involved in the definition. We propose to ignore these in this book, and to use a calculus of probability based upon the classical definition of the probability of occurrence of an event E as the relative frequency with which it occurs in a very large number of trials. By the word "trial" is meant some action, or experiment, in a given class of possible actions. For example, suppose that we observe the cars which cross a given line on a road in a traffic stream. Let the cars be of n possible types, say $T_1, ..., T_n$, and let a "trial" consist of the observation of the type of a car as it crosses the line. If N cars are observed let N_i be the number observed to be of type T_i, so that $N_1 + ... + N_n = N$. Then, if C is a car, the probability of the event "C is of type T_i" is defined to be p_i where

$$p_i = \lim_{N \to \infty} (N_i/N) ,$$

assuming that this limit almost always exists. It is obvious that the probability thus defined is a number between 0 and 1, and that $p_1 + p_2 + ... + p_n = 1$.

The reader should be aware of another notation which is frequently used. Let E_i be the event "C is of type T_i" so that the possible events are $E_1, ..., E_n$. It is customary to write $P(E_i)$ for the probability of the event E_i, and then

$$P(E_1) + P(E_2) + ... + P(E_n) = 1 .$$

We now come to the idea of compounding of events. If A and B are two events, with probabilities $P(A)$ and $P(B)$, we consider two new events:

(i) the event A or B, and (ii) the event A and B. In case (i) denote the event by $A + B$ and in case (ii) by AB. We call $A + B$ the *union* of A and B, and AB the *intersection* of A and B. The problem is to find $P(A + B)$ and $P(AB)$. For this purpose consider the above example of cars crossing a line, and suppose that some of the cars are red. If C denotes a car, let

A be the event "C is of type T_i",
B be the event "C is red".

Suppose that, on observing N cars, it is found that N_i are of type T_i, N_r are red, N_{ri} are red and of type T_i, so that

$$P(A) = N_i/N , \quad P(B) = N_r/N ,$$

where, here and below, we suppose that in any ratio which gives a probability the limit as $N \to \infty$ is taken. Now AB means the event "C is red and of type T_i", so that $P(AB) = N_{ri}/N$. The event $A + B$ means "C is red or of type T_i", and the number of cars possessing this property is clearly $N_r + N_i - N_{ri}$. Hence

$$P(A + B) = (N_i + N_r - N_{ri})/N = P(A) + P(B) - P(AB) .$$

This is a fundamental formula, valid for any two events A and B, linking the probabilities of the union and intersection of the events.

Suppose now that no cars of type T_i are red, but that there are possibly red cars of other types. Then the occurrence of the event A (that is, that "C is of type T_i") excludes the possibility of the occurrence of the event B (that is, that "C is red"), and vice versa. We say that A and B are *mutually exclusive events*. In this case, since $N_{ri} = 0$, we clearly have $P(AB) = 0$ and

$$P(A + B) = P(A) + P(B) .$$

11. Conditional probability

It frequently happens that the certain occurrence of one event affects the probability of occurrence of another event. For example, in the above case, if it is known that a car C is red, then the probability that C is of type T_i is N_{ri}/N_r and this is different from $P(A)$ which is N_i/N. We call the former a *conditional* probability, and write $P(A|B)$ for the probability of A, conditional on B having occurred. Thus,

$$P(A|B) = \frac{N_{ri}}{N_r} = \frac{N_{ri}}{N} \bigg/ \frac{N_r}{N} = \frac{P(AB)}{P(B)} ,$$

that is

$$P(AB) = P(A|B)\, P(B) .$$

It may similarly be shown that

$$P(AB) = P(B|A)\, P(A) ,$$

and these results are also fundamental in the theory of probability.

Suppose now that we make two extended observations on the cars passing the line:

(i) observe the relative frequency, N_i/N, of cars of type T_i,

(ii) observe, amongst all of the N_r red cars only, the relative frequency N_{ri}/N_r of cars of type T_i.

If these two frequencies are the same, that is if

$$N_i/N = N_{ri}/N_r ,$$

then the event A, "C is of type T_i", is *independent* of the event B, "C is red", in the sense that whether a car is of type T_i does not depend in any way on whether it is red. In this case, we have

$$P(A|B) = N_{ri}/N_r = N_i/N = P(A)$$

and the above formula for $P(AB)$ becomes

$$P(AB) = P(A)\,P(B) ,$$

that is, in the case of independent events A and B, the probability of both A and B occurring is the product of the probabilities of A and of B.

There is another formula, relating to conditional probability which we shall find useful. In the above example of cars crossing a line, the events $E_1, ..., E_n$, where E_i means "C is of type T_i", exhaust all the possibilities, for a car is certainly of one of the n types. If we consider another event, say "C is red", then it is clear that this is the same as the event "C is red and of type T_1, or C is red and of type T_2, or ... C is red and of type T_n". In symbols this is expressed thus:

$$B = BE_1 + BE_2 + ... + BE_n ,$$

where B denotes, as before, the event "C is red". Since BE_1, ..., BE_n, are mutually exclusive, we have

$$P(B) = P(BE_1) + P(BE_2) + ... + P(BE_n) ,$$

and, for each intersection, BE_i, we have

$$P(BE_i) = P(B|E_i)\,P(E_i) .$$

Thus

$$P(B) = \sum_{i=1}^{n}{}' P(B|E_i)\, P(E_i)\,.$$

This formula may be verified directly by observing that

$$P(B|E_i) = N_{ri}/N_i, \quad P(E_i) = N_i/N, \quad P(B) = N_r/N\,,$$

and $N_r = N_{r1} + N_{r2} + \ldots + N_{rn}$. It may be stated generally as *the theorem of total probability:*

If $E_1, \ldots, E_n$ is a set of mutually exclusive events and it is certain that one occurs, and if A is any other event then

$$P(A) = \sum_{i=1}^{n}{}' P(A|E_i)\, P(E_i)\,.$$

It is frequently useful in cases where the conditional probabilities $P(A|E_i)$ may be evaluated more easily than the value of $P(A)$ directly. For an application in a continuous case the reader is referred to the section below on the addition of random variables.

12. Random variables and probability distributions

The notion of a random variable arises when we attempt to measure some attribute or aspect of an experiment which, it is supposed, may be repeated a very large number of times. An example is the variable demand for petrol by a sequence of customers at a petrol station. The "experiment" is the demand, and the "attribute" measured is the size of the demand. However many customers have bought petrol in the past, the owner of the station cannot say with certainty what the demand of the next customer will be. The size, x, of the demand is called a *random variable*, and it is to be understood that the value of x in any one trial, is determined by chance.

The possible values of x may be taken from a finite or (theoretically) infinite range, R. We consider two cases:

(i) R is the set of positive integers, with or without zero,

(ii) R is the continuous interval $(0, \infty)$.

In case (i), Let

$$P(x = n) = p_n \quad (n = 0, 1, 2, ..., \infty)$$

that is, p_n is the probability that the value of x in a single trial is n. We call the sequence $(p_0, p_1, ...)$ a *probability density distribution.*

In case (ii), consider an interval du between u and $u +$ du. Let

$$P(u < x < u + \mathrm{d}u) = f(u)\,\mathrm{d}u \quad (0 < u < \infty)$$

that is, $f(u)$ du is the probability that x has a value in the interval $(u, u + \mathrm{d}u)$. The function $f(u)$ is also called a probability density distribution. To distinguish between the two cases the distribution is said to be *discrete* in case (i) and *continuous* in case (ii). Note that in either case the sum of the probabilities taken over the complete range is 1, that is,

$$\sum_{i=0}^{\infty} p_i = 1\,, \quad \int_0^{\infty} f(u)\,\mathrm{d}u = 1\,,$$

where it is assumed that $f(u)$ is integrable.

It is very important to distinguish between the probability density distribution and what is called the *probability distribution*, or, more accurately, the *cumulative probability distribution.* The latter is a function, $F(u)$, specifying the probability that x does not exceed a given value, u, that is, $F(u) = P(x \leqslant u)$. In the discrete case, if $u = n$, we have

$$F(n) = P(x \leqslant n) = \sum_{i=0}^{n} p_i\,,$$

while in the continuous case,

$$F(u) = P(x \leqslant u) = \int_0^{u} f(t)\,dt\,.$$

It is to be particularly noticed that $F(n)$ and $F(u)$ are non-decreasing functions of n and u, with the properties, $F(0) = 0$ (if $p_0 = 0$), $F(\infty) = 1$. It is important to be able to pass to the density distribution, given the probability distribution. In the discrete case we have, at once, $p_n = F(n) - F(n-1)$, but the continuous case demands more attention. If $F(u)$ is given as a *differentiable* function, then we have

$$f(u) = \mathrm{d}\, F(u)/\mathrm{d}u\,,$$

but, $F(u)$ may not be differentiable, or it may have differentiable and non-differentiable components. Consider, for example, the simple case where it is *certain* that x has the value a in every trial. Then $F(u)$ is a step function satisfying

$$F(u) = 0 \quad (u < a), \qquad F(u) = 1 \quad (u > a)\,,$$

and the probability density function is the Dirac δ-function, $\delta(u-a)$, introduced in the previous section on Analysis. As an example of a distribution with continuous and discontinuous components, consider a random variable, x, such that

$$P(0 < x \leqslant u) = F(u) \quad (u > 0)$$

and

$$P(x = 0) = p_0\,.$$

Then the probability density function, $f(u)$, is given by

$$f(u) = \mathrm{d}F(u)/\mathrm{d}u + p_0\delta(u)\,.$$

Such a case arises in Chapter IV, § 6. Note that, since

$$\int_0^\infty f(u)\,\mathrm{d}u = 1\,, \quad \text{we must have} \quad F(\infty) = 1 - p_0\,.$$

The Moments of a Distribution. The rth moment of the discrete distribution, where $P(x = n) = p_n$, is defined to be μ_r, where

$$\mu_r = \sum_{n=0}^{\infty} p_n\, n^r \qquad (r = 1, 2, 3, \ldots)\,.$$

In the case of a continuous distribution, with density function $f(u)$, the rth moment is defined by

$$\mu_r = \int_0^\infty u^r f(u)\,\mathrm{d}u\,,$$

while, in the general case of a distribution with continuous and discontinuous components the definition is

$$\mu_r = \int_0^\infty u^r \, \mathrm{d}\, F(u) \,,$$

where this is a Stieltjes' integral and $F(u)$ is the distribution function. This case, of course, includes the previous two as special cases.

The first moment μ_1 is called the *mean* of x, or *expected value* of x. For any function $g(x)$ we define the expected value to be $E[g(x)]$ where

$$E[g(x)] = \int_0^\infty g(u) \, \mathrm{d}\, F(u) \,.$$

Thus $\mu_1 = E(x)$ and $\mu_r = E(x^r)$. The *variance* of x is defined to be $E[\{x - E(x)\}^2]$, that is, the second moment about the mean. Write $x = E(x)$. Then, clearly,

$$E[(x - \bar{x})^2] = E(x^2) - 2\bar{x}E(x) + \bar{x}^2$$

$$= \mu_2 - \{E(x)\}^2 \,.$$

We denote the variance by σ^2 where σ is called the *standard deviation*. The result just written is then

$$\sigma^2 + \bar{x}^2 = \mu_2 \,.$$

13. Probability generating functions

In the case of a discrete distribution, it is frequently of great convenience to work with what is called the *probability generating function* (p.g.f.) of the distribution. This is the power series where the coefficient of x^n is $p_n (n = 0, 1, 2, \ldots)$, that is, $\Pi(z)$, where

$$\Pi(z) = E(z^x) = \sum_{n=0}^{\infty} p_n z^n \,.$$

The convenience referred to arises in the following way. In many situations the problem of determining $(p_0, p_1, \ldots)$ in terms of the variables at hand may arise. This may be a lengthy or practically impossible task. On the other hand it is frequently a relatively easy matter to determine $\Pi(z)$, and then p_n may, at least in principle, be determined by expanding $\Pi(z)$ into a power series and equating coefficients. This technique will be applied in several places in this book especially in the Chapters on queueing and stock control.

Examples: (i) For the Poisson distribution, where

$p_r = \lambda^r e^{-\lambda}/r!$ $(r = 0,1,2,...)$ it is found that $\Pi(z) = e^{\lambda(z-1)}$.

(ii) For the geometric distribution, where

$p_r = (1 - a)\, a^{r-1}$ $(r = 0, 1, 2, ...)$ we have

$$\Pi(z) = (1 - a)(1 - az)^{-1} .$$

(iii) For the binomial distribution, where

$$p_r = \binom{n}{r} \alpha^r \beta^{n-r} \qquad (\alpha + \beta = 1; \quad r = 0, 1, 2, ..., n)$$

the expression for $\Pi(z)$ is

$$\Pi(z) = (\beta + \alpha z)^n .$$

14. The addition of random variables: convolutions

Let x and y be independent random variables, that is, such that the value of x in any trial does not depend in any way upon the value of y in any trial. Then z, where $z = x + y$, is a random variable; and an important problem is that of determining the distribution function of z, given the distribution functions of x and y. We shall solve this problem in two cases:

(i) x and y are positive integral valued variables,

(ii) x and y are positive continuous variables.

Firstly, take the discrete case, and let

$$P(x = n) = p_n, \quad P(y = n) = q_n \quad (n = 0, 1, 2, ...) .$$

Then, since x and y are independent, we have

$$P(z = n) = \sum_{r=0}^{n} P(x = r)\, P(y = n - r) ,$$

so that if $(c_0, c_1, c_2, ...)$ is the probability density distribution of z, that is, $c_n = P(z = n)$, we have

$$c_n = \sum_{r=0}^{n} p_r q_{n-r} = \sum_{s=0}^{n} p_{n-s} q_s .$$

Thus, this case is easy, and for the distribution function we have

$$P(z \leqslant n) = \sum_{s=0}^{n} c_s = \sum_{s=0}^{n} \sum_{r=0}^{n} p_r q_{n-r} .$$

It is sometimes convenient, as we shall see below, to write c_n in the form

$$c_n = \sum_{r=0}^{\infty} p_r q_{n-r} = \sum_{s=0}^{\infty} p_{n-s} q_s ,$$

where $p_k = q_k = 0$ for $k < 0$.

Secondly, in the continuous case, let x, y and z have probability density functions $f(u)$, $g(u)$ and $h(u)$ respectively. The problem is to find $h(u)$ in terms of $f(u)$ and $g(u)$. Take a fixed value of y, in the interval $(v, v + \mathrm{d}v)$ so that, if

$$w < z < w + \mathrm{d}w \quad \text{then} \quad w - v < x < w - v + \mathrm{d}w .$$

Now

$$P(w - v < x < w - v + \mathrm{d}w) = f(w - v)\, \mathrm{d}w$$

and

$$P(v < y < v + \mathrm{d}v) = g(v)\, \mathrm{d}v .$$

Hence, considering that y can have any value in the interval $(0, w)$, we have by the theorem of total probability,

$$h(w)\, \mathrm{d}w = P(w < z < w + \mathrm{d}w)$$

$$= \mathrm{d}w \int_0^w f(w - v)\, g(v)\, \mathrm{d}v .$$

A similar result may be obtained if we firstly consider x fixed instead of y. The final result for the probability density $h(w)$ of z is

$$h(w) = \int_0^w f(w - v)\, g(v)\, \mathrm{d}v = \int_0^w g(w - u) f(u)\, \mathrm{d}u .$$

This result can easily be converted into one connecting the distribution functions $F(u)$, $G(u)$ and $H(u)$ of x, y and z. For

$$H(w) = \int_0^w h(t)\,\mathrm{d}t = \int_0^w \int_0^t f(t - v)\,g(v)\,\mathrm{d}v\,\mathrm{d}t\,.$$

If we interchange the order of integration, remembering that the double integral is evaluated over the triangle bounded by the lines $v = 0$, $v = t$ and $t = w$, we obtain

$$H(w) = \int_0^w g(v)\,\mathrm{d}v \int_v^w f(t - v)\,\mathrm{d}t = \int_0^w g(v)\,\mathrm{d}v \int_v^{w-v} f(x)\,\mathrm{d}x$$

$$= \int_0^w F(w - v)\,g(v)\,\mathrm{d}v\,.$$

By using the alternative expression for $h(w)$, we obtain, similarly,

$$H(w) = \int_0^w G(w - u)\,f(u)\,\mathrm{d}u\,.$$

The reader should observe that in most accounts of probability theory the formulae for $h(w)$ and $H(w)$ involve integrals taken over an infinite range of integration. This arises in the case where x and y are defined over the interval $(-\infty, \infty)$. In this case, in deriving the formula for $h(w)$ it is necessary to observe that y can have any value in the interval $(-\infty, \infty)$, instead of $(0, w)$, as above for $z = x + y$, and it is possible to have $w < z < w + \mathrm{d}w$ with $x \rightarrow \infty$, $y \rightarrow -\infty$ and with $x \rightarrow -\infty$, $y \rightarrow \infty$. Thus

$$h(w) = \int_{-\infty}^{\infty} f(w - v)g(v)\,\mathrm{d}v\,,$$

and, in the special case where $f(x) = g(x) = 0$ for $x < 0$, this becomes the earlier formula. It may be shown also that

$$H(w) = \int_{-\infty}^{\infty} F(w - v)g(v)\,\mathrm{d}v\,,$$

in the case of a range $(-\infty, \infty)$ for x, y and z, remembering that in this case, for example, $F(u)$ is the integral of $f(u)$ over the range $(-\infty, u)$.

The important notion of a convolution may now be introduced. Let $\{a\}$, $\{b\}$ and $\{c\}$ be the sequences,

$$\{a\} = \{a_0, a_1, \ldots\}, \quad \{b\} = \{b_0, b_1, \ldots\}, \quad \{c\} = \{c_0, c_1, \ldots\}.$$

We call $\{c\}$ the *convolution* of $\{a\}$ and $\{b\}$ if

$$c_n = \sum_{r=0}^{n} a_r b_{n-r},$$

It is to be noted that if

$$A(u) = \sum_{r=0}^{\infty} a_r u^r, \quad B(u) = \sum_{r=0}^{\infty} b_r u^r, \quad C(u) = \sum_{r=0}^{\infty} c_r u^r,$$

then

$$C(u) = A(u)\,B(u).$$

Now suppose that $A(u)$ and $B(u)$ are the probability generating functions of two random variables x and y. Then, since $\{c\}$ is the probability density function of $x + y$, it follows that the generating function of $x + y$ is $A(u)\,B(u)$. We shall refer to this result as the *convolution theorem.* By repeated application of the theorem it follows that if S_N, where

$$S_N = x_1 + x_2 + \ldots + x_N,$$

is the sum of $N (N$ fixed) independent random variables each with the same probability generating function, $A(u)$, then the generating function of S_N is $\{A(x)\}^N$. We shall make use of this result in Chapter VII.

In the continuous case let $f(u)$, $g(u)$ and $h(u)$ be three functions, defined over the interval $(0, \infty)$, such that

$$h(u) = \int_0^u f(u - v)\,g(v)\,dv.$$

We call $h(u)$ the *convolution* of $f(u)$ and $g(u)$. It is clear that, in the particular case where $f(u)$ and $g(u)$ are the probability density functions of random variables x and y, $h(u)$ is the density function of $x + y$. Later, in the discussion on Laplace transforms, we shall derive a result, in the continuous case, analogous to the convolution theorem.

Examples: (i) For the *Poisson distribution*, where

$$P(x = n) = a_n = \lambda^n e^{-n}/n! \quad (n = 0, 1, 2, ...)\,,$$

we have $A(x) = e^{\lambda(x-1)}$. Thus S_N, where $S_N = x_1 + ... + x_N$, and x_r follows a Poisson distribution with parameter, λ_r, has the generating function $e^{\mu(1-x)}$, where $\mu = \sum_{i=1}^{N} \lambda_i$. Hence *the sum of any number of Poisson distributions is also a Poisson distribution.*

(ii) Let $x_1, ..., x_N$ all have the same exponential distribution, with density function $f(u)$ where $f(u) = \lambda e^{-\lambda u}$, and let $f_N^{(u)}$ be the density function of S_N, where $S_N = x_1 + ... + x_N$. Then clearly

$$f_N(v) = \int_0^v f_{N-1}(v-u) f(u) du\,.$$

It may easily be shown that

$$f_N(v) = \lambda^N v^{N-1} e^{-\lambda v}/(N-1)\,!$$

S_N has a mean value N/λ and it is usual to write $\lambda = \mu N$, so that the distribution with density, $\varphi(u)$, where

$$\varphi(u) = \frac{(\mu N)^N u^{N-1} e^{-\mu N u}}{(N-1)!}$$

has a mean $1/\mu$. This, called the *Erlang distribution*, E_N, *is the distribution of the sum of N exponential distributions with the same parameter*. It will be used a good deal in the chapters on queueing theory.

15. The Laplace transform of a probability distribution

Let the random variable x have the distribution function, $F(u)$. The Laplace transform of $F(u)$ is defined to be $f^*(s)$ where

$$f^*(s) = \int_0^\infty e^{-su} dF(u)\,.$$

In the continuous case, where there is a density function $f(x)$ such that $f(u) = dF/du$, this becomes the usual definition,

$$f^*(s) = \int_0^\infty e^{-su} f(u)\, du\,,$$

and in the case of a discrete variable x, where $P(x=n)=p_n$ $(n=0, 1, 2, ...)$, we have

$$f^*(s)=\sum_{n=0}^{\infty} p_n e^{-sn} .$$

It is to be noticed that in each case $f^*(s)=E(e^{-su})$. If the exponentials are expanded, then it is evident that $f^*(s)$ may be written in terms of the moments, μ_r, of x (whether continuous or discrete) in the form

$$f^*(s)=\sum_{r=0}^{\infty} (-)^r \mu_r s^r / r\,!$$

This is an important result, for if $f^*(u)$ is known, but $f(u)$ not, then the moments of x may be found, at least in principle, by expanding $f^*(s)$ into a power series in s and equating coefficients. This will be done in Chapter IV, § 7.

There are two other properties of the Laplace transform which it will be useful to have. The probability generating function $\Pi(z)$ of the discrete variable x is given by

$$\Pi(z)=\sum_{n=0}^{\infty} p_n z^n = E(z^n) .$$

The relation of this function to the Laplace transform may be obtained by putting $z=e^{-s}$. We then have

$$\Pi(e^{-s})=E(e^{-su})=f^*(s) .$$

Finally, consider the Laplace transform of the convolution, $h(w)$, of the density functions $f(u)$ and $g(u)$ of two random variables x and y. We have

$$h(w)=\int_0^w f(w-v)\, g(v) dv .$$

Now,

$$h^*(s)=\int_0^\infty e^{-sw} h(w) dw=\int_0^\infty e^{-sw}\int_0^w f(w-v) g(v)\, dv\, dw$$

$$=\int_0^\infty g(v)\, dv \int_v^\infty e^{-sw} f(w-v)\, dw$$

$$= \int_0^\infty g(v)\, \mathrm{d}v \int_0^\infty \mathrm{e}^{-s(v+u)} f(u)\, \mathrm{d}u$$

$$= f^*(s)\, g^*(s)\,.$$

Thus the Laplace transform of the convolution of $f(u)$ and $g(u)$ is the product of the transforms of $f(u)$ and $g(u)$, and this is the analogue of the convolution theorem stated earlier for a pair of discrete variables.

16. The Poisson process

Let us consider again the cars which cross a given line in a traffic stream. Our interest now is in the instants of time at which successive cars cross the line, and the intervals of time between successive arrivals at the line. We shall exclude at once the possibility of cars overtaking near the line, so that two or more cars cannot arrive at the line at the same time. It is reasonable to suppose that the number of cars arriving in an interval, u, of time depends upon u but not upon the number of arrivals that took place in any intervals prior to u. This will be the case, for example, when the fact that a car is travelling in the stream has no influence on whether or not another car joins the stream. It is also reasonable to suppose that in any small interval of time the probability of arrival of a car is proportional to the length of the interval, that is, that there is a homogeneity about the intervals of time whereby if we expect one car to arrive in a small interval h, then we expect two cars to arrive in an interval $2h$. When these three conditions are satisfied we shall say that the arrivals constitute a *Poisson process.* More formally, we shall say that an infinite sequence of independent events, each occurring at an instant of time, forms a Poisson process if the following two conditions are satisfied:

(i) the total number of events in any interval, u, of time does not depend on any of the events which occurred before the beginning of the interval, u,

(ii) the probability of an event in a small interval, δt, of time is $\lambda \delta t + O(\delta t^2)$, where λ is a constant and $O(x^2)$ means any function $f(x)$ of the order of x^2, that is such that $|f(x)/x^2| < K$, as $x \to 0$, for some constant $K > 0$.

It may be noted at once that since the events are independent the condition (ii) means that the probability of two events in time δt is $O(\delta t^2)$, that is, is negligibly small as $\delta t \to 0$.

For a Poisson process we shall now derive two theorems:

THEOREM 1: (POISSON DISTRIBUTION): For a Poisson process the number of events occurring in an interval t is a random variable which follows a Poisson distribution of parameter λt, that is, the chance of n events in time t is $(\lambda t)^n e^{-\lambda t}/n!$,

THEOREM 2: (EXPONENTIAL DISTRIBUTION): For a Poisson process the intervals of time between successive events follow an exponential distribution, that is,

$$P(u < \tau < u + du) = \lambda e^{-\lambda u} .$$

For the proof of Theorem 1, let $P_r(t)$ be the chance of r arrivals in a time interval t, where $r = 0, 1, 2, \ldots$. In an interval of length $t + \delta t$ there may occur r arrivals in two ways, either r arrivals in the interval t and none in δt, or $r - 1$ arrivals in t and 1 arrival in δt. Thus,

$$P_r(t + \delta t) = P_r(t)\,(1 - \lambda\delta t) + P_{r-1}(t)\,\lambda\delta t .$$

We write this in the form

$$\frac{P_r(t + \delta t) - P_r(t)}{\delta t} = \lambda P_{r-1}(t) - \lambda P_r(t) ,$$

and then take the limit as $\delta t \to 0$. We then obtain

$$P_r'(t) = \lambda P_{r-1}(t) - \lambda P_r(t) \qquad (r = 1, 2, 3, \ldots)$$

In the case, $r = 0$, we have

$$P_0(t + \delta t) = P_0(t)(1 - \lambda\delta t)$$

so we obtain

$$P_0'(t) = -\lambda P_0(t) .$$

Now, clearly $P_0(0) = 1$, this expressing that the chance of an arrival at a particular instant is zero. Hence the last equation gives $P_0(t) = e^{-\lambda t}$, and then it is easy to show that the solution of the general equation is given by

$$P_r(t) = (\lambda t)^r e^{-\lambda t}/r!$$

This is Theorem 1. The method of finding $P_r(t)$, based on a system of differential-difference equations, will be used a good deal in Chapter IV.

The proof of Theorem 2 is very simple. Let t be the interval between successive arrivals and let

$$f(u)\mathrm{d}u = P(u < t < u + \mathrm{d}u)\,.$$

Then $f(u)\,\mathrm{d}u$ is the chance that there is no arrival in the interval, u, and there is an arrival in the interval, $\mathrm{d}u$, that is

$$f(u)\mathrm{d}u = P_0(u)\lambda\mathrm{d}u\,,$$

which means that $f(u) = \lambda P_0(u) = \lambda \mathrm{e}^{-\lambda u}$. In Chapters IV and V much use will be made of the Poisson and exponential distributions.

17. Some problems of waiting time

In Chapter IV the waiting time involved in queueing will be studied in some detail. As preparation for the types of problems involved the reader may care to consider the following four problems, due to Burr (1). The first three are particularly simple.

An individual, C, arrives at a bus stop where there is a choice of n independent systems of buses. In each system buses run at fixed intervals T. The waiting time, τ, of C is the interval between the time of his arrival and the arrival of the first bus.

PROBLEM 1: What is the probability density distribution of τ?

PROBLEM 2: What is the density distribution of τ, if it is known that no bus passed during an interval, v, immediately preceding the arrival of C?

PROBLEM 3: What is the density distribution if it is known that a bus definitely passed at a time v before the arrival of C?

So far we have not considered other prospective passengers. Suppose, then, that C on arrival finds r other individuals waiting, and that the arrival of prospective passengers is a Poisson process of parameter λ.

PROBLEM 4: What is the density distribution of τ if there are r individuals waiting when C arrives, and it is assumed that the latest bus to pass picked up all passengers then waiting?

SOLUTIONS: Let the instant of arrival of C be taken as zero time.

1. The chance that a particular bus arrives in the interval $(u, u + du)$ is du/T, and the chance that none of the other $(n - 1)$ buses arrive in the interval $(0, u)$ is $(1 - u/T)^{n-1}$. Hence, considering all n possibilities, if $f_n(u, T)\,du$ is the density distribution of the waiting time, τ, we have

$$f_n(u, T)\mathrm{d}u = P(u < \tau < u + \mathrm{d}u) = n(1 - u/T)^{n-1}\mathrm{d}u/T\,,$$

that is

$$f_n(u, T) = nT^{-1}(1 - u/T)^{n-1}\,.$$

2. Since no buses passed during the time interval $(-v, 0)$ it is certain that a bus will arrive during the interval $(0, T - v)$ (instead of $(0, T)$ as in Problem 1). Apart from this the conditions are as in Problem 1. Hence the density function in the case of Problem 2 is $f_n(u, T - v)$.
3. Let the bus, B, which passes at a time v preceding the arrival of C belong to the system, S. Then the first bus to arrive after C arrives will belong to one of the $n - 1$ systems other than S. No bus of any of these $n - 1$ systems passed during the interval v preceding the arrival of C, so the situation is as in Problem 2 with $n - 1$ in place of n. Thus the density function in the case of Problem 3 is $f_{n-1}(u, T - v)$, when $n \geqslant 2$. If $n = 1$ there is, of course, only a single waiting time, $T - v$.
4. This problem is more advanced than the others. The last bus to pass before the arrival of C may have passed at any time in the interval $(-T, 0)$. Let $p_r(t, T)\,\mathrm{d}t$ be the chance that a bus last passed in the interval $(-t - \mathrm{d}t, -t)$, *on the hypothesis that there are r individuals waiting when C arrives.* Then, if $F(u)\,du$ is the chance that the waiting time is between u and $u + du$, we have, by reference to Problem 3, with $v = t$, and on remembering that the last bus may have passed at any time in the interval $(-(T - u), 0)$,

$$F(u)\mathrm{d}u = \mathrm{d}u \int_0^{T-u} p_r(t, T) f_{n-1}(u, T - t)\mathrm{d}t\,.$$

Thus the problem is to find $p_r(t, T)$, which is a conditional probability.

Let A be the event "a bus last passed in the interval $(-t-\mathrm{d}t, -t)$",

B_r be the event "there are r individuals waiting when C arrives" where $r = 0, 1, 2, \ldots$.

Then

$$P(A|B_r)\, P(B_r) = P(B_r|A)\, P(A)\,.$$

Now we want $P(A|B_r)$. The values of the other three probabilities are given as follows. The event A involves a bus passing in the interval $\mathrm{d}t$ and no bus passing in the interval $(-t, 0)$. Thus

$$P(A) = n\,\frac{\mathrm{d}t}{T}\left(1-\frac{t}{T}\right)^{n-1} = f_n(t, T)\mathrm{d}t\,,$$

as in Problem 1. The event $B_r|A$ is that r individuals arrive in an interval t. Thus, since the arrivals form a Poisson process,

$$P(B_r|A) \equiv p_r(t) = \mathrm{e}^{-\lambda t}(\lambda t)^r/r!$$

To find $P(B_r)$ we note firstly that the r individuals waiting when C arrives may have arrived at any times in the interval $(-T, 0)$. The chance that they arrived in the interval $(-u, 0)$ is $p_r(u)$ and the chance that a bus last passed in the interval $(-u-\mathrm{d}u, -u)$ is $f_n(u, T)\,\mathrm{d}u$. Hence

$$P(B_r) \equiv \frac{1}{K_r} = \int_0^T p_r(u)\, f_n(u, T)\mathrm{d}u\,.$$

We now have

$$p_r(t, T)\mathrm{d}t = P(A|B_r) = P(B_r|A)P(A)/P(B_r) = K_r p_r(t) f_n(t, T)\mathrm{d}t\,.$$

Hence we have

$$F(u) = K_r \int_0^{T-u} p_r(t)\, f_n(t, T)\, f_{n-1}(u, T-t)\mathrm{d}t\,.$$

It is easy to show that

$$f_n(t, T)\, f_{n-1}(u, T-t) = nT^{-1} f_{n-1}(u+t, T)\,,$$

so that finally the density distribution in Problem 4 is given by

$$F(u) = \frac{nK_r}{T} \int_0^{T-u} p_r(t) f_{n-1}(u+t, T) \mathrm{d}t .$$

18. The solution of a type of partial differential equation

In Chapter V on queueing theory it will be necessary to solve an equation of the form

$$P \frac{\partial z}{\partial x} + Q \frac{\partial z}{\partial y} = R ,$$

where P, Q and R are functions of x, y and z. This is an equation of standard type and an outline only is given of the method of solution.

Let $u(x, y, z) = \text{const}$, and $v(x, y, z) = \text{const}$ be two independent integrals of the subsidiary equations,

$$\frac{\mathrm{d}x}{P} = \frac{\mathrm{d}y}{Q} = \frac{\mathrm{d}z}{R} .$$

Then the general solution of the first equation is

$$F\{u(x, y, z), v(x, y, z)\} = 0$$

where $F(\xi, \eta)$ is an arbitrary function of ξ and η. Sometimes it is more convenient to take the solution in the form

$$v(x, y, z) = G\{u(x, y, z)\} ,$$

particularly if G does not involve z, and v involves z in such a way that z may be found explicitly as a function of x and y.

Two examples will be given. These arise in Chapter V, § 2.

Example 1. For the equation

$$\frac{\partial \Pi}{\partial t} + \mu(z-1) \frac{\partial \Pi}{\partial z} = \lambda(z-1) \Pi ,$$

the auxiliary equations are

$$\frac{\mathrm{d}t}{1} = \frac{\mathrm{d}z}{\mu(z-1)} = \frac{\mathrm{d}\Pi}{\lambda(z-1)\Pi} .$$

Two independent solutions of the latter are

$$u \equiv (1 - z)e^{-\mu t} = \text{const}, \quad v \equiv \Pi e^{-\lambda z/\mu} = \text{const},$$

so that the general solution of the given equation is

$$\Pi = e^{\lambda z/\mu} G\{(1 - z) e^{-\mu t}\},$$

where $G(\xi)$ is an arbitrary function of ξ.
If, as in Chapter V, § 2, $\Pi = z^a$ when $t = 0$, it follows that

$$z^a = e^{\lambda z/\mu} G\{(1 - z)\},$$

which gives

$$G(u) = (1 - u)^a e^{-\lambda(1-u)/\mu}.$$

Hence

$$\Pi = e^{\vartheta(z,t)} \varphi(z,t),$$

where

$$\vartheta(z,t) = -\lambda(1 - z)(1 - e^{-\mu t})/\mu, \quad \varphi(z,t) = \{1 - (1 - z) e^{-\mu t}\}^a.$$

Example 2. For the equation

$$\frac{\partial \Pi}{\partial t} + (z - 1)(\lambda z + \mu) \frac{\partial \Pi}{\partial z} = m\lambda(z - 1)\Pi,$$

two independent solutions of the auxiliary equations are found to be

$$u \equiv (1 - z) e^{-kt}/(\mu + \lambda z) = \text{const}, \quad v \equiv \Pi/(\mu + \lambda z)^m = \text{const},$$

where $k = \lambda + \mu$, so the general solution is

$$\Pi = (\mu + \lambda z)^m G\{(1 - z) e^{-kt}/(\mu + \lambda z)\}.$$

If $\Pi = 1$ when $t = 0$, it follows that

$$G(u) = (1 + \lambda u)^m / k^m,$$

and thus

$$\Pi = [(\mu + \lambda e^{-kt}) + \lambda z (1 - e^{-kt})]^m / k^m.$$

This example occurs in Chapter V, § 2 (iii).

REFERENCES

1. E. J. BURR, "Transport problems", *Math. Gaz.*, **XLII** (1958), 307–9.
2. P. A. M. DIRAC, *Principles of Quantum Mechanics*, Clarendon Press, Oxford, 1956.
3. A. ERDELYI (Editor), *Tables of Integral Transforms*, vol. I., McGraw-Hill, N. Y., 1954.
4. D. V. LINDLEY, "The theory of queues with a single server", *Proc. Camb. Phil. Soc.*, **48** (1952), 277–89.
5. N. W. MCLACHLAN and P. HUMBERT, Formulaire pour le calcul symbolique, *Mémorial des Sciences Mathématiques*, Gauthier-Villars, Paris, 1941.
6. K. PEARSON, *Tables of the incomplete Gamma-function*, H.M.S.O., London, 1922.
7. E. C. TITCHMARSH, *Introduction to the Theory of Fourier Integrals*, Clarendon Press, Oxford, 1937.
8. N. WIENER and E. HOPF, Über eine Klasse singulärer Integralgleichungen", *S. B. Berl. Akad. Wiss.* (1931), 696–706.

CHAPTER II

LINEAR PROGRAMMING

1. Introduction

In various domains of industrial activity there arise situations where it is important to try and minimize, or maximize, some variable which is a measure of the efficiency of the operation concerned. The variable may, for example, be the time required to execute the operation, or the cost of the operation; or, in the case of production, the total output over a given period of time. In the field of personnel assignment, where several individuals, each capable of performing each of several tasks, have assigned rating factors it may be desirable to allot the individuals to the tasks so that the most efficient use is made of the available human resources. It frequently happens that the problem of determining the optimum operating conditions in situations such as these can be formulated mathematically, and, at least to a close degree of approximation, in linear algebraic terms. When this is possible methods are available for solving the problem and it is the purpose of this chapter to present an account of the chief method called the Simplex Method, and to give some examples of its applications.

It has been necessary to strike a balance between purely mathematical aspects and the practical details of some of the applications. We have chosen to steer a middle course, and while the main features of the mathematical methods are described there are places where the argument is not entirely rigorous nor exhaustive; and places where the applications considered are either small-scale or else involve simplifying assumptions which imply some departure from reality. It is hoped nevertheless that the account is sufficiently satisfying for the mathematical reader and sufficiently realistic for the man of practical affairs.

The methods of Linear Programming divide naturally into three classes, the Simplex Method and its variants, the Transportation Method and the Assignment Method. In this chapter an account is given of the Simplex Method (see the following chapter for Transportation and Assignment), after the definition of the general problem of Linear Programming. There is a certain degree of overlap amongst these methods. The Simplex Method, at least in principle, is of universal application; but in practice it frequently happens that for special problems the special character of the Transportation and Assignment Methods makes the use of one of these much more desirable from the point of view of the amount of computation involved. Indeed, the two special methods owe their existence to the fact that, when applicable, they are much more efficient as regards computation; and in any serious practical problem an early task should be to examine whether one of these methods may be used.

Two remarks on computation may not be out of place. A detailed account and appraisal of all the niceties of computation in Linear Programming (including the many special situations arising in the use of electronic computers) would be beyond the scope of this book. Attention has been confined to a few aspects, of a somewhat fundamental character, and in various places references to more detail are given for the guidance of the reader. The other remark concerns the present dynamic state of development of the subject. Practical problems have the habit, as is well-known to anyone who has moved in this field, of acquiring large-scale characteristics. The number of variables involved may, for example, run to three or four figures, and the situation may be aggravated by the process of trying to approximate an essentially non-linear problem by a series of linear steps. All this points to the fact that, from the mathematical and numerical point of view, the greatest need is for the development of efficient computational algorithms. Much work has been done in this field in recent years, and reference is made to this in several places. Nevertheless, there remains a considerable field for exploration, and this presents a real challenge to those mathematicians interested in numerical analysis.

2. The problem of Linear Programming

Consider an operation, or process, in which the variables are $x_1, ..., x_n$, and suppose that the operation is subject to a number m of constraints which may be expressed *linearly* (or at least approximately linearly) in the form

$$\sum_{j=1}^{n} a_{ij}x_j = b_i \quad (i = 1, ..., m) \tag{1}$$

where the a_{ij} and the b_i are known constants. Only non-negative values of $x_1, ..., x_n$ are allowable and it is supposed that the m constraints are linearly independent. Associated with the operation there is a variable L, which may, for example, be some measure of the efficiency of the operation, and it is supposed that L is expressible linearly in terms of $x_1, ..., x_n$, that is

$$L \equiv \sum_{j=1}^{n} c_i x_i \tag{2}$$

where $c_1, ..., c_n$ are given constants. If $m < n$, that is the number of constraints is less than the number of variables, there may be a family of solutions to the equations (1) and the problem to be considered is that of finding the solution, or family of solutions, which minimizes or maximizes L.

The term "Linear Programming" (hereafter abbreviated to L. P.) is the generic title given to the methods whereby a problem of the type stated may be solved. The solution is regarded as the "Programme", and the nomenclature is reasonable because, in a practical case, the solution specifies numerically the values of the various operational variables. In what follows we shall find it convenient to use the word *optimize* for the expression *maximize or minimize.*

It is convenient to mention here a variant of the constraints (1). It frequently happens that a constraint arises naturally in the form of an inequality, say

$$u \leqslant \sum_{j=1}^{n} a_j x_j \leqslant v\,.$$

This can always be replaced by two constraints of the equality type, namely

$$\sum_{j=1}^{n} a_j x_j - y_j = u, \quad \sum_{j=1}^{n} a_j x_j + z_j = v,$$

where y_i and z_j are non-negative variables. The form (1) will be called the *standard form* of constraints and we shall suppose from now on that the constraints have been written in this form (and that they are m in number). The new variables introduced in order to achieve the standard form, such as u and v, are called *additional variables* (following the terminology of Vajda (15)).

Matrix Form of the Problem. Denote by A the $m \times n$ matrix, whose (i, j) th element is a_{ij}. Let $\mathbf{x} = \{x_1, ..., x_n\}$, $\mathbf{b} = \{b_1, ..., b_n\}$, $c = \{c_1, ..., c_n\}$. If $x_i \geqslant 0$ for $i = 1, ..., n$ we shall write $\mathbf{x} \geqslant 0$. Then the problem of L. P. may be stated thus: of the solutions $\mathbf{x}$ to the equation $A\mathbf{x} = \mathbf{b}$, find those such that $\mathbf{x} \geqslant 0$ which optimize L where $L = \mathbf{c}'\mathbf{x}$. From this form we may deduce very easily an important result.

Suppose that $\mathbf{x}_1, ..., \mathbf{x}_r$ are linearly independent solutions of $A\mathbf{x} = \mathbf{b}$, which all yield the same optimal value L_0, that is $L_0 = \mathbf{c}'\mathbf{x}_1 = ... = \mathbf{c}'\mathbf{x}_r$. Then solutions of the family $e_1\mathbf{x}_1 + ... + e_r\mathbf{x}_r$ where $e_1, ..., e_r$ are non-negative variable parameters such that $e_1 + ... + e_r = 1$, also yield the optimal value.

This follows since

(i) $A(e_1\mathbf{x}_1 + ... + e_r\mathbf{x}_r) = e_1\mathbf{b} + ... + e_r\mathbf{b} = (e_1 + ... + e_r)\mathbf{b} = \mathbf{b}$, so that $e_1\mathbf{x}_1 + ... + e_r\mathbf{x}_r$ is a solution,

(ii) $\mathbf{c}'(e_1\mathbf{x}_1 + ... + e_r\mathbf{x}_r) = e_1 L_0 + ... + e_r L_0 = L_0$.

Later on we shall have occasion to use this result.

3. The Simplex Method

Before describing the Simplex Method it is necessary to introduce some definitions. For this purpose the matrix form of the L. P. problem is written in a slightly different way. Let $P_1, ..., P_n$ be the column vectors of A. Then the equation $A\mathbf{x} = \mathbf{b}$ may be written

$$x_1 P_1 + ... + x_n P_n = \mathbf{b}. \tag{3}$$

Since the vectors $P_1, ..., P_n$ are each of length m it is evident that, at most, m of $P_1, ..., P_n$ are linearly independent. Suppose there is at least one set of m vectors, say $P_1, ..., P_m$, which are linearly independent. Then there is a unique solution to the equation

$$x_1P_1 + ... + x_mP_m = \mathbf{b},$$

say, $x_r = x'_r (r = 1, ..., m)$. This solution together with the value zero for each of the remaining $n - m$ variables is an admissible solution of (3) only if $x'_r \geqslant 0$ $(r = 1, ..., m)$; and this leads to the following definitions.

DEFINITION 1. The variables $x_1, ..., x_m$ are said to form a *basic set* if the matrix of their coefficients is non-singular, that is, if $P_1, ..., P_m$ are linearly independent. The remaining variables are said to be *non-basic*.

Note that there are at most $\binom{n}{m}$ basic sets of variables.

DEFINITION 2. The solution of (3) in which the non-basic variables are put equal to zero is said to be *basic*.

Note that a basic solution contains $n - m$ zeros at least and that there is only a finite number of basic solutions $\left(\text{at most } \binom{n}{m}\right)$. If a basic solution contains more than $n - m$ zeros it is said to be *degenerate*.

DEFINITION 3. A solution in which the variables have non-negative values is said to be *allowable*.

We shall be particularly interested in BAND-solutions, that is, solutions which are basic, allowable and non-degenerate.

The Simplex Method for optimizing L consists of an iterative process which commences with a BAND-solution, having an associated value L_0, and determines a new BAND-solution with an associated value L_1, where $L_1 \gtrless L_0$ according as the problem is to maximize or minimize L. At each stage a rule is available for indicating if the optimum value of L has been reached. If not, the process is applied repeatedly together with the rule until the optimum is obtained. It will be shown that only a finite number of applications is necessary to reach the optimum when L is bounded, which is the only case of practical interest.

The problem of determining an initial BAND-solution will not be discussed. In some cases, such as transportation, it is easy to write down an initial solution. We shall assume that a solution is provided, for example by inspection, or from the physical context in which the problem arises. The mathematical devices whereby a BAND-solution can be obtained when one is not readily available are discussed in the standard texts (4, 11, 15) and the interested reader is referred to these sources for details.

A very important preliminary result is the expression of the general solution of the equation $A\mathbf{x} = \mathbf{b}$ in terms of a given BAND-solution. Suppose the variables $x_1, ..., x_n$ are ordered in such a way that $P_1, ..., P_m$ are linearly independent vectors and the associated solution $(x'_1, ..., x'_m, 0, ..., 0)$ satisfies $x'_i > 0$, so that it is a BAND-solution. We express the vectors $P_{m+1}, ..., P_n$ in terms of $P_1, ..., P_m$ thus:

$$P_k = \sum_{j=1}^{m} b_{kj} P_j \quad (k = m+1, ..., n) .$$

Then we have:

$$\begin{aligned} \mathbf{b} &= x_1 P_1 + ... + x_n P_n \\ &= x_1 P_1 + ... + x_m P_m + \sum_{s=m+1}^{n} x_s \sum_{i=1}^{m} b_{si} P_i \\ &= \sum_{i=1}^{m} (x_i + \sum_{s=m+1}^{n} b_{si} x_s) P_i . \end{aligned}$$

But

$$\mathbf{b} = \sum_{i=1}^{m} x'_i P_i .$$

Hence

$$\sum_{i=1}^{n} (x'_i - x_i - \sum_{s=m+1}^{n} b_{si} x_s) P_i = 0 .$$

Now, since $P_1, ..., P_m$ are linearly independent it follows that

$$x_i = x'_i - \sum_{s=m+1}^{n} b_{si} x_s \quad (i = 1, ..., m) \tag{4}$$

where $x_{m+1}, ..., x_n$ are arbitrary. This is the general solution. Also, if

$$L' = c_1 x'_1 + ... + c_m x'_m ,$$

then

$$L = c_1x_1 + \ldots + c_nx_n = L' + \sum_{k=m+1}^{n} x_k(c_k - \gamma_k) \tag{5}$$

where

$$\gamma_k = \sum_{i=1}^{m} b_{ki}c_i \quad (k = m + 1, \ldots, n) .$$

We use the solution (4) and the expression (5) for L to obtain various results.

(i) Suppose there is a row, say the kth of the $(n - m) \times m$ matrix (b_{kj}) such that all its elements are negative or zero, that is

$$b_{kj} \leqslant 0 \text{ for } j = 1, \ldots, m .$$

From the solution (4) it follows that if we take all of $x_{m+1}, \ldots, x_n$ to be zero, except x_k then because $b_{kj} \leqslant 0$ the value of x_k may be taken as large as we please and the solution $(x_1, \ldots, x_m, 0, \ldots, 0, x_k, 0, \ldots, 0)$ remains allowable. Then from (5) it follows that, as we let $x_k \to \infty$, L is unbounded above if $c_k > \gamma_k$ and unbounded below if $c_k < \gamma_k$. Thus we have this result:
If for some value of k (chosen from the numbers $m + 1, \ldots, n$) $b_{ki} \leqslant 0$ for every i, then $L_{\max} = \infty$ if $c_k > \gamma_k$ *and $L_{\min} = -\infty$ if $c_k < \gamma_k$.*

(ii) Suppose $c_k > \gamma_k$ for all k in the range $m + 1, \ldots, n$. Then (5) shows that any positive values that we may take for $x_{m+1}, \ldots, x_n$ (such that $x_1, \ldots, x_m$ as given by (4) are non-negative) will make $L > L'$. Similarly if $c_k < \gamma_k$ for all k then (5) shows that $L < L'$ for admissible positive $x_{m+1}, \ldots, x_n$. Hence *if $c_k > \gamma_k$ for all k then L' is the minimum value of L; if $c_k < \gamma_k$ for all k then L' is the maximum of L.*

The case where $c_k = \gamma_k$ for some value of k will be discussed in § 4. It is connected with the existence of a *family* of optimal solutions.

Having disposed of cases (i) and (ii) there are two others to consider. These are:

(iii) $c_k > \gamma_k$ for *some* (but not all k), and $b_{ki} > 0$ for some (possibly all) i,

(iv) $c_k < \gamma_k$ for *some* (but not all k), and $b_{ki} > 0$ for some (possibly all) i.

For (iii) and (iv) an iterative process is available whereby we may proceed, in a finite number of steps, to the *maximum* of L in case (iii) and the *minimum* of L in case (iv). But before describing the process it is necessary to introduce the following:

Fundamental Theorem. The optimum value of L, when it is finite, occurs at a basic (allowable) solution. The proof of this theorem is not given here. Algebraic proofs are available in (11), Chapter XXI, and in Ref. 4. The theorem is important in the Simplex Method because it implies that in the search for the optimum value of L attention may be confined to basic solutions, and, as noted on p. 37, the number of such solutions in finite. The iterative process described below leads from one BAND-solution to another BAND-solution with a value of L nearer to the optimum, and hence it follows that *the optimum will be reached in a finite number of applications of the process.*

We now consider cases (iii) and (iv) mentioned above. These are characterized by the fact that there exists a value of k (in the range $m+1, ..., n$), say $k = r$, such that $b_{ri} > 0$ for some set of i in the range $i, ..., m$. This fact plays an important part in what follows. We specialize solutions (4) to a BAND-solution other than the obvious initial BAND-solution $(x'_1, ..., x'_m, 0, ..., 0)$. For this purpose take all of $x_{m+1}, ..., x_n$, except x_r, to be zero and put $x_r = \vartheta$ where ϑ will be determined. Then from (4)

$$x_i = x'_i - \vartheta b_{ri} \quad (i = 1, ..., m)$$

$$x_r = \vartheta$$

and this, with the vanishing of the remaining variables, constitutes a solution for arbitrary ϑ. It is a basic solution, different from $(x'_1, ..., x'_m, 0, ..., 0)$ only if one of $x_1, ..., x_m$ vanish, that is $\vartheta = x'_i/b_{ri}$ for some i in the range $i, ..., m$. In addition it is allowable and non-degenerate only if every non-vanishing variable is positive. This means (i) $\vartheta > 0$ and hence in the consideration of the ratios x'_i/b_{ri} only those values of i such that $b_{ri} > 0$ are to be considered (if $b_{ri} < 0$ then $x_r > 0$ for all $\vartheta > 0$), (ii) all of $x_1, \ldots, x_m$ except one which vanishes, are positive and hence

$$\vartheta = \min_i \, (x'_i \,/\, b_{ri}) \,,$$

where i is such that $b_{ri} > 0$. If this minimum occurs for $i = s$ then x_s is the variable which vanishes. We omit here the case of a tie, where the minimum occurs for more than one value of i. We have now proved this result.

If $(x'_1, \ldots, x'_m, 0, \ldots, 0)$ is a BAND-*solution, S_0, then another* BAND-*solution, S_1, is given by*

$$(x_1, \ldots, x_{s-1}, 0, x_{s+1}, \ldots, x_m, 0, \ldots, 0, x_r, 0, \ldots, 0)\,,$$

that is by insertion of x_r, and removal of x_s where

(i) *r is one of the set $m + 1, \ldots, n$ such that $b_{ri} > 0$ for some set of values of i,*

(ii) *having chosen r, s is chosen from* $1, \ldots, m$ *so that* $\min_i (x'_i/b_{ri})$, *where $b_{ri} > 0$, occurs for $i = s$,*

(iii) $x_r = \vartheta$, $x_i = x'_i - \vartheta b_{ri} (i = 1, \ldots, m)$ *where* $\vartheta = x'_s/b_{rs}$.

We shall speak of S_1 as the *derived* solution (that is derived from S_0) and S_0 as the *initial* solution.

Consider now the value $L(S_1)$ of L associated with S_1 in cases (iii) and (iv). If $c_k \gtrless \gamma_k$ for $k = r$ then we have

$$L(S_1) = L' + \vartheta(c_r - \gamma_r) \begin{cases} > L', & \text{in case (iii) since } c_r > \gamma_r \\ < L', & \text{in case (iv) since } c_r < \gamma_r. \end{cases}$$

Thus, in each case, the value of L for the derived solution is nearer to the optimum than the value for the initial solution. It is evident that by iteration of this process, if necessary, (that is starting with the derived solution as the new initial solution), we shall reach either case (i) (if L is unbounded) or case (ii) (if L has an optimal value), in a *finite* number of stages; for

(a) the BAND-solution and the value of L are changed at each iteration,

(b) there is only a finite number of BAND-solutions.

Thus we shall have reached our goal of finding the optimal value of L.

There is a practical point which it is convenient to mention here, relating to the indices r and s. The latter is determined, when r has been chosen, as the index i for which x_i'/b_{ri} is minimal, where $b_{ri} > 0$. This gives a unique value for s, except in the case of ties which are excluded here. For r the choice may not be unique. Consider case (iii), where L has a maximum. The condition on r is that $c_r > \gamma_r$ and that $b_{ri} > 0$ for some values of i. This may yield several values of r. There is no criterion for determining which is the best value to take (in the sense of minimizing the number of iterations necessary to reach the maximum of L), but the practice has grown up, and there is good justification for it in light of experience, of taking that value of r for which $c_r - \gamma_r$ is a maximum.

4. Remarks on the Simplex Method

(a) *A Family of Optimal Solutions.* In case (ii) of § 3 we excluded the possibility, $c_k = \gamma_k$ for some k, and we now consider the position when this equality occurs. Let $c_r = \gamma_r$ where, of course, $m + 1 \leqslant r \leqslant n$, and suppose that $c_k > \gamma_k$ for all k in the range $m + 1, ..., n$ except r. Then expression (5) for L does not contain x_r and thus a variation in the value of x_r does not affect L. Moreover $L_{\min} = L'$. Thus the optimal value of L occurs for a *family* F_1 of solutions. A BAND-solution belonging to F_1 is the initial solution S_0. Another BAND-solution in F_1 is given by taking $x_r = \min_i (x_i'/b_{ri})$ where $b_{ri} > 0$. Suppose this minimum occurs for $i = s$, so that the solution is S_1, as given on page 41. Then, by the general result on the superposition of solutions given on page 36, it follows that the family F_1 consists of all solutions of the form $e_0S_0 + e_1S_1$ where $e_0 + e_1 = 1$; $e_0, e_1 \geqslant 0$. Note that the solutions of this family are all non-basic (since they contain $m + 1$ non-zero values for the variables), except the two BAND-solutions S_0 snd S_1.

This result may be generalized. If $c_r = \gamma_r$ for t values of r in the range $m + 1, ..., n$, then there is a family F_t of solutions containing, in addition to S_0, r BAND-solutions $S_1, ..., S_t$; here S_j is obtained from S_0 by inserting x_j, where $x_j = \min_i (x_i'/b_{ji})$ for

$b_{ji} > 0$ and, if the minimum occurs for $i = k$, removing x_k. Then F_t consists of the solutions $e_0S_0 + ... + e_tS_t$ where $e_0, ..., e_t \geqslant 0$ and $e_0 + ... + e_t = 1$.

(b) *Degeneracy and Cycling.* An essential part of the process in cases (iii) and (iv) is the determination of ϑ as $\min(x_i'/b_{ri})$, for $b_{ri} > 0$. If this minimum is not unique but occurs for d values of i, where $d > 1$, then the solution S_1 derived from S_0 contains only $m - d + 1$ non-zero values for the variables and hence is degenerate, even though the solution S_0 is non-degenerate ($x_i' > 0$ for $i = 1, ..., m$).

Now consider what happens if the procedure of § 4 is applied to S_1, regarded as the *initial* solution. One of the basic variables is now zero and hence $\vartheta = 0$. This means that the solution S_2, derived from S_1, is the same as S_1, although the set of basic variables is different. And since $S_2 = S_1$, it follows that the change in the basic variables has not altered the value of L. Thus if one starts with a degenerate solution and applies repeatedly the Simplex Method it is evident that all the derived solutions will be degenerate and the value of L will be invariant. Only the set of basic variables changes during the iteration. Two situations are now possible. Either ultimately case (ii) will be reached and it will have been shown that the invariant value of L is the optimal value (and in this case all is well), or else at some stage one returns to the initial set of basic variables. In this case a *cycle* of iterations will have been set up, and it will then be impossible to escape from this cycle and improve the value of L. Thus the Simplex Method breaks down in this case.

It is possible to avoid the phenomenon of cycling by a perturbation method due to Charnes, using certain sets of polynomials in an infinitesimal parameter ε. We shall not, however, describe this method here. The interested reader may consult references (4) (11) or (15). It is worth noting that cycling appears to occur relatively infrequently in practical problems, but the experience of Prinz (13), on the computer should be noted.

(c) *Improvements on the Simplex Method.* Many modifications of the Simplex Method have been proposed. The aim has been mainly to develop improved computational algorithms for either reducing the amount of numerical work involved in a problem of given size or extending the size of the problem that may be solved with given facilities. Some of the methods have arisen as a result of limitations in the use of electronic computers, for example, because of limited storage facilities it may be necessary to read in the matrix at each iteration and this may be a slow process. In one recent method, due to Aczel and Russell (1) for reducing this limitation, the main idea is to choose from the non-basic variables a set S consisting of those for which there is, on the grounds of experience with the particular problem concerned, a strong presumption that in the final solution the variables contained in S will have zero values. These variables are given the value zero, and the resulting *restricted* problem is solved. It is shown how the solution may be conveniently tested to determine if, in the original problem, it is also optimal.

Another method, which has lately received increased attention, is the double gradient method due to Professor R. Frisch of the Institute of Economics at Oslo. This was originally developed for application to large-scale macro-economic problems. It is basically different from the Simplex Method. Instead of proceeding from the solution S_0 to S_1 a direction is determined whereby one proceeds from S_0 to a solution S_2 which is much closer to the final solution. Progress towards the optimum is made the more rapid by the process of *truncation* which consists in modifying, after a few applications of the double-gradient method, the set of basic variables so that

(i) variables not previously in the basis and now thought to have non-zero values in the final solution are brought into the basis,
(ii) variables which it is thought likely have zero values in the final solution are made into non-basic variables and given the value zero.

The Frisch Method is important because the likely number of iterations required for a problem, where there are N non-basic variables is about $6 \log_{10} N$, and since this is only 18 for $N = 1000$, it is possible to cope with problems where N is quite large (say up to 4 figures). For the details of the Frisch method the original memoranda from the University Institute of Economics, Oslo, should be consulted (7). A good introductory account is given by Aczel and Russel (1). Special methods are sometimes applicable when the matrix A, in the original set of equations $A\mathbf{x} = \mathbf{b}$ has a high proportion of zero elements. The situation is described as one of *sparseness*. The methods utilize this sparseness in an attempt to avoid approaching the capacity of the memory of an electronic computer. Hoffman (9) has given an account of them with references. A special case occurs when A, partitioned into blocks of matrices, consists of a number of diagonal or near-diagonal blocks. This case has been studied by Dantzig (5).

5. Example of the use of the Simplex Method

In the following example the vector $\mathbf{b}$ occurring in the equation $A\mathbf{x} = \mathbf{b}$ is taken in the form of a set parameters rather than in numerical form. This permits a semi-analytical discussion and allows us to cover various features, including the case where there is a family of optimal solutions. The example arises in the Trim Problem, discussed in § 7.

PROBLEM: The seven non-negative variables $x_1, ..., x_7$ are subjected to the three restrictions

$$\begin{aligned} x_4 + x_5 + x_7 &= x \\ x_2 + 2x_3 + x_5 + 2x_6 &= y \\ 6x_1 + 4x_2 + 2x_3 + 3x_4 &= z \end{aligned} \tag{6}$$

where x, y and z are non-negative parameters. The problem is to *minimize* L where

$$L \equiv 2x_1 + ax_2 + 2x_5 + 6x_6 + 9x_7 \tag{7}$$

a being a variable parameter.

This problem will be solved only in the case where z *is large* compared with x and y; the question of how large will be answered as the discussion proceeds. Since there are 3 restrictions an optimal solution will involve at most 3 non-zero variables. The first task is to choose an initial basic set of variables (3 in number) and the corresponding allowable solution. It is clear that if z is sufficiently large the variable x_1 must appear in a basic solution since x_2, x_3 and x_4 are at most of the order of magnitude of x and y, and x_1, appearing only in the third restriction, must therefore be of the order of the magnitude of z. It is next observed that x_3 and x_4 do not appear in the expression of L, so it seems likely that these variables would appear in a basic solution, since then we would have $x_2 = x_5 = x_6 = x_7 = 0$ and $L = 2x_1$. So we set out with x_1, x_3 and x_4 as a trial set of basic variables. From the equations (6) it is easy to express x_1, x_3 and x_4, and then L in terms o fthe other variables, thus:

$$6x_1 = (z - y - 3x) - 3x_2 + 4x_5 + 2x_6 + 3x_7$$

$$2x_3 = y - x_2 - x_5 - 2x_6$$

$$x_4 = x - x_5 - x_7$$

$$3L = (z - y - 3x) + 3(a - 1)\, x_2 + 8x_5 + 20x_6 + 30x_7 . \quad (8)$$

If $a > 1$ the coefficients of the non-basic variables are all positive, and hence the minimum value of L will be given by taking $x_2 = x_5 = x_6 = x_7 = 0$. Then $6x_1 = z - y - 3x$ and so for the solution to be allowable we must have $z > 3x + y$. For the remainder of this example we shall assume that z satisfies this inequality. In this case we have this result:

If $a > 1$ and $z > 3x + y$ the unique solution giving a minimal value L_m of L is

$$x_2 = x_5 = x_6 = x_7 = 0$$

$$x_1 = \tfrac{1}{6}(z - y - 3x)$$

$$x_3 = \tfrac{1}{2}y$$

$$x_4 = x$$

and

$$L_m = \tfrac{1}{3}(z - 3x - y) .$$

The Case $a = 1$: The expression (8) for L does not contain x_2 in this case and L will still have the minimal value $\frac{1}{3}(z - 3x - y)$ given by $x_5 = x_6 = x_7 = 0$. However, there is a *family* of solutions giving this minimal value, namely:

$$\begin{aligned} x_1 &= \tfrac{1}{6}(z - 3x - y) - \tfrac{1}{2}\lambda \\ x_2 &= \lambda \\ x_3 &= \tfrac{1}{2}(y - \lambda) \\ x_4 &= x \end{aligned} \tag{9}$$

where λ is a parameter such that $0 \leqslant \lambda \leqslant \min\left\{y, \tfrac{1}{3}(z - 3x - y)\right\}$. There are two cases:

(i) $z > 3x + 4y$. Then $0 \leqslant \lambda \leqslant y$, and the family is derived from the two basic solutions A and B as follows:

SOLUTION A: $$\begin{aligned} x_1 &= \tfrac{1}{6}(z - 3x - y) \\ x_3 &= \tfrac{1}{2}y \\ x_4 &= x\,. \end{aligned}$$

SOLUTION B: $$\begin{aligned} x_1 &= \tfrac{1}{6}(z = 3x = 4y) \\ x_2 &= y \\ x_4 &= x\,. \end{aligned}$$

Solution (9) is given by $A(1 - \lambda/y) + B\,\lambda/y$.

(ii) $3x + y < z < 3x + 4y$. Then $0 \leqslant \lambda \leqslant \tfrac{1}{3}(z - 3x - y)$,

and the family is derived from the basic solutions A and C where A is as above and C is as follows:

SOLUTION C: $$\begin{aligned} x_2 &= \tfrac{1}{3}(z - 3x - y) \\ x_3 &= \tfrac{1}{6}(3x + 4y + z) \\ x_4 &= x\,. \end{aligned}$$

The Case $a < 1$: In this case, since the coefficient of x_2 in expression (8) for L is negative, it follows that (x_1, x_3, x_4) is not a minimal basic set of variables; x_2 must be brought into the basis. The variable to be removed is found as follows. The equations may be written in the matrix form

$$(P_1, \ldots, P_7)\,\mathbf{x} = \begin{pmatrix} 0 & 0 & 0 & 1 & 1 & 0 & 1 \\ 0 & 1 & 2 & 0 & 1 & 2 & 0 \\ 6 & 4 & 2 & 3 & 0 & 0 & 0 \end{pmatrix} \begin{pmatrix} x_1 \\ \vdots \\ x_7 \end{pmatrix} = \begin{pmatrix} x \\ y \\ z \end{pmatrix}. \tag{10}$$

Since we have taken x_1, x_3 and x_4 as the initial basic set of variables, and we wish to introduce x_2 into the basis it is necessary to express the vector P_2 in terms of P_1, P_3 and P_4. The expression is

$$P_2 = \tfrac{1}{2} P_1 + \tfrac{1}{2} P_3 .$$

Now the basic solution corresponding to the basis x_1, x_3 and x_4 is

$$x'_1 = \tfrac{1}{6}(z - 3x - y)$$
$$x'_3 = \tfrac{1}{2} y$$
$$x'_4 = x ,$$

and x_2 is the variable to be introduced into the basis. Hence, using the expression $P_2 = \frac{1}{2} P_1 + \frac{1}{2} P_3$ we determine ϑ where

$$\vartheta = \min_{i=1,3,4} \frac{x'_i}{b_{2i}} = \min \left\{ \tfrac{1}{3}(z - 3x - y), y \right\}$$

$$= \begin{cases} y \text{ if } z > 3x + 4y \text{ (then remove } x_3 \text{ from the basis)} \\ \tfrac{1}{3}(z - 3x - y) \text{ if } z < 3x + 4y \text{ (then remove } x_1 \text{ from the basis).} \end{cases}$$

There are thus two cases to consider:

(i) $z < 3x + 4y$. The basis is (x_2, x_3, x_4). It is found that

$$3L = (z - 3x - y) + 6(1 - a)\, x_1 + (6 + 4a)\, x_5 + 2(9 + a)x_6 + 3(9 + a)x_7 .$$

The coefficients of the non-basic variables are positive if $a > -\frac{2}{3}$ and in this case we have the minimal value $L_m = \frac{1}{3}(z - 3x - y)$, the corresponding basic solution being $x_2 = \frac{1}{3}(z - 3x - y)$, $x_3 = \frac{1}{6}(3x + 4y - z)$, $x_4 = x$.

(ii) $z > 3x + 4y$. The basis is (x_1, x_2, x_4), and it is found that

$$3L = (z - 3x - 4y + 3ay) + 6(1 - a)x_3 + + (13 - 6a)x_5 + 2(13 - 3a)x_6 + 30x_7 .$$

Since $a < 1$ the coefficients of the non-basic variables are positive and we have reached the minimal value, $L_m = \frac{1}{3}(z - - 3x - 4y) + ay$, the corresponding solution being

$$x_1 = \tfrac{1}{6}(z - 3x - 4y),\ x_2 = y,\ x_4 = x.$$

NOTE: In the limiting case where $z = 3x + 4y$, there is a tie in the choice of ϑ and one of the basic variables takes on the value zero. Thus Case (i) gives the solution $x_2 = \frac{1}{3}(z - 3x - y) = y, x_3 = 0, x_4 = x$ and Case (ii) gives $x_1 = 0, x_2 = y, x_4 = x$. However, the expressions for L show that it is unnecessary to change the basis (no further improvement being possible) and so cycling, which may arise in cases of degeneracy, does not in fact arise here. The minimal value of L is ay.

6. The Caterer Problem

Special problems in linear programming may sometimes be solved by special methods, and an example in this category is the Caterer Problem. This first appeared as a well-defined problem in a paper by Jacobs (10) in 1954. It arose in the aircraft industry as a spare engine problem and has been paraphrased to read as follows:

> During n consecutive days a caterer is required to serve a number of meals each day, namely r_j on the jth day, where $j = 1, ..., n$. He will thus need r_j fresh napkins on the jth day. The laundry provides a slow service, whereby napkins are returned at the end of the pth day after receipt, and a quick service with napkins returnable at the end of the q th day, where $q < p$. The costs of laundering are b and c pence per napkin for the slow and quick service respectively ($b < c$). The caterer starts by making a purchase of napkins at a pence each. How many napkins does the caterer purchase and how does he schedule the laundering of the napkins so as to minimize the total cost for the n days?

Let S be the number of napkins purchased. It is clear at the outset that $S \geqslant \max_j r_j$, and that if S is sufficiently large compared with $r_1, ..., r_n$, then it will not be necessary to use the more expensive, that is the fast, laundering service. In this case there is no problem of scheduling, but the total cost of the operations will not be minimal since the caterer will have purchased more napkins than necessary. On the other hand if S is "rather small", then the caterer may have to send most of the napkins to the fast laundering service, thereby incurring more cost than the cost of purchasing extra napkins. Thus there are really two problems, namely

(i) to determine S,

(ii) given S, to determine how to divide the napkins between the slow and the fast laundering service, so as to minimize the laundering costs. We shall not discuss problem (i) but, *for a given* S, show how problem (ii) may be solved, using a method developed by Bellman (3). Suppose that, at the end of the kth day, the r_k napkins used that day are divided into u_k, sent to the q-day laundry, and v_k sent to the p-day laundry. The cost of laundering for the kth day is thus $bv_k + cu_k$, and the total cost for n days is C where

$$C = b \sum_{k=1}^{n-1} v_k + c \sum_{k=1}^{n-1} u_k .$$

Now $u_k + v_k = r_k$ and hence

$$C = c \sum_{k=1}^{n-1} r_k - (c - b) \sum_{k=1}^{n-1} v_k .$$

Thus, since $c > b$, the problem of minimizing C is the problem of maximizing $\sum_{k=1}^{n-1} v_k$.

The restraints on the variables $v_1, \ldots, v_{n-1}$ obviously include the set $0 \leqslant v_k \leqslant r_k$, and the others are determined in this way. Let x_k be the number of clean napkins at the start of the kth day. Now at the end of the $(k - 1)$th day the clean napkins returned from the laundry number $u_{k-q} + v_{k-p}$. Hence

$$x_k = x_{k-1} - r_{k-1} + u_{k-q} + v_{k-p} ,$$

where $u_i = v_i = 0$ for $i \leqslant 0$.

This difference equation for x_k may be easily solved, subject to the initial condition, $x_1 = S$; and the solution takes the form

$$x_k = S - \mathcal{L}_k(v) \quad (k = 1, 2, ..., n)$$

where $\mathcal{L}_k(v)$ is linear in $v_1, ..., v_{n-1}$, on using the fact that $u_k + v_k = r_k$. Now $x_k \geqslant r_k$ and thus the restraints on the $v_1, ..., v_{n-1}$ are

$$\begin{gathered} 0 \leqslant v_k \leqslant r_k \\ \mathcal{L}_k(v) \leqslant S - r_k . \end{gathered} \tag{11}$$

Thus the caterer problem is formulated as a problem in linear programming, namely to maximize $\sum_{i=1}^{n-1} v_i$ subject to the constraints (11). Bellman has pointed out that the level of difficulty in solving this problem explicity depends not on the individual values of p and q, but only on the difference $p - q$. We shall solve for the case $q = 1$, $p = 2$ (the case $q = m$, $p = m + 1$ is as easy) and describe Bellman's method for the case $q = 1$, $p = 3$.

The case $q = 1$, $p = 2$: The difference equation for x_k is

$$x_k - x_{k-1} = v_{k-2} - v_{k-1},$$

where $x_1 = S$, and $v_0 = 0$. Hence

$$x_k = S - v_{k-1} \geqslant r_k .$$

Thus the problem is to find the maximum of L where $L = \sum_{i=1}^{n-1} v_i$, subject to the conditions $0 \leqslant v_k \leqslant r_k$ and

$$v_k \leqslant S - r_{k+1} \quad (k = 1, 2, ..., n - 1) .$$

It is obvious that the solution is to choose each v_k individually as large as possible, that is to take

$$v_k = \min(r_k, S - r_{k+1}) \quad (k = 1, 2, ..., n - 1) .$$

The case $q = 1$, $p = 3$: In this case x_k satisfies the equation

$$x_k - x_{k-1} = v_{k-3} - v_{k-1},$$

and the solution is $x_k = S - v_{k-1} - v_{k-2} \leqslant r_k$.

Thus, in addition to $0 \leqslant v_k \leqslant r_k$, the conditions on the v_k are

$$v_1 \leqslant S - r_2, \quad v_{k+1} + v_k \leqslant S - r_{k+2} \quad (k = 1, 2, ..., n-2).$$

It follows that our problem is of this form:

Maximize L, where $L = \sum_{i=1}^{n-1} v_i$, subject to the conditions

$$\begin{aligned} 0 \leqslant v_k \leqslant r_k & \quad (k = 1, ..., n) \\ v_1 \leqslant b_1 & \\ v_i + v_{i+1} \leqslant b_{i+1} & \quad (i = 1, 2, ..., n-2), \end{aligned} \qquad (12)$$

where $b_1, ..., b_n$ are constants. For a solution consider the variables $v_1, ..., v_{n-1}$ in turn, starting with v_1, which is subject to the conditions, $v_1 \leqslant r_1$, $v_1 \leqslant b_1$, $v_1 + v_2 \leqslant b_2$. The maximum value of v_1 is clearly v_1' where $v_1' = \min(r_1, b_1, b_2)$. Now v_2 is subject to the conditions $v_2 \leqslant r_2$, $v_1' + v_2 \leqslant b_2$, $v_2 + v_3 \leqslant b_3$. Hence the maximum value of v_2 is v_2' where $v_2' = \min(r_2, b_2 - v_1', b_3)$. Proceeding in this way we find that the maximum value of $v_i (i = 1, ..., n-1)$ is v_i' where

$$v_i' = \min(r_i, b_i - v_{i-1}', b_{i+1}) \quad (i = 1, 2, ..., n-1).$$

Thus we determine a set of values $v_1', ..., v_{n-1}'$ and a value L' of L where

$$L' = \sum_{i=1}^{n-1} v_i'.$$

It may be shown that L' is the solution to our problem, namely the *maximum* value of L, subject to the conditions (12). For the proof the reader may consult the paper (3) of Bellman, who observed that when v_1 is chosen, there remains a problem of the original type on $n - 2$ variables, instead of $n - 1$. Thus, define

$$f_k(x) = R_{k\,\max} \sum_{i=k}^{n-1} v_i,$$

where R_k is the region given by

$$0 \leqslant v_k \leqslant x, 0 \leqslant v_i \leqslant r_i (i = k, ..., n-1)$$

and

$$v_k + v_{k+1} \leqslant b_{k+1}, \ldots, v_{n-2} + v_{n-1} \leqslant b_{n-1} .$$

Then Bellman proves by induction that

$$f_k(x) = \min(P_k, x + Q_k) \quad (k = 1, \ldots, n-2)$$

where P_k and Q_k are defined recursively by

$$P_k = \min(P_{k+1} + b_{k+1}, Q_{k+1} + b_{k+1}),$$

$$Q_k = \min(P_{k+1}, r_{k+1} + Q_{k+1}),$$

for $k = 1, 2, \ldots, n-2$ the final values being

$$P_{n-2} = b_{n-1}, \quad Q_{n-2} = r_{n-1} .$$

The maximum value of L is $f_1(x)$ where $x = \min(r_1, b_1, b_2)$, and the policy for maximizing L is $v_k = \min(x, b_{k+1})$ at each stage.

Example: Maximize L, where $L = \sum_{i=1}^{5} v_i$ subject to

$$\begin{aligned} v_1 &\leqslant 3 & v_1 &\leqslant 4 \\ v_1 + v_2 &\leqslant 2 & v_2 &\leqslant 2 \\ v_2 + v_3 &\leqslant 5, & v_3 &\leqslant 3 \\ v_3 + v_4 &\leqslant 4 & v_4 &\leqslant 3 \\ v_4 + v_5 &\leqslant 7 & v_5 &\leqslant 2 . \end{aligned}$$

Here we have $P_4 = 7$, $Q_4 = 2$ and

$$\begin{aligned} P_3 &= \min(11, 6) = 6, & Q_3 &= \min(7, 5) = 5, \\ P_2 &= \min(11, 10) = 10, & Q_2 &= \min(6, 8) = 6, \\ P_1 &= \min(12, 8) = 8, & Q_1 &= \min(10, 8) = 8 . \end{aligned}$$

Hence the maximum value of L is L_m where $L_m = \min(8, x + 8) = 8$, and the solution is $v_1 = 2$, $v_2 = 0$, $v_3 = 3$, $v_4 = 1$, $v_5 = 2$. It should be noted that the solution is not unique, another being $v_1 = 1$, $v_2 = 1$, $v_3 = 3$, $v_4 = 1$, $v_5 = 2$.

Formulation as a Transportation Problem. The original formulation of the caterer problem by Jacobs (10) in 1954 was followed by a paper (8) in the same year by Gaddum, Hoffman and Sokolowsky on some features of the computation involved. Quite a different approach was made by Prager (12) in 1956, when it was shown that the caterer problem may be formulated as a transportation problem (in the sense of Chapter III) with a very special cost matrix. For this the reader is referred to Prager's paper or to the outline by Vajda (14).

7. The Trim Problem

In various industries material is produced in the form of a strip or ribbon rolled into coils, for example paper, textiles, plastics, metals. A customer's order is frequently filled by taking a number of like coils called standard coils, and trimming or slitting these, that is cutting along a line or several lines parallel to the edge of the strip. Usually a loss of material is incurred in slitting, and this material is called the *scrap*; for example, if the width of a standard coil is W, and the coils derived from it by slitting have widths $d_1, ..., d_m$ then scrap arises if $d_1 + ... + d_m < W$. In practice it is necessary to slit a number of coils to fill a given order, and these coils will be slit in different ways, as will be evident below. It is desirable to minimize the total scrap incurred in slitting all the coils and thus we have the problem of how to arrange the slitting programme so as to achieve this minimization. We shall formulate this problem in general terms and then solve in detail a particular example. If the reader finds the general formulation difficult he is asked to proceed to the example directly.

Suppose that material is ordered in widths $w_1, ..., w_r$, and let $m_1, ..., m_r$ be a set of integers ($\geqslant 0$) such that

$$m_1 w_1 + ... + m_r w_r \leqslant W.$$

Then a standard coil can be slit to produce m_1 coils of width w_1, m_2 coils of width w_2, ..., m_r coils of width w_r, and a scrap t where $t = W - \sum_{i=1}^{r} m_i w_i$. This method of slitting will be called *the set-up corresponding to the set* $(m_1, ..., m_r)$. There are many set-ups corresponding to the various possible choices of $m_1, ..., m_r$ and by the ith set-up we shall mean that corresponding to the set $(m_1^{(i)}, ..., m_r^{(i)})$. Suppose that there are N possible set-ups so that $i = 1, 2, ..., N$. Then if, in filling the order for n_j coils of width w_j $(j = 1, ..., r)$, we slit x_i standard coils according to the ith set-up, we shall have

$$\sum_{i=1}^{N} x_i m_j^{(i)} = n_j \quad (j = 1, ..., r). \tag{13}$$

The scrap incurred on slitting one coil according to the ith set-up is t_i where $t_i = W - \sum_{j=1}^{r} m_j^{(i)} w_j$, and the total scrap is L where

$$L = \sum_{i=1}^{N} t_i x_i . \tag{14}$$

Now in practice it is desirable to minimize the total scrap. Thus we have a problem in linear programming, namely to determine integers $x_1, ..., x_N$ satisfying the equations (13) so as to minimize the expression (14) for the scrap.

Example: Consider coils 20 in. wide to be cut into coils of widths 11 in., 7 in. and 3 in. Suppose that the numbers of coils required in these widths are x, y and z respectively (thus $x = n_1$, $y = n_2$, $z = n_3$). Enumerate the various set-ups and find, for given x, y and z the numbers of coils to be cut according to these set-ups so that the scrap is minimized.

It is easily found that there are seven possible set-ups, with associated scrap t as follows:

Width	Set-up						
	1	2	3	4	5	6	7
11 in.	0	0	0	1	1	0	1
7 in.	0	1	2	0	1	2	0
3 in.	6	4	2	3	0	0	0
Scrap t	2	1	0	0	2	6	9

Of these set-ups only the first five would normally be used; set-up 6 would be used only if a great number (see later) of 7 in. coils were required, and set-up 7 only if a great number of 11 in. coils were required.

Let $x_1, ..., x_7$ be the numbers of standard coils cut according to set-ups 1, ..., 7 respectively, in order to fulfil the order for x coils of 11″, y of 7″ and z of 3″. Then we have

$$\begin{aligned} x_4 + x_5 + x_7 &= x \\ x_2 + 2x_3 + x_5 + 2x_6 &= y \\ 6x_1 + 4x_2 + 2x_3 + 3x_4 &= z \end{aligned} \tag{15}$$

and the total scrap L is given by

$$L = 2x_1 + x_2 + 2x_5 + 6x_6 + 9x_7 \, .$$

The problem is to find *integers* $x_1, ..., x_7$, satisfying the equations (15), which minimize L. It must be said at once that the requirement that $x_1, ..., x_7$ be integers adds a real difficulty of a mathematical character to the problem. Suppose S is the solution obtained by the Simplex Method. S will not usually involve integral values for $x_1, ..., x_7$ and it cannot be assumed that the proper solution is "near" to S, although often it will be. However, we shall ignore this difficulty here and discuss the solution S. There is a justification for doing this, as follows. In practice the problem is not to devise the best slitting programme for a *single* period, but rather to work out the programme at the start of each of a sequence of periods (days or weeks, say), when order requirements are known. Now usually it will be the practice to keep a small stock of the sizes of coils commonly ordered. Suppose that for some period the numbers of coils ordered are x, y and z, and let the solution obtained by the Simplex Method be S where $S = (x_1, ..., x_7)$. If some of $x_1, ..., x_7$ are not integral we adjust to nearby integers, giving a set S' where $S' = (x_1', ..., x_7')$ say. A slitting programme based on S' will yield numbers x', y' and z' of coils, and these numbers will not differ appreciably from x, y and z. Then the ordered numbers x, y and z may be obtained from x', y' and z' by making use of the stock, that is adding or withdrawing as required. With this mode of operation it will be seen that if at the start of each period the slitting programme taken is S', then over a long interval of time slitting will have been carried out, from a practical point of view, in an almost optimal manner.

From the theory of linear programming it is known that in a basic solution, S, there are only three non-zero values in the set $x_1, \ldots, x_7$ since the equations (15) are three in number. There may, of course, be non-basic solutions with more than three non-zero values, obtained by linearly combining basic solutions in the way indicated at the end of § 2. This actually happens in the example at hand, as will be seen below. The form of the solution S depends upon the relative magnitudes of x, y and z. If we regard x, y and z as variable parameters it is found that there are FOUR possible cases.

Case I ($z > 3x + y$): Here the solution of the example in § 6 applies, in the case where $a = 1$. Thus there are two families of solutions as follows: (i) $z > 3x + 4y$. The general solution is given by

$$\begin{aligned} x_1 &= \tfrac{1}{6}(z - 3x - y) - \tfrac{1}{2}\lambda \\ x_2 &= \lambda \\ x_3 &= \tfrac{1}{2}(y - \lambda) \\ x_4 &= x\,, \end{aligned}$$

where λ can have any value in the range $0 \leqslant \lambda \leqslant y$.
(ii) $3x + 4y > z > 3x + y$. The general solution is the same but λ has the range

$$0 \leqslant \lambda \leqslant \tfrac{1}{3}(z - 3x - y)\,.$$

Note that the two families of solutions have in common the solution given by

$$\begin{aligned} x_1 &= \tfrac{1}{6}(z - 3x - y) \\ x_3 &= \tfrac{1}{2}y \\ x_4 &= x\,, \end{aligned}$$

and the scrap L is, for each family, given by

$$L = 2x_1 + x_2 = \tfrac{1}{3}(z - 3x - y)\,.$$

Case II ($3x + y > z > \max\{(y - x), 3(x - y)\}$): There is a single solution given by

$$x_3 = \tfrac{1}{8}(-3x + 3y + z)$$

$$x_4 = \tfrac{1}{4}(x - y + z)$$

$$x_5 = \tfrac{1}{4}(3x + y - z)$$

and the scrap L is given by

$$L = 2x_5 = \tfrac{1}{2}(3x + y - z)\,.$$

Case III ($z < 3(x - y)$): There is a single solution,

$$x_4 = \tfrac{1}{3}z, \quad x_5 = y, \quad x_7 = x - y - \tfrac{1}{3}z,$$

and

$$L = 2x_5 + 9x_7 = 9x - 7y - 3z.$$

Case IV ($z < y - x$): There is a single solution,

$$x_3 = \tfrac{1}{2}z, \quad x_5 = x, \quad x_6 = \tfrac{1}{2}(-x + y - z)$$

and

$$L = 2x_5 + 6x_6 = -x + 3y - 3z.$$

It is to be noted that Case III applies when a relatively large number of 11 in. coils are required, and a relatively small number of 3 in. coils, that is $x > y$ and $z < 3(x - y)$. This is why set-up 7 appears in the solution. Similarly Case IV applies when a relatively large number of 7 in. coils are required and hence set-up 6 appears in the solution. In practice, of course, set-ups 6 and 7 are not likely to be used very often because of the large scrap entailed. It would be better to use some of the other set-ups and place the surplus 3 in. coils in stock, provided the stock of such coils did not become too large.

Yield. In judging the efficiency of the slitting programme determined by the solution S an obvious criterion of the efficiency is the yield, η, defined by

$$\eta = 1 - L/T,$$

where L is the scrap incurred and T is the initial amount of material.

Consider, for example, Case I where the programme is given by

$$x_1 = \tfrac{1}{6}(z - 3x - y) - \tfrac{1}{2}\lambda,\ x_2 = \lambda,\ x_3 = \tfrac{1}{2}(y - \lambda),\ x_4 = x.$$

The initial amount of material consists of $(x_1 + x_2 + x_3 + x_4)$ coils, each of 20 in. width. Thus

$$T = 20(x_1 + x_2 + x_3 + x_4) = 10(3x + 2y + z)/3.$$

It follows that

$$\eta = 1 - L/T = \frac{3(11x + 7y + 3z)}{10(3x + 2y + z)}.$$

Similarly the values of η may be calculated for the other cases.

For varying values of x, y and z it is of interest to know the maximum and minimum attainable values of η, for a fixed initial amount of material, say $T = k$. It is clear that minimum η corresponds to maximum scrap L, so that in Case I where $L = \tfrac{1}{3}(z - 3x - y)$, the minimum η is given by $x = y = 0$ and thus has the value 0·9. Similarly the maximum value of η, given by $z = 3x + y$, is 1. The other cases may be treated in the same way. The final results are tabulated as follows:

Case	Condition	Yield, η	Maximum	Minimum
I	$z > 3x + y$	$\frac{3(11x+7y+3z)}{10(3x+2y+z)}$	1; $z = 3x+y$	0·90; $x = y = 0$
II	$3x+y>z$ $z>3(x-y)$ $z>y-x$	$\frac{2(11x+7y+3z)}{5(5x+3y+z)}$	1; $z=3x+y$	0·90; $x=y, z=0$
III	$z<3(x-y)$ $x>y$	$\frac{11x+7y+3z}{20x}$	1; $y=0$, $z=3x$	0·55; $y=z=0$
IV	$z<y-x$ $y>x$	$\frac{11x+7y+3z}{10(x+y)}$	1; $x=0$, $y=z$	0·70; $x=z=0$

Geometrical Interpretation. The results on yield may be understood more clearly by making use of a geometrical representation. Let an order for x, y and z coils of widths 20 in., 11 in. and 7 in. respectively be represented by a point $P(x, y, z)$ in a three-dimensional Cartesian space. We are interested only in the positive octant, $x > 0$, $y > 0$, $z > 0$. This octant is divided into 4 regions, corresponding to the 4 cases in the following way.

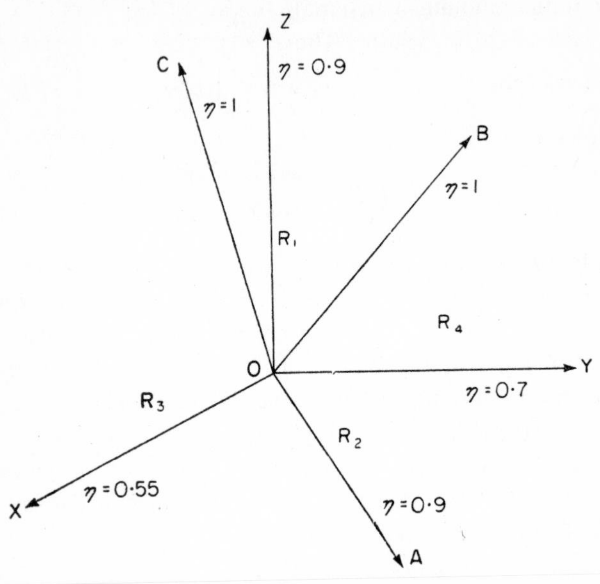

FIG. 1.

In Fig. 1 let OA, OB and OC denote the lines

$$OA\colon\ z = 0,\ x = y,$$

$$OB\colon\ x = 0,\ y = z,$$

$$OC\colon\ y = 0,\ z = 3x.$$

Then the octant is divided into 4 wedges, R_1, R_2, R_3 and R_4, each with vertex at O, and each having three edges thus:

Region	R_1	R_2	R_3	R_4
Edges	OB, OC, OZ	OB, OC, OA	OA, OC, OX	OA, OB, OY

Case I corresponds to the region R_1 in the sense that all points satisfying $z > 3x + y$ are in this region. Similarly Cases II, III and IV correspond to the regions R_2, R_3 and R_4 respectively.

It will be noticed that the lines OZ, OA, OX and OY correspond to the minimum yields in the four cases; and maximum yield occurs for the plane BOC in R_1 and R_2, and for the lines OC in R_3 and OB in R_4.

Improvement in Yield. Consider an order for x coils at 11 in., y at 7 in. and z at 3 in., and let the slitting programme producing these coils have an efficiency η. In view of the fact that small stocks of coils are kept, it would be possible to use a programme where the numbers of coils produced are x', y' and z', and make adjustments by reference to the stocks provided the differences $x' \sim x$, $y' \sim y$ and $z' \sim z$ are small. This would be desirable if the efficiency of this second programme exceeded η. The problem then is to determine if an increase in efficiency is produced by increasing or decreasing x, y and z. It is easy to see from Fig. 1 that in the case of R_1 or R_2 one would move from the point $P(x, y, z)$ to some point $P'(x', y', z')$ nearer to the plane BOC; in the case of R_3 to a point P' nearer to the line OC and in the case of R_4 to a point P' nearer to OB. The answer is given more precisely in terms of a simple result on ratios, as follows:

Let $r = N/D$ where

$$N = a_1x_1 + \ldots + a_nx_n, \qquad D = \alpha_1x_1 + \ldots + \alpha_nx_n,$$

and $x_1, \ldots, x_n$ are non-negative variables. Then r is increased by

$$\text{(i) an increase in } x_i, \text{ if either } \begin{pmatrix} a_i, \alpha_i > 0 \\ a_i/\alpha_i > r \end{pmatrix} \text{ or } \begin{pmatrix} a_i, \alpha_i < 0 \\ a_i/\alpha_i < r \end{pmatrix},$$

$$\text{or (ii) a decrease in } x_i, \text{ if either } \begin{pmatrix} a_i, \alpha_i > 0 \\ a_i/\alpha_i < r \end{pmatrix} \text{ or } \begin{pmatrix} a_i, \alpha_i < 0 \\ a_i/\alpha_i > r \end{pmatrix}.$$

In order to prove this result write

$$N = a_ix_i + R_i, \qquad D = \alpha_ix_i + S_i,$$

and consider an increase of x_i from x_i to $x_i + \varepsilon$ ($\varepsilon > 0$). The new value r_1 of r is given by

$$r_1 = \frac{a_i(x_i + \varepsilon) + R_i}{\alpha_i(x_i + \varepsilon) + S_i} = \frac{N + a_i\varepsilon}{D + \alpha_i\varepsilon},$$

and

$$r_1 - r = \frac{(Da_i - N\alpha_i)\varepsilon}{D(D + \alpha_i\varepsilon)}.$$

It follows that if $a_i, \alpha_i > 0$ then $r_1 > r$ if $a_i/\alpha_i > r$, while if $a_i, \alpha_i < 0$, then $r_1 > r$ if $a_i/\alpha_i < r$. This is result (i) and the second result follows in a similar way.

If we apply this result to the formulae for η in the four cases we obtain the programmes, given in the following table, for improving η.

Case	Programme
I ($0{\cdot}90 < \eta < 1$)	Increase x or y; decrease z
II ($0{\cdot}90 < \eta < 1$)	Decrease x; decrease y if $\eta > \frac{14}{15}$ and increase y if $\eta < \frac{14}{15}$; decrease z.
III ($0{\cdot}55 < \eta < 1$)	Decrease x; increase y or z.
IV ($0{\cdot}70 < \eta < 1$)	Increase x; decrease y; increase z.

Remark on the Trim Problem. The above analysis may be carried out whenever there is only a small number of coil sizes. In many practical cases, however, where the number of coil sizes is too large, recourse must be had to a numerical solution, devised for the case at hand. Very little has been published on such cases but the reader may care to consult the paper by Eisemann (6).

REFERENCES

For a more extensive list of references see the bibliography by G. F. Virginia Rohde in *Operat. Res. Quart.*, **5** (1957), 45–62.

1. M. A. ACZEL and A. H. RUSSELL, "New Methods of Solving Linear Programmes", *Operat. Res. Quart.*, **8** (1957), 206–19.
2. R. BELLMAN, "On the computational solution of linear programming problems involving almost-block diagonal matricies", *Mgmt Sci.*, **3** (1957), 403–6.

3. R. BELLMAN, "On a dynamic approach to the caterer problem", *Mgmt Sci.*, **3** (1957), 270–8.
4. A. CHARNES, W. W. COOPER and A. HENDERSON, *An Introduction to Linear Programming*, J. Wiley, N. Y. (1953).
5. G. B. DANTZIG, "Upper bounds, secondary constraints, and block triangularity in linear programming", *Econometricia*, **23** (1955), 174–83.
6. K. EISEMANN, "The trim problem", *Mgmt Sci.*, **3** (1957), 279–84.
7. R. FRISCH, *Principles of Linear Programming*, Memorandum, Inst. of Economics, Oslo Univ. (1954).
8. J. W. GADDUM, A. J. HOFFMAN and D. SOKOLOWSKY, "On the solution of the caterer problem", *Nav. Res. Logistics Quart.*, **1** (1954), 223–9.
9. A. J. HOFFMAN, "How to solve a linear programming problem", *Proceedings of the Second Symposium on Linear Programming*, June 27–9, 1955, vols. I and II, pp. 397–424, published by the National Bureau of Standards, Office of Scientific Publications, Washington, D. C.
10. W. W. JACOBS, "The caterer problem", *Nav. Res. Logistics Quart.*, **1** (1954), 154–65.
11. T. C. KOOPMANS (Editor), *Activity Analysis of Production and Allocation*, Cowles Commission for Research in Economics, Monograph No. 13, J. Wiley, N. Y. (1951).
12. W. PRAGER, "On the caterer problem", *Mgmt Sci.*, **3** (1956), 15–27.
13. D. G. PRINZ, "Some experiences on the Manchester Computer with the Simplex Method", *Report of the Conference on Linear Programming*, May, 1954, arranged by Ferranti Ltd., London.
14. S. VAJDA, *Readings in Linear Programming*, Pitman, London, 1958.
15. S. VAJDA, *The Theory of Games and Linear Programming*, Methuen, London, 1956.

CHAPTER III

TRANSPORTATION AND ASSIGNMENT

1. Introduction

The problem of transportation, in its basic form, is concerned with the following situation. There are m sources $S_1, ..., S_m$ and n destinations $D_1, ..., D_n$. Suppose that at S_i there are p_i units of some commodity P and that the cost of transporting one unit from S_i to D_j is $c_{ij}(i = 1, ..., m;\ j = 1, ..., n)$. Further suppose that at destination D_j there is a requirement of q_j units of P, where obviously $\sum_i p_i = \sum_j q_j$. The problem is to determine how many units, x_{ij}, should be transported from S_i to D_j so that the total cost of transporting all the units to their destinations shall be a minimum. Mathematically it may be expressed as follows: find mn numbers x_{ij}, either zero or positive integers, such that

$$\text{(i)} \quad \sum_j x_{ij} = p_i\,; \qquad \sum_i x_{ij} = q_j\,,$$

(ii) T is a minimum where

$$T = \sum_{i,j} c_{ij} x_{ij}\,.$$

A related problem is that of assignment. This arises in personnel management in the following way. Suppose that there are n men each capable of performing each of n tasks; and let there exist a numerical rating for each man on each task. The problem is to assign the men to the tasks (one man to one task) so that the sum of the n ratings for the assigned tasks is a maximum. Such an assignment is called optimal, and there may be several optimal assignments. The total number of possible assignments is clearly $n!$, so that it is impracticable, even for moderate values of n, to calculate all the assignments and choose those which are optimal by inspection.

The problem may be expressed in mathematical form as follows:

Let r_{ij} be the rating for the ith man on the jth task, and let R denote the $n \times n$ matrix (r_{ij}). Find n elements of R, no two of which lie in the same row or column, such that their sum is a maximum.

If X is an $n \times n$ matrix, each of whose elements is 0 or 1, the problem may be otherwise expressed thus: find a matrix X, such that

(i) in every row and column of X there is one and only one non-zero element,

(ii) T is a minimum where

$$T = \sum_{i,j} x_{ij} r_{ij} .$$

It is clear that the problems of transportation and assignment are special problems in linear programming and thus the Simplex Method, or any other general method, is, at least in principle, available for their solution. But in practice the size of the problem is frequently too great for a reasonable degree of computation and special methods are necessary. Two methods (one for transportation and one for assignment) are presented in this chapter. No proofs are given; the aim in each case is to demonstrate a method rather than to prove that it is correct.

THE PROBLEM OF TRANSPORTATION

2. The initial solution

We shall firstly determine an initial solution and then systematically improve it until a solution is obtained which makes the total cost T of transportation a minimum. There are various ways of obtaining an initial solution, and the method presented here has been found to be reasonably efficient in that the total cost associated with the solution is not too far removed from the minimal cost.

As an example suppose that there are three sources and five destinations ($m = 3$, $n = 5$) and let the p_i, q_j and costs c_{ij} be as indicated in Fig. 1.

p			K		
$S_1 : 4$	2	11	10	3	7
$S_2 : 8$	1	4	7	2	1
$S_3 : 9$	3	9	4	8	12
q	3	3	4	5	6
	D_1	D_2	D_3	D_4	D_5

FIG. 1.

The matrix K of costs, where $K = (c_{ij})$ is called the *cost matrix* and the requirements figures $q_1, ..., q_j$ are called the *deficiencies*. We first determine an *ordering* of the columns as follows. Consider the jth column, C_j, and its deficiency number, q_j. However we allocate q_j units amongst the cells of C_j the difference between the maximum and minimum possible costs of allocation is $q_j(\max_i c_{ij} - \min_i c_{ij})$, assuming temporarily that the figures p_i for the sources are no restriction. This is the maximum possible saving in the cost of allocating to column C_j the q_j units in the position of $\min_i c_{ij}$. Hence we order the columns according to the magnitude of

$$q_j(\max_i c_{ij} - \min_i c_{ij})$$

for $j = 1, 2, ..., n$. Having determined this order we now allocate the deficiencies of the 1st, 2nd, 3rd, ... columns under this ordering, in such a way that the row restrictions are taken into account; and we do this until the surpluses in one row have been exhausted.

Example:

Cost Matrix

p	D_1	D_2	D_3	D_4	D_5
$S_1 : 4$	2	11	10	3	7
$S_2 : 8$	1	4	7	2	1
$S_3 : 9$	3	9	4	8	12
q	3	3	4	5	6

$D_{max} - D_{min}$:	2	7	6	6	11
$\times q$:	6	21	24	30	66
order :	5	4	3	2	1

Allocation :

			3	0
0	0	0	2	6
			0	0

Next repeat the process on the remaining rows and columns, thus:

S_1 : 1	2	11	10
S_3 : 9	3	9	4

Max − min :	1	2	6
$\times q$:	3	6	24
order :	3	2	1

Allocation :

1	0	0
2	3	4

Combining this with the first partial allocation we get a starting solution thus:

Solution $\mathfrak{S}_1$ $T = 70$

1	0	0	3	0
0	0	0	2	6
2	3	4	0	0

This solution contains 7 non-zero entries. In the general case it is essential for the solution to contain $m + n - 1$ entries before we can proceed.

3. Testing a solution

For any solution, $\mathfrak{S}_1$, it is necessary to have (i) a test showing if the solution is optimal, (ii) a method for improving the solution if it is not optimal. To cope with (i) we proceed as follows.

Construct an $m \times n$ matrix, H, and in the cells of H corresponding to the occupied cells of solution $\mathfrak{S}_1$ place the corresponding costs, with for reference purposes a mark in each cell as shown in Fig. 2.

	H					*C*
	○ 2	8	3	○ 3	2	2
	1	7	2	○ 2	○ 1	1
	○ 3	○ 9	○ 4	4	3	3
R	0	6	1	1	0	

FIG. 2.

Adjoin a row R and a column C of cells, as shown, and place a zero in any cell of R or C. Here it is taken arbitrarily in the first cell of R. Next, evaluate numbers r_i and c_j to be placed in the cells of R and C in such a way that

$$r_i + c_j = c_{ij} \tag{1}$$

where c_{ij} is the cost in the ith row and jth column. It will always be possible to evaluate the r_i and c_j, provided the solution being tested is not degenerate. Having found the r_i and c_j we complete the filling of the cells of H by using the same formula (1). Next we subtract from H the cost matrix, as shown in Fig. 3.

H

○ 2	8	3	○ 3	2
1	7	2	○ 2	○ 1
○ 3	○ 9	○ 4	4	3

−

K

2	11	10	3	7
1	4	7	2	1
3	9	4	8	12

=

L

*	–	–	*	–
0	3	–	*	*
*	–	*	–	–

FIG. 3.

In the resulting matrix L (called the test matrix) the entries in the cells corresponding to the occupied cells of the solution being tested are zero (they are here marked with an asterisk), and the other entries may be negative, zero or positive.

Rule: If the entries in L are all negative or zero the solution being tested is optimal. If any entries are positive the solution may be improved.

4. Improvement of a solution

If the test of § 3 indicates a solution is not optimal it may be improved by the following process. There are three steps.

STEP 1: Take the largest number h in the matrix L ($h = 3$ in the example above), and, on the diagram exhibiting solution $\mathfrak{S}_1$, mark a *circuit* (see Fig. 4) which proceeds as follows. Take the cell P_0 corresponding to h and

(i) in the row containing P_0 proceed to the nearest occupied cell, say P_1, which lies in a column which contains another occupied cell, say P_2,

(ii) proceed from P_1 to P_2,

(iii) repeat operations (i) and (ii) with reference to the cell P_2 (in the example thus obtaining P_3 and P_4) and continue as necessary (in the example obtain P_5 and P_0) until eventually the initial cell P_0 is reached. This completes the circuit.

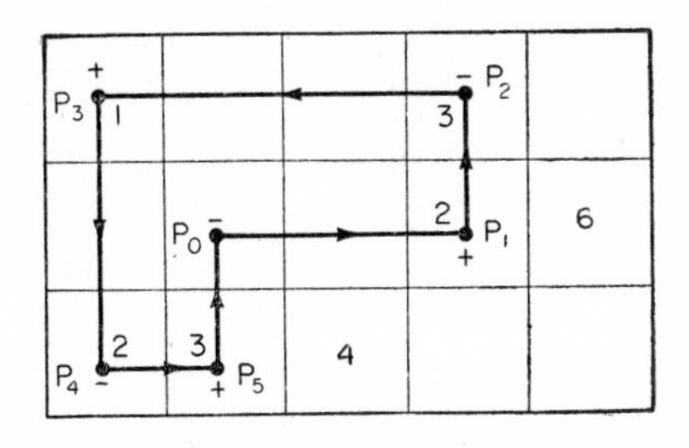

FIG. 4.

STEP 2: At the corners of the circuit attach alternately positive and negative signs, commencing with a negative sign at P_0. Thus $P_0 P_1 P_2 P_3 P_4 P_5 P_0$ produces the sequence $- + - + - +$. Next determine the *minimum*, k, of the numbers in the occupied cells (on the corners of the circuit) which carry a *positive* sign. In the example, $k = 1$, since P_1, P_3 and P_5 carry positive signs and allocation numbers 2, 1, and 3 respectively.

STEP 3. In the cells which contain corners of the circuit, alternately allocate $+k$ and $-k$, placing k in the cells which carry a negative sign and $-k$ in the others. Thus in the example, cells P_0, P_1, P_2, P_3, P_4 and P_5 will now carry allocation numbers 1, 1, 4, 0, 3 and 2 respectively. In this way a new solution $\mathfrak{S}_2$ is obtained and this solution will have an associated cost which is *less* than that of $\mathfrak{S}_1$. Thus $\mathfrak{S}_2$ is an improvement on $\mathfrak{S}_1$.

The solution must now be tested for optimality. If it is not optimal an iteration based on the above procedure will ultimately lead to an optimal solution since at each stage the cost is reduced. In the example above the new solution is as follows:

$\mathfrak{S}_2$:

0	0	0	4	0
0	1	0	1	6
3	2	4	0	0

$T = 67$

The cost is 67 (as against 70 for $\mathfrak{S}_1$), and application of the test shows that this solution is optimal, the test matrix being of the form

L :

–	–	–	*	–
–	*	–	*	*
*	*	*	–	–

Later we shall see that, since all entries of L other than those bearing an asterisk (*) are negative, $\mathfrak{S}_2$ is the *only* optimal solution.

5. Degenerate solutions

Consider a transportation problem with an $m \times n$ cost matrix. Let $N = m + n - 1$. A solution may involve N allocation numbers (all integral) or less.

DEFINITION: If a solution to an $m \times n$ transportation problem involves less than N allocation numbers it is said to be *degener-*

ate. If there are M ($< N$) allocation numbers, $N - M$ is called the *degree of degeneration* of the solution.

The problem now to be considered is how to test if a degenerate solution is optimal, and, in the case where it is not optimal, how to improve it. If an attempt be made to apply the test described in § 3 it will be found impossible, in the case of a degenerate solution, to fill all the cells in the matrix H. To cope with this situation proceed as follows:

STEP 1. Evaluate as much as possible the entries for H, R and C, starting with a zero in some cell of R or C.

STEP 2. Place a small (unspecified) number ε in a cell of the solution matrix, choosing the cell corresponding to some vacant cell in H after the application of Step 1. Evaluate as much as possible of the cells in H, R and C.

STEP 3. If there remain any unevaluated cells in H, R or C, repeat Step 2, using a second (different) ε.

Continue to apply Steps 2 and 3 until all cells in H, R and C have been evaluated. It is then possible to proceed with § 3 and test whether the initial degenerate solution is optimal. If it is not optimal, an improvement may be obtained in the manner described in § 4. Repeated application may be necessary, since the first application may merely result in a transfer of ε from one cell to another. Ultimately, however, an optimal solution will be obtained. It is to be noted that this optimal solution may or may not be degenerate, and in the complete process of passing from the initial degenerate solution to the optimal solution the intermediate solutions may be either degenerate or non-degenerate.

As an example of the above procedure consider the 3×5 problem specified by the following table.

Cost Matrix

19	14	5	3	7	2
7	10	9	4	15	13
14	1	12	6	11	8
	11	4	6	9	10

The method of § 2 leads to a degenerate starting solution, $\mathfrak{S}_1$.

$\mathfrak{S}_1$:

			9	10
	4	3		
11		3		

$T = 160$

An application of the above process, with ε initially taken in the (1,1) cell leads to a shift of ε into the (1,2) cell. Repeated application of the process leads to an improved solution $\mathfrak{S}_2$.

$\mathfrak{S}_2$:

	3		6	10
	1	6		
11			3	

$T = 154$

On testing it is found that $\mathfrak{S}_1$ is optimal (and, as will be seen later, the only optimal solution).

6. Alternative optimal solutions

It frequently happens that a transportation problem has several optimal solutions. A method is now described whereby these may be obtained.

Suppose that, for a given problem, a starting solution has been obtained by the method of § 3, and improved (perhaps repeatedly) by the method of § 4 until an optimal solution has emerged. This means that the entries of the test matrix L are all negative or zero.

Rule: If the test matrix L, corresponding to an optimal solution contains any zeros (called essential zeros), other than in the cells marked with an asterisk, there exist alternative optimal solutions.

To find the alternative solutions apply the improvement process of § 4, where now $h = 0$. It may be that there are several essential zeros in the test matrix L, and in this case one makes an application to these zeros in turn. A set of alternative optimal solutions is obtained and for each of these the test matrix L must be evaluated. These new test matrices may contain essential zeros which lead to further alternative solutions. Ultimately a complete set of optimal solutions is obtained.

As an example consider the 4×6 problem specified by the following table:

Cost Matrix

7	2	11	3	12	10	8
12	3	2	5	3	4	2
14	1	9	2	4	1	4
9	4	7	8	9	5	7
	5	3	8	11	6	9

The starting solution is:

		7			
			11		1
				6	8
5	3	1			

$T = 143$

This is degenerate, so that improvement involves the use of the ε technique. One obtains the non-degenerate optimal solution I.

		7			
	3		4		5
		1	7	6	
5					4

$T = 133$

SOLUTION I

and the test matrix of this solution is found to be of the form

–	–	*	–	–	–
–	*	–	*	–	*
–	–	*	*	*	–
*	0	–	–	0	*

An application of the improvement process of § 4 to the essential zeros in the cells (4, 2) and (4, 5) leads respectively to two further optimal solutions, II and III.

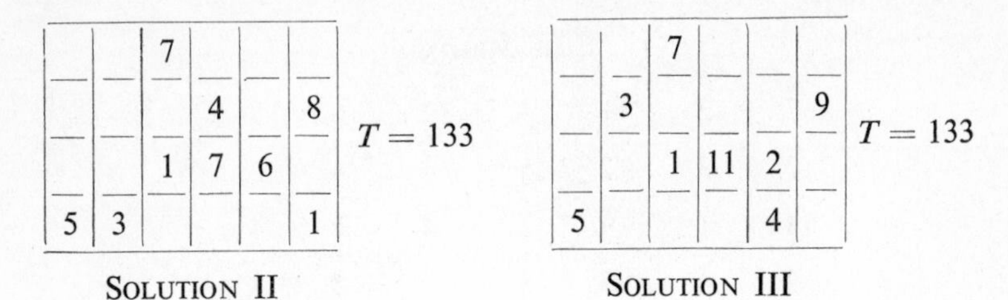

		7			
			4		8
		1	7	6	
5	3				1

$T = 133$

SOLUTION II

		7			
	3				9
		1	11	2	
5				4	

$T = 133$

SOLUTION III

Application of the improvement process to the test matrices of these solutions leads to no further solutions, so the final result consists of the three optimal solutions, I, II and III. It is to be noted that I and III are degenerate, and II non-degenerate.

7. Basic and derived solutions

In the preceding treatment the solutions of an $m \times n$ transportation problem always involved $m + n - 1$ non-zero allocation numbers or less. Such solutions are called *basic*.

Let $\mathfrak{S}_1, \mathfrak{S}_2, ..., \mathfrak{S}_r$ be a set of basic solutions, each of which involves the *same* cost T. Let $\lambda_1, ..., \lambda_r$ be any non-negative numbers such that

$$\lambda_1 + \lambda_2 + ... + \lambda_r = 1.$$

It is easy to show that $\mathfrak{S}$, where $\mathfrak{S} = \lambda_1\mathfrak{S}_1 + ... + \lambda_r\mathfrak{S}_r$, is also a solution and that it involves the cost T. The solutions $\mathfrak{S}$, for varying $\lambda_1, ..., \lambda_r$, are called *derived* solutions. If the basic solutions are optimal it follows that solutions derived from them are also optimal.

To illustrate the ideas consider the three basic optimal solutions I, II and III of the example of § 6. By considering $a\text{I} + b\text{II} + c\text{III}$ where $a + b + c = 1$, it is found that the solution at the top of page 75 is optimal.

In this solution the allocation numbers will not normally be integers and in practical problems it may happen that only integral

		7			
	$3(a+c$		$4(a+b)$		$5a+8b$ $+9c$
		1	$7a+7b$ $+11c$	$6a+6b$ $+2c$	
5	$3b$				$4a+b$

$T = 133$

solutions are admissible. The solution will be integral only if $3b$, $4c$, $4a+b$, $7a+7b+11c$, $6a+6b+2c$, $3(a+c)$, $4(a+b)$, $5a+8b+9c$ are integral and $a+b+c=1$. Write

$$3b = r, \quad 4c = s,$$

where r and s are integers. Then $a = 1 - \frac{1}{3}r - \frac{1}{4}s$ and it is easily verified that the above conditions are satisfied. The final result is this.

There are twenty integral optimal solutions to the problem of § 6. These may be written in the form

		7			
	$3-r$		$4-s$		$5+r+s$
		1	$7+s$	$6-s$	
5	r			s	$4-r-s$

where $r = 0, 1, 2$ *or* 3 *and* $s = 0, 1, 2, 3$ *or* 4. *The* 3 *basic solutions, (I, II and III above) are given by* $r = s = 0$; $r = 3$, $s = 0$ *and* $r = 0$, $s = 4$ *respectively. The* 17 *derived solutions involve* 10 *or* 11 *non-zero allocation numbers.*

THE PROBLEM OF ASSIGNMENT

8. The theorem of König

Of fundamental importance in the solution of the assignment problem is a combinatorial theorem due to the Hungarian mathematician Dénes König. This theorem relates to a matrix some of whose elements are zero. Consider, for example, the matrix M, where

$$M = \begin{pmatrix} 2 & 0 & 4 & {}^\circ 0 \\ 3 & {}^\circ 0^* & 5 & 3 \\ {}^\circ 0 & 2 & 0^* & 0 \\ 6 & 3 & 4 & 0^* \end{pmatrix}$$

It is observed that the *minimum* number, a, of lines (rows or columns) containing *all* the zeros of M is three (the 3rd row and the 2nd and 4th columns); and that this is also the *maximum* number, b, of zeros with the property that no two lie in the same row or column (two sets of such zeros are marked, one with a * and one with a °). The theorem of König states that for any matrix, $a = b$. Before stating it formally we introduce the following definitions:

DEFINITION 1: Two elements of a matrix are said to be *independent* if they belong to two distinct rows and columns. Several elements are independent if the elements of each pair are independent.

DEFINITION 2: A line means a row or a column of a matrix. Thus there are $2n$ lines associated with an $n \times n$ matrix, R.

DEFINITION 3: If the symbol c is written at the bottom of a column or to the right of a row of R the corresponding line is said to be **covered**. Any element in a covered line is said to be covered. It is clear that an element may be uncovered (when the row and the column containing the element are not covered), once covered or twice covered.

We can now state the

Theorem of König. The maximum number of independent zeros of a matrix, R, equals the minimum number of lines required to cover all the zeros of R. A proof of this theorem may be found in the book (6) by König.

9. Solutions to the problem of assignment

Various methods have been devised for solving the assignment problem. One of the earliest is that of Easterfield (2), who, by a process of successive adjustment to the columns of a matrix arrives at the solution. Another method, due to Dwyer (1), uses a 'method of optimal regions'. Recently, Kuhn (7) developed what he called 'the Hungarian method', which relies heavily upon the theorem of König. This method has been clearly outlined by Flood (5), and variants of the method have been described and compared by Kuhn (8). An efficient algorithm for solving the problem was published in 1957 by Munkres (11), and we shall present the steps of this algorithm below.

In the introduction to this chapter the problem of assignment was formulated with reference to an $n \times n$ matrix, R, of positive numbers, r_{ij}. Let

$$r = \max_{i,j} r_{ij} \qquad (i, j = 1, ..., n)$$

and denote by S the matrix (s_{ij}) where $s_{ij} = r - r_{ij}$. Then another formulation is this: find a permutation $(i_1, ..., i_n)$ of the numbers $(1, ..., n)$ such that T is a *minimum*, where

$$T = s_{1i_1} + s_{2i_2} + ... + s_{ni_n} \, .$$

It is to be noted that T is a sum of n independent elements of S. We shall consider the problem in this form. Suppose that a number, v, is subtracted from each of the elements of some column of S. Then the $n!$ possible values of T are all decreased by the amount v and hence the permutation leading to a minimal value of T is unchanged. A similar result holds if a number, u, is subtracted from the elements of any row. Thus we have the following important

LEMMA: The permutation making T minimal for the matrix (s_{ij}) is unaltered if we replace s_{ij} by $s_{ij} - u_i - v_j$, where u_i and v_j are arbitrary numbers.

This lemma together with the theorem of König provides a basis for our solution. Firstly, subtract from the elements of each row of S, the minimum element in the row; and from the matrix so obtained subtract from the elements of each column the minimum element in the column. If the resulting matrix is S^*, it is clear that there is at least one zero in every row and column of S^*, for example,

$$S = \begin{pmatrix} 3.1 & 2.5 & 1.7 \\ 2.4 & 5.3 & 4.6 \\ 1.2 & 3.7 & 5.7 \end{pmatrix}, \quad S^* = \begin{pmatrix} 1.4 & 0 & 0 \\ 0 & 2.1 & 2.2 \\ 0 & 1.7 & 4.5 \end{pmatrix}$$

The matrix S^* obtained in this way will be called a *standard form*. By the lemma, the permutation for which T is a minimum is the same for S and S^*. In what follows it will be assumed that S itself has been taken initially in standard form.

For any matrix M, let $\nu(M)$ denote the maximum number of independent zeros in M. The second step is to find $\nu(S)$ where S is in standard form. This, by König's theorem, equals the minimum number of lines required to cover all the zeros of S. For matrices of small order the number ν may be found by inspection, but a systematic and exhaustive procedure is necessary for higher order matrices. Such a procedure is provided by the algorithm of Munkres given below.

If $\nu = n$ (the order of S) then there are n independent zeros in S and the corresponding elements in the original form of S provide a solution to our problem.

If $\nu < n$ it is necessary to reduce S as follows. There are ν lines covering all the zeros of S. Let S_1 be the matrix formed by the non-covered elements of S (S_1 may be a rectangular matrix), and let h be the least element of S_1. Subtract h from each non-covered element of S, add h to each element of S which is twice covered, and let S^* be the resulting matrix (of order n). For S^* now find $\nu(S^*)$ by the process described above in relation to S. As before, if $\nu = n$, our problem is solved; if $\nu < n$ we derive a second matrix, S^{**}, from S^* by the same process used to derive S^* from S, and we find the value of $\nu(S^{**})$. This iterative procedure is carried out until a matrix is obtained for which $\nu = n$. At this stage our problem is solved, and a set of n independent zeros is given by the algorithm of Munkres. It is, of course, necessary to show that the iteration terminates after a finite number of stages. This we do in the following way.

Consider the process whereby S^* is derived from S, namely the subtraction of h from each non-covered element of S and the addition of h to each element of S which is twice covered. This is clearly the same as the addition of h to the elements of each of the ν covered lines of S (so that $2h$ is added to elements twice covered) followed by the subtraction of h from the resulting matrix. Let $\Sigma(S)$ denote the sum of the elements of S. The second process, just described, involves the addition of $hn\nu$ to $\Sigma(S)$ and the subtraction of hn^2. Thus

$$\sum(S^*) = \sum(S) - nh(n - \nu) < \sum(S).$$

It follows that the iterative procedure, $S \to S^* \to S^{**}_{\to} \ldots$, involves at each stage a reduction in Σ so that the process must terminate.

We have now effectively solved the problem of assignment. An example is given in § 11. The reader should note that we have yet to give a procedure for determining, for a given matrix M, (i) the number $\nu(M)$, (ii) a set of $\nu(M)$ independent zeros. This is given in the next section.

10. The algorithm of Munkres†

In applying this algorithm the reader should note at the outset that it is frequently necessary to attach a star or a prime to a zero, thus forming 0^* or $0'$. We shall use the language: "star a zero" or "prime a zero".

Let S be taken in standard form. Star any set $\mathfrak{S}_0$ of independent zeros and cover their columns.

(*) Consider an uncovered column. This, since S is in standard form, contains at least one zero. Let A be a zero of the column. If the row of A does not contain a 0^* then A is independent of the zeros of $\mathfrak{S}_0$, so star A, add it to $\mathfrak{S}_0$ and cover the column

† The algorithm is followed by an example. In case of difficulty the reader should consider the example in conjunction with the algorithm. The latter consists of a slight modification of the procedure given by Munkres (11).

of A; otherwise leave the column of A uncovered. Repeat from (*) until the only uncovered columns, consisting of a set, $C_1^{(1)}, \ldots, C_r^{(1)}$, are such that the row of every zero which lies in one of these columns contains a 0*. Let $\mathfrak{S}_1$ be the set of such zeros.
(**) Take a zero of $\mathfrak{S}_1$, prime it, cover its row, and uncover the column of the 0* in its row. Repeat until all zeros in $C_1^{(1)}, \ldots, C_r^{(1)}$, are covered. Let the process involve the uncovering of columns $C_1^{(2)}, \ldots, C_s^{(2)}$ and note that each of these columns contains a 0*. Consider the set $\mathfrak{S}_2$ of uncovered zeros in $C_1^{(2)}, \ldots, C_s^{(2)}$. A zero of $\mathfrak{S}_2$ may or may not have a 0* in its row. If it has *not*, then underline it. If it *has*, then prime it, cover the 0* and uncover the column of the 0*. Repeat until all zeros of $\mathfrak{S}_2$ are covered, and suppose that in the process columns $C_1^{(3)}, \ldots, C_t^{(3)}$ are uncovered.

Now apply to $C_1^{(3)}, \ldots, C_t^{(3)}$ the same process as just applied to $C_1^{(2)}, \ldots, C_s^{(2)}$ and repeat if necessary. Ultimately we obtain a set of covered rows and columns, containing *all* the zeros of S, except those underlined.

Consider the set $\mathfrak{S}$ of underlined zeros, and let Z_0 be a zero of $\mathfrak{S}$. Z_0 is in a column containing a 0*, Z_1, and in a row not containing a 0* (this row and column are not covered). Also since the column of Z_1 is not covered, the row of Z_1 is covered and hence it contains a 0*, say Z_2. Now Z_2 may or may not be a column containing a 0*. If the column does contain a 0*, say Z_3, then this column is uncovered, and thus the row of Z_3 is covered, and hence contains a 0′, Z_4. Continue this process until finally, for some integer i, a set of zeros,

$$Z_0, Z_1, Z_2, \ldots, Z_{2i-1}, Z_{2i},$$

is obtained where Z_{2i} is a 0′ with no 0* in its column.

Note that $Z_1, Z_3, \ldots, \ldots, Z_{2i-1}$ are starred and $Z_0, Z_2, \ldots, Z_{2i}$ are primed zeros. Define the path $Z_0, Z_1, \ldots, Z_{2i}$ to be a *circuit associated with* Z_0 and note that this circuit involves $i+1$ rows and $i+1$ columns of S. Now star $Z_0, Z_2, \ldots, Z_{2i}$ and unstar Z_1, $Z_3, \ldots, Z_{2i-1}$. This process clearly augments by ONE the number of starred zeros, and these are all independent.

Next note that it may be possible to repeat the procedure of the last paragraph with respect to another underlined zero $\bar{Z}_0$ of $\mathfrak{S}$. This will certainly be possible if the circuits associated with Z_0 and $\bar{Z}_0$ are independent, that is, if they do not involve a common row or column. The procedure should be carried out on as many zeros of $\mathfrak{S}$ as is practicable. Then, with the augmented set $\mathfrak{S}_0$ of starred zeros so obtained, repeat the whole process, if necessary; that is, remove all primes, uncover all rows, cover the column of every starred zero in $\mathfrak{S}_0$, determine the set $\mathfrak{S}_1$ of zeros in uncovered columns, and repeat from (**).

Ultimately one obtains a set of rows and columns, $\nu(S)$ in number, covering *all* the zeros of S. And the set of starred zeros so obtained is a maximal independent set.

Example: It is observed that since the application of the algorithm does not involve altering the value of any element of S (the essential fact is whether each element is or is not zero) it is sufficient to take each element of S to be 0 or 1. This we shall do in the following example.

Consider a matrix of order 6, namely,

$$S = \begin{pmatrix} 1 & 0 & 1 & 0 & 1 & 1 \\ 0^* & 1 & 1 & 1 & 1 & 1 \\ 1 & 1 & 0^* & 1 & 1 & 1 \\ 1 & 0 & 1 & 1 & 1 & 1 \\ 1 & 1 & 1 & 0^* & 0 & 1 \\ 1 & 0^* & 0 & 1 & 1 & 0 \end{pmatrix}$$
$$\begin{matrix} c & c & c & c & & \end{matrix}$$

and let $\mathfrak{S}_0$ consist of the four starred zeros shown. It is easily seen that the first set, $C_1^{(1)}$, $C_2^{(1)}$ of uncovered columns consists of columns 5 and 6, and that the set $\mathfrak{S}_1$ consists of the two zeros in these columns.

Now prime the zeros of $\mathfrak{S}_1$, cover their rows and uncover columns 2 and 4. Then $C_1^{(2)}, C_2^{(2)}$, are these columns, and the coverings are as follows:

$$S = \begin{pmatrix} 1 & \underline{0} & 1 & \underline{0} & 1 & 1 \\ 0^* & 1 & 1 & 1 & 1 & 1 \\ 1 & 1 & 0^* & 1 & 1 & 1 \\ 1 & \underline{0} & 1 & 1 & 1 & 1 \\ 1 & 1 & 1 & 0^* & 0' & 1 \\ 1 & 0^* & 0 & 1 & 1 & 0' \end{pmatrix} \begin{matrix} \\ \\ \\ \\ c \\ c \end{matrix}$$
$$\begin{matrix} c & & c & & & \end{matrix}$$

Now $\mathfrak{S}_2$ consists of the three uncovered zeros in columns 2 and 4, and each of these, since it does not have a 0* in its row, is underlined. Also it is clear that the four covered lines shown cover all zeros except those underlined. Thus $\mathfrak{S}_2 = \mathfrak{S}$.

There are now two possibilities with regard to the treatment of the zeros of $\mathfrak{S}$. Either two independent circuits can be drawn, as shown in I, leading at once to the final solution, Ia, with $\nu(S) = 6$; or else the single circuit shown in II, leading to the intermediate result IIa with a set of FIVE independent zeros. In this last matrix it is not possible to provide a circuit for either of the underlined zeros. Hence the complete procedure must be applied to IIa. This is shown in III, with the intermediate result IIIa, and the final result IIIb, which is the same as Ia.

$$\text{I} \begin{pmatrix} 1 & \underline{0} & 1 & \underline{0}\,Z_0 & 1 & 1 \\ 0^* & 1 & 1 & 1 & 1 & 1 \\ 1 & 1 & 0^* & 1 & 1 & 1 \\ 1 & \underline{0}\,Z_0 & 1 & 1 & 1 & 1 \\ 1 & 1 & 1 & 0^*Z_1 & 0'\,Z_2 & 1 \\ 1 & 0^*Z_1 & 0 & 1 & 1 & 0'\,Z_2 \end{pmatrix} \rightarrow \text{Ia} \begin{pmatrix} 1 & 0 & 1 & 0^* & 1 & 1 \\ 0^* & 1 & 1 & 1 & 1 & 1 \\ 1 & 1 & 0^* & 1 & 1 & 1 \\ 1 & 0^* & 1 & 1 & 1 & 1 \\ 1 & 1 & 1 & 0 & 0^* & 1 \\ 1 & 0 & 0 & 1 & 1 & 0^* \end{pmatrix}$$

Final Solution: $\nu(S) = 6$.

$$\text{II} \begin{pmatrix} 1 & \underline{0}\,Z_0 & 1 & \underline{0} & 1 & 1 \\ 0^* & 1 & 1 & 1 & 1 & 1 \\ 1 & 1 & 0^* & 1 & 1 & 1 \\ 1 & \underline{0} & 1 & 1 & 1 & 1 \\ 1 & 1 & 1 & 0^* & 0' & 1 \\ 1 & 0^*Z_1 & 0 & 1 & 1 & 0'\,Z_2 \end{pmatrix} \rightarrow \text{IIa} \begin{pmatrix} 1 & 0^* & 1 & \underline{0} & 1 & 1 \\ 0^* & 1 & 1 & 1 & 1 & 1 \\ 1 & 1 & 0^* & 1 & 1 & 1 \\ 1 & \underline{0} & 1 & 1 & 1 & 1 \\ 1 & 1 & 1 & 0^* & 0' & 1 \\ 1 & 0 & 0 & 1 & 1 & 0^* \end{pmatrix}$$

$$\text{III}\begin{pmatrix}1 & 0^* & 1 & 0 & 1 & 1\\ 0^* & 1 & 1 & 1 & 1 & 1\\ 1 & 1 & 0^* & 1 & 1 & 1\\ 1 & 0 & 1 & 1 & 1 & 1\\ 1 & 1 & 1 & 0^* & 0 & 1\\ 1 & 0 & 0 & 1 & 1 & 0^*\end{pmatrix} \rightarrow \text{IIIa}\begin{pmatrix}1 & 0^*Z_1 & 1 & 0'Z_2 & 1 & 1\\ 0^* & 1 & 1 & 1 & 1 & 1\\ 1 & 1 & 0^* & 1 & 1 & 1\\ 1 & \underline{0}\,Z_0 & 1 & 1 & 1 & 1\\ 1 & 1 & 1 & 0^*Z_3 & 0'Z_4 & 1\\ 1 & 0' & 0 & 1 & 1 & 0^*\end{pmatrix}\begin{matrix}c\\ \\ \\ \\ c\\ c\end{matrix}$$

$$\begin{matrix}c & c & c & c & & c\end{matrix} \qquad \qquad \begin{matrix}c & & c & & & \end{matrix}$$

$$\downarrow$$

$$\text{IIIb}\begin{pmatrix}1 & 0 & 1 & 0^* & 1 & 1\\ 0^* & 1 & 1 & 1 & 1 & 1\\ 1 & 1 & 0^* & 1 & 1 & 1\\ 1 & 0^* & 1 & 1 & 1 & 1\\ 1 & 1 & 1 & 0 & 0^* & 1\\ 1 & 0 & 0 & 1 & 1 & 0^*\end{pmatrix}$$

Final Solution: $\nu(S) = 6$.

11. The complete solution in a particular case

In this section the method described in § 9 is illustrated by solving the assignment problem considered by Easterfield (2), where the rating matrix, S, is given in original and in standard form by

$$\begin{pmatrix}9 & 22 & 58 & 11 & 19 & 27\\ 43 & 78 & 72 & 50 & 63 & 48\\ 41 & 28 & 91 & 37 & 45 & 33\\ 74 & 42 & 27 & 49 & 39 & 32\\ 36 & 11 & 57 & 22 & 25 & 18\\ 3 & 56 & 53 & 31 & 17 & 28\end{pmatrix} \qquad \begin{pmatrix}6 & 11 & 31 & 0^* & 2 & 9\\ 10 & 37 & 15 & 9 & 16 & 0^*\\ 23 & 2 & 49 & 11 & 13 & 0\\ 71 & 31 & 0^* & 38 & 22 & 14\\ 33 & 0^* & 30 & 11 & 8 & 0\\ 0 & 45 & 26 & 20 & 0^* & 10\end{pmatrix}$$

respectively. For the purpose of applying the algorithm of § 10, let the initial set $\mathfrak{S}_0$ of independent zeros be those shown with a star in the standard form. In this case the only uncovered column is the first and the only zero in this column is in the (6,1) position. On covering row 6 and uncovering column 5 the application of the algorithm is completed, and it is seen that all the zeros of S are covered by FIVE lines, that is $\nu(S) = 5$.

The matrix, S_1, consisting of the uncovered elements of S is a 5×2 matrix whose least element is 2. Using the process described in § 9 we obtain the modified form S^* of S and apply the algorithm again. It is found that $\nu(S^*) = 5$, as before. Repetition of this procedure leads to a matrix S^{**} for which again $\nu(S^{**}) = 5$, and another application leads to the matrix.

$$\begin{pmatrix} 4 & 17 & 39 & 0^* & 0 & 17 \\ 0 & 35 & 15 & 1 & 6 & 0^* \\ 13 & \underline{0} & 49 & 3 & 3 & \underline{0} \\ 61 & 29 & 0^* & 30 & 12 & 14 \\ 25 & 0^* & 32 & 5 & 0 & 2 \\ 0 & 53 & 36 & 22 & 0^* & 20 \end{pmatrix}$$

On applying the algorithm to this matrix it is found that there is a set $\mathfrak{S}$ of TWO underlined zeros, namely those in the (3,2) and (3,6) positions. The circuits associated with these zeros are as follows:

$$\begin{pmatrix} 4 & 17 & 39 & 0^* & 0' & 17 \\ 0' & 35 & 15 & 1 & 6 & 0^* \\ 13 & \underline{0} & 49 & 3 & 3 & \underline{0} \\ 61 & 29 & 0^* & 30 & 12 & 14 \\ 25 & 0^* & 32 & 5 & 0' & 2 \\ 0' & 53 & 36 & 22 & 0^* & 20 \end{pmatrix} \quad \begin{pmatrix} 4 & 17 & 39 & 0^* & 0' & 17 \\ 0' & 35 & 15 & 1 & 6 & 0^* \\ 13 & \underline{0} & 49 & 3 & 3 & \underline{0} \\ 61 & 29 & 0^* & 30 & 12 & 14 \\ 25 & 0^* & 32 & 5 & 0' & 2 \\ 0' & 53 & 36 & 22 & 0^* & 20 \end{pmatrix}$$

These lead to two sets of six independent starred zeros, namely those shown in the following matrices,

$$\begin{pmatrix} 4 & 17 & 39 & 0^* & 0 & 17 \\ 0 & 35 & 15 & 1 & 6 & 0^* \\ 13 & 0^* & 49 & 3 & 3 & 0 \\ 61 & 29 & 0^* & 30 & 12 & 14 \\ 25 & 0 & 32 & 5 & 0^* & 2 \\ 0^* & 53 & 36 & 22 & 0 & 20 \end{pmatrix} \quad \begin{pmatrix} 4 & 17 & 39 & 0^* & 0 & 17 \\ 0^* & 35 & 15 & 1 & 6 & 0 \\ 13 & 0 & 49 & 3 & 3 & 0^* \\ 61 & 29 & 0^* & 30 & 12 & 14 \\ 25 & 0^* & 32 & 5 & 0 & 2 \\ 0 & 53 & 36 & 22 & 0^* & 20 \end{pmatrix}$$

By reference to the original form of S, it is seen that there are two solutions to the problem, namely

$$3 + 28 + 27 + 11 + 25 + 48 = 142,$$

$$43 + 11 + 27 + 11 + 17 + 33 = 142$$

12. General remarks

The problems of transportation and assignment may be solved by different methods from those presented in earlier sections of this chapter, and it is convenient here to comment briefly on these, and other matters. The reader is referred to the original papers for details.

(i) *MITAB.* An interesting machine has recently been constructed at the Willow Run Laboratories of the University of Michigan. It is MITAB (Michigan Transportation and Assignment Blackboard) and has proved very useful in the solving of assignment problems up to a size of 19 × 19 or transportation problems up to a size of 9 × 18. It is not a computer but mechanizes many of the tedious operations involved in applying the algorithm of Munkres (11) to large scale problems. The machine has been described by Machol (9), and a detailed description of the circuit has been given by Weinert, Munkres and Cargo (13).

(ii) *The Methods of Egerváry.* In a little known paper (3), published in 1931, the Hungarian mathematician Jenö Egerváry developed some combinatorial properties of matrices. This paper, which centres around König's theorem, is of interest because it provides essentially the basis for the solution of the problem of assignment, as developed much later by Munkres and by Kuhn. Now, after a long period of silence, Egerváry has published (4) an extension of his paper of 1931, showing that the problem of transportation may be solved by a similar method provided certain multiplicities are attached to the rows and columns of the cost matrix. The reader may care to compare this method with the algorithm of Munkres (11), which was developed for solving transportation problems on MITAB.

(iii) *Transhipment.* In the problem of transportation considered in §§ 2–11, only direct transport from some source S_i to some destination D_j was considered. The problem may be extended to include the possibility of any source or destination acting as an intermediate point; that is, one considers shipment from S_i to D_j via one or more sources or destinations. This is known as the transhipment problem and it has been solved by

Orden (12), using an adaption of the method for solving the transportation problem.

(iv) *The "Travelling-Salesman" Problem.* A salesman finds it necessary to travel from his home, C_1, to $n-1$ locations, C_2, $C_3, ..., C_n$, and then return home. Let $c(i, j)$ be the distance, or the cost of travelling, or the time taken to travel, from C_i to C_j. The problem is to find in what order, $C_{i_2}, C_{i_3}, ..., C_{i_n}$ the locations should be visited so as to minimize the total distance (or cost or time). Otherwise expressed, the problem is to find that permutation $(1, i_2, i_3, ..., i_n)$ of the numbers $(1, 2, ..., n)$, so that the quantity

$$c(1, i_2) + c(i_2, i_3) + ... + c(i_n, 1)$$

shall be a minimum.

It must be stated at once that no satisfactory mathematical solution to this problem has so far been given, even though the problem was first formulated some twenty-five years ago. For a good review of the attempts up to 1955 the reader is referred to a paper (5) by Flood. There is also an interesting paper by Morton and Land (10), where the problem is treated by a method of Linear Programming.

Since the problem is closely related to that of assignment it is of interest to point out the essential difference which causes the travelling-salesman problem to be of a different order of difficulty. The assignment problem, as formulated in § 1, amounts to that of finding any permutation matrix† X, such that $\sum_{i,j} x_{ij} r_{ij}$ is a minimum††. The travelling salesman problem is that of finding a permutation matrix X, such that (i) $\sum_{i,j} x_{ij} c(i,j)$ is a minimum, (ii) X has the extra restriction that it be cyclic, that is, the equation $X^p = I$, where I is the unit matrix of order n, is satisfied for $p = n$ but not for $p < n$. This restriction arises because

$$\sum x_{ij} c(i, j) = c(1, i_2) + c(i_2, i_3) + ... + c(i_n, 1)\,,$$

† A permutation matrix is a square matrix whose elements are all 0 or 1 with exactly one unit element in each row and column.

†† It is easily shown that $\sum_{i,j} x_{ij} r_{ij}$ is the trace of the matrix XR', where $R = (r_{ij})$ and R' is the transpose of R.

and thus since $1, i_2, i_3, ..., i_n$ are all different, none of the non-zero elements of X can appear on the diagonal of X. It is this restriction to cyclic permutations which is the core of the difficulty in the travelling-salesman problem.

REFERENCES

1. P. S. DWYER, "Solution of the personnel classification problem with the method of optimal regions", *Psychometrica,* **19** (1954), 11–26.
2. T. E. EASTERFIELD, "A combinatorial algorithm". *J. Lond. Math. Soc.,* **21** (1946), 219–26.
3. J. EGERVÁRY, "Matrixok kombinatorikus tulajdonságairól". *Math. Phys. Lapok,* **38** (1931), 16–28. Translated by H. W. KUHN, "On combinatorial properties of matrices", *Logistics Papers,* George Washington Univ., Issue 11, Paper 4 (1955).
4. J. EGERVÁRY, "Kombinatorikus módszer a szállitási probléma megoldására". *Publications of the Mathematical Institute of the Hungarian Academy of Sciences,* IV (1959), 15–28.
5. M. M. FLOOD, "The travelling-salesman problem". *Operations Res.* 4 (1956), 61–75.
6. D. KÖNIG, *Theorie der endlichen und unendlichen Graphen,* Ch. 14, § 3, Chelsea, N.Y., 1950.
7. H. W. KUHN, "The Hungarian method for the assignment problem". *Nav. Res. Logistics Quart.,* **2** (1955), 83–97.
8. H. W. KUHN, "Variants of the Hungarian method for assignment problems". *Nav. Res. Logistics Quart.,* **3** (1956), 253–8.
9. R. E. MACHOL, "The mechanical blackboard", *Operat. Res.,* **5** (1957), 422–8.
10. G. MORTON and A. H. LAND, "A contribution to the Travelling-Salesman problem", *J. R. Statist. Soc.,* **17** (1955), 165–203.
11. J. MUNKRES, "Algorithms for the assignment and transportation problems". *J. Soc. Ind. Appl. Math.,* **5** (1957), 32–8.
12. A. ORDEN, "The transhipment problem", *Mgmt Sci.,* **2** (1956), 276–85.
13. B. R. WEINERT, J. R. MUNKRES and G. T. CARGO, Report WR-38-T, Michigan Univ., Engrg Res. Instit.

CHAPTER IV

QUEUEING THEORY: THE SINGLE CHANNEL QUEUE

1. Introduction

The theory of queues is a new branch of applied mathematics, having its origin in a paper of 1909 by A. K. Erlang on a problem of congestion in telephone traffic. In recent years much research into the theory has been carried out, particularly in the field of operations research, and at the present time the subject continues to grow vigorously. The present chapter is concerned with the mathematical development of the theory and with a survey of some of the applications. As in the chapter on linear programming an attempt has been made to satisfy the interests of those primarily interested in the applications as well as those whose interests are mainly in the mathematical aspects.

The fundamental idea in the theory is the *congestion* caused by an interruption in a flow pattern and the *waiting* associated with the congestion. The flow is usually discrete, for example, the arrival and departure of individuals at a service counter, but it may be continuous, such as the flow of a fluid into and out from a reservoir. The earliest recognition of a situation of this kind occurred in the study of telephone traffic. Incoming calls constitute the flow, which is interrupted at the telephone exchange by the operators dealing with the calls. During a busy period intending callers suffer some *delay* because the operators are unable to deal with the calls as rapidly as they are made. The original problem treated by Erlang in his paper of 1909 (6,17) was concerned with the calculation of this delay in the case of one operator, and in 1917 the results were extended to the case of several operators (6,18). Development in the field of telephone traffic continued, largely along the lines initiated by Erlang, and the main publications are those of Molina in 1927 (34) and Fry in 1928 (20).

A period of research concentrated on mathematical aspects started in 1930 with a paper by Pollaczek (38). This was followed in 1931 by Kolmogorov (28) and in 1932 and 1933 by Khintchine (26, 27). Then there was a rather quiet period until after the last war, since when there has been widespread activity, especially in industrial problems.

The situations to which queueing theory has been applied include

(1) Congestion in road traffic,
(2) The servicing of a group of machines liable to breakdown,
(3) Scheduling of air traffic at an airport,
(4) The optimal size of dams and other storage systems,
(5) Production scheduling,
(6) Inventory control,
(7) Waiting in a hospital outpatients department.

The extent to which the theory has grown may be gauged from the bibliography by Miss Alison Doig in *Biometrika*, **44** (1957), 490. This lists over 800 papers.

2. General concepts and definitions

The simplest type of queue is depicted in Fig. 1. Individuals, called *customers*, arrive at a point A and, if there are already customers at A, wait until it is possible to receive attention at the *service point*, P. After service the customers pass on, possibly to another service point, and the exit stream is called the *output*. The stream by which customers arrive at A is called the *input*.

There are two statistical distributions associated with the specification of a queue. These are:

(i) *the input distribution*, describing the type of arrival; this is the distribution of the intervals of time between successive customers arriving at A.

(ii) *the service-time* (*or holding-time*) *distribution*, describing the type of service; this is the distribution of the times taken to serve customers at a service point.

The *queue* is defined to be the collection of customers either waiting at A or being served, and the *queue length*, $n(t)$, at any instant t, is taken to be the number of customers in this collection.

Various questions may be of interest in the study of a queue. For given input and service distributions these include:

(1) the distribution of the length of the queue,

(2) the distribution of the waiting time in the queue,

(3) the proportion of a long period of time during which the service system is idle.

If the input and service distributions are not given it may be desirable to examine the effect of various assumed distributions on the queue length or the waiting time. This has been done in various contexts, including the design of appointments systems in hospitals (1) and some scheduling problems, for example, in production and in traffic flow.

An important concept in the theory is the *queue discipline*. This is the manner in which the customers are chosen from the queue for service. Until recently most of the theory covered only the cases of 'first come, first served', that is, where customers are served in order of arrival, and completely random service, where every customer in the queue has the same chance of being chosen next. Erlang's paper of 1917 covered the first case, and the second case has been treated by Mellor (33), Vaulot (44), Palm (36), Riordan (40) and Wilkinson (47), all with reference to telephone systems. But during the last several years the theory has been extended to cover various other types of queue discipline, including priority service, bulk service, 'last-come, first served', and the case where breakdown in the servicing facility may occur (this case can be treated as a type of priority (46)). The notion of priority was apparently first incorporated into the theory by Cobham in 1954–5 (10). Other papers quickly followed, including those by Cohen (11), R. E. Cox (13), and Runnenburg and Kesten (41). Priority is discussed in §10. The term 'bulk service', due to Bailey (2), refers to the discipline where the operator deals simultaneously with a batch of customers. The mathematical treatment of this type of service has been discussed by Downton (14, 15).

In practice most queues are not so simple as that shown in

Fig. 1. Various *compound* forms are possible, and a few words on nomenclature are necessary. It may happen that there are several service points, *in series* (or *in tandem*), as shown in Fig. 2.

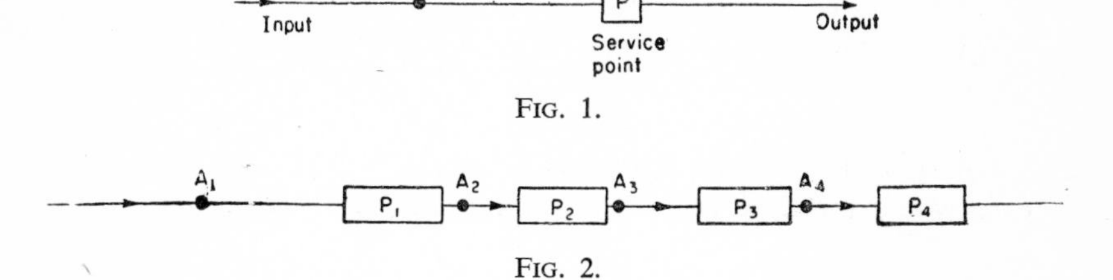

FIG. 1.

FIG. 2.

Customers queueing at A_1 are serviced at P_1 and form a queue at A_2 awaiting service at P_2; this process is repeated for a number of stages before the final output. The single line of flow is called a *lane* (or *channel*), even when there is only one service point P. A more complex queue is one involving several lanes, such as shown in Fig. 3.

The lanes are said to be in *parallel*, and may be identical or different both as regards the number of service points in a lane and the service-time distributions. Finally it is possible to have a queue which consists of a *network* of queues, each of the type shown in Fig. 2 or Fig. 3. These more complicated forms have only been considered very recently (7, 23, 24, 39) and as yet there is no very fully developed theory.

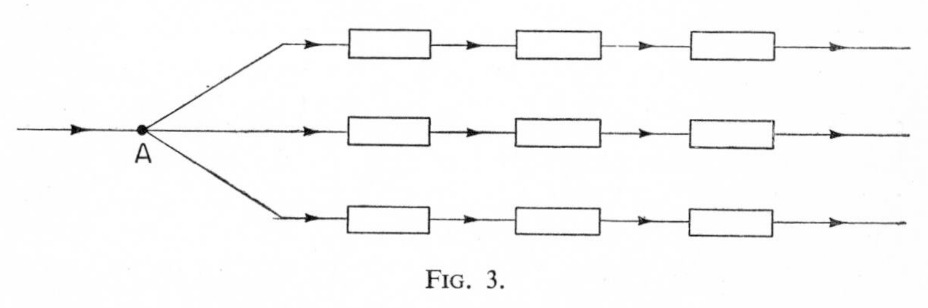

FIG. 3.

3. Types of distributions and a notation for queues

Input and service-time distributions may be of any reasonable form and in practice a large variety of forms are encountered. However, the *theory* of queues will be developed with reference to three special types of distribution: regular, random (exponential) and Erlangian.† These are defined as follows.

Let x (a time interval) be a positive random variable, with distribution function $F(x)$.

(i) *Regular distribution.*
$$F(x) = 0 \quad (x < a)$$
$$\quad = 1 \quad (x \geqslant a),$$

where a is a constant. This is the distribution in the deterministic case where the time interval has the constant value a.

(ii) *Random (exponential) distribution.*

$$F(x) = 1 - e^{-\lambda x},$$

where λ is a positive constant. In this case the time interval is of random length and has an average length $1/\lambda$.

(iii) *Erlangian distribution.*

$$F(x) = \int_0^x f(t)dt,$$

where the frequency distribution $f(x)$ is given by

$$f(x) = \frac{(\lambda k)^k}{\Gamma(k)} x^{k-1} e^{-\lambda k x},$$

and k and λ are positive constants with $k \geqslant 1$. If $k = 1$ we obtain case (ii), while (i) is obtained as $k \to \infty$. Thus (iii) provides a continuous range of distributions (parameter k) between (i) and (ii). We denote the Erlangian distribution by E_k. In the case where k is integral, E_k may be obtained as the sum of k exponential distributions, as shown in Chapter 1, § 14, Ex. (ii).

NOTATION: Denote by D, M and E_k the distributions (i), (ii) and (iii) respectively and by G a general distribution. A queue, apart from the specification of the discipline, is defined by

† Apart from these, general distributions have been treated in only a few papers, notably those of Lindley and of Smith (see § 8).

(a) the type of input distribution,
(b) the type of service-time distribution,
(c) in the case of a queue involving several identical lanes in parallel, the number of lanes.

Let s be the number of lanes. Then, in the case of a 'first come, first served' discipline the queue will be denoted by $X/Y/s$ where X and Y are either D, M, G or E_k. Thus $M/M/1$ denotes a single channel queue with random input and service-times; and $M/G/s$ denotes a queue with s parallel channels and with random input and general service-time distribution.

4. The problems of queueing theory

An existing queue will be judged differently by different people. Thus a customer will observe the length of the queue on arrival, and will be interested in his waiting time. The server may be interested in the slack periods, when there are no customers to serve, and he would like to know the probability of there being no queue, and to have some information about the duration of the slack and busy periods. Again suppose the queue arises in some industrial situation (for example, production or traffic flow). Management may wish to determine

(i) how many channels to provide in order that the average queue length be not unreasonable, or
(ii) how to schedule arrivals so that the queue length does not fluctuate too much.

The theory of queues has been developed in an attempt to answer questions such as these and in this chapter and the next we shall be concerned to a considerable extent with the calculation of the waiting time and the queue length. Emphasis will be placed on the formulation of queueing problems and the methods of solution.

It is convenient here to introduce certain notation. Let

u, v, w and $n(t)$ be random variables defined as follows:

u = the inter-arrival time (between two successive customers),

v = the service time of a customer,

w = the waiting time of a customer, not including the service time,

$n(t)$ = the number of customers in the queue at time t (the queue *length*), including the customer(s) being served.

Further, let

$P_n(t)$ = the chance that the queue length at time t is n,

$A(x)$ = the distribution function of u, that is the chance that $u \leqslant x$,

$B(x)$ = the distribution function of v,

$F(x)$ = the distribution function of w,

λ = the mean number of customers arriving in unit time,

μ = the mean number of customers served in unit time.

Note that $1/\lambda$ and $1/\mu$ are the mean inter-arrival time and mean service time respectively, that is

$$\frac{1}{\lambda} = \int_0^\infty u \, \mathrm{d} A(u), \qquad \frac{1}{\mu} = \int_0^\infty v \, \mathrm{d} B(v).$$

A quantity which appears frequently in the theory is λ/μ. Write

$$\varrho = \lambda/\mu ,$$

and call ϱ the *traffic intensity*.

We shall be concerned in the following sections with the calculation of $F(x)$, $n(t)$ and $P_n(t)$, mainly in the limiting case of *statistical equilibrium*, that is a steady state which is assumed to be reached as $t \to \infty$. For this state we write

$$n = \lim_{t\to\infty} n(t), \qquad p_n = \lim_{t\to\infty} P_n(t) ,$$

and for $A(x)$ and $B(x)$ we shall use the types introduced in § 3. The possible states depend on the value of ϱ, but the theory is too advanced to be discussed in this book. It is a part of ergodic theory and the reader will find an excellent account in Kendall's paper (25), where the matter is developed in terms of Feller's theory of recurrent events. The equilibrium state is ultimately reached when $\varrho < 1$, and in this chapter, apart from § 9, it is assumed that this condition is satisfied.

5. The queue $M/G/1$: formulae for $E(n)$ and $E(w)$

In this section an elementary method is used to derive formulae for the mean queue length and mean waiting time for a queue with random input and general service-time when the system is in a state of statistical equilibrium. Let n_0, n_1 be the queue lengths immediately after two successive customers C_0, C_1 have been served, v be the service time of C_1, r be the number of customers arriving while C_1 is being served. Then $n_1 = r$ if $n_0 = 0$ and $n_1 = n_0 + r - 1$ if $n_0 \neq 0$.
The two cases may be formally combined into one on introducing a random variable δ defined thus:

$$\delta = 1 \quad \text{if} \quad n_0 = 0, \qquad \delta = 0 \quad \text{if} \quad n_0 \neq 0 .$$

Then it follows that

$$n_1 = n_0 + r - 1 + \delta \tag{1}$$

It is to be noted that†

$$\delta^2 = \delta, \qquad n_0\delta = 0 ,$$

and hence, from (1), on averaging, we obtain

$$E(n_1) = E(n_0) + E(r) - 1 + E(\delta) .$$

But in a state of equilibrium, $E(n_1) = E(n_0)$ and $E(r)$, being the expected number of arrivals in a time $E(v)$, satisfies

$$E(r) = \lambda E(v) = \lambda/\mu = \varrho .$$

Thus

$$E(\delta) = 1 - E(r) = 1 - \varrho .$$

---

† Note also that from the definition of δ, $E(\delta)$ is the chance that a customer on being served leaves no customers to follow. Since δ is only defined at the instants when customer service is completed it cannot be asserted that $E(\delta)$ is the chance that there is no queue (at any random instant). However, it happens that the formula $l - \varrho$ for $E(\delta)$ is the chance that there is no queue, and this is established in § 6.

Now square both sides of (1) and average, remembering that $n_0\delta = 0$, and that $E(n_1^2) = E(n_0^2)$. Then

$$0 = E[(r-1)^2] + E(\delta^2) + 2E[n_0(r-1)] + 2E[\delta(r-1)]$$
$$= E(r^2) - 2\varrho + 1 + (1-\varrho) + 2E(n_0)\,E(r-1) + 2E(\delta)\,E(r-1)\,,$$

where

$$E[n_0(r-1)] = E(n_0)\,E(r-1), \quad E[\delta(r-1)] = E(\delta)\,E(r-1)\,,$$

since the input is random and thus r is statistically independent of n_0 and δ. It easily follows that

$$E(n_0) = \varrho + \frac{E(r^2) - \varrho}{2(1-\varrho)}\,.$$

It is now necessary to calculate $E(r^2)$, which is the mean square of the number of arrivals in the service-time v. Notice that the averaging must be carried out with respect to the *two* random variables r and v. Now because the input is random the chance of r arrivals in time v is $e^{-\lambda v}(\lambda v)^r/r!$. Hence, for a fixed v, the mean square of the number of arrivals in time v is M where

$$M = \sum_{r=1}^{\infty} \frac{r^2 e^{-\lambda v}(\lambda v)^r}{r!} = \lambda v(1 + \lambda v)\,,$$

on using the result $\sum_{n=1}^{\infty} n^2 x^n/n! = x(1+x)\,e^x$. Thus

$$E(r^2) = \int_0^{\infty} \lambda v(1+\lambda v)\,dB(v) = \lambda \int_0^{\infty} v\,dB(v) + \lambda^2 \int_0^{\infty} v^2 dB(v)\,.$$

The first integral, being the mean of the service-time, has the value $1/\mu$, and the second has the value $\sigma_v^2 + 1/\mu^2$ where σ_v^2 is the variance of $B(v)$. Thus

$$E(r^2) = \varrho + \lambda^2(\sigma_v^2 + 1/\mu^2) = \varrho + \varrho^2 + \lambda^2\sigma_v^2\,.$$

The formula for $E(n_0)$ now becomes

$$E(n) = \varrho + \frac{\varrho^2 + \lambda^2\sigma_v^2}{2(1-\varrho)}\,, \qquad (2)$$

and this gives the *average queue length* in the case of random input and an arbitrary service-time distribution. Note that if $B(v)$ is an exponential distribution of parameter μ, then $\sigma_v^2 = 1/\mu^2$ and $E(n) = \varrho/(1 - \varrho)$.

It is now an easy matter to derive a formula for $E(w)$. If w is the waiting time (before service) of C_1, then n_1 customers arrive in a time $v + w$. Thus, since the mean arrival rate is λ,

$$E(n) = \lambda E(v + w) = \lambda/\mu + \lambda E(w) .$$

It follows that

$$\lambda E(w) = E(n) - \varrho = \frac{\varrho^2 + \lambda^2 \sigma_v^2}{2(1 - \varrho)} ,$$

a result which is usually written in the form

$$\frac{E(w)}{E(v)} = \frac{\varrho}{2(1 - \varrho)} \{1 + \mu^2 \sigma_v^2\} . \tag{3}$$

This formula is due to Pollaczek (38), and it is a convenient measure of the efficiency of the system, since it gives the ratio of the mean time a customer waits for service to commence to the mean service time. There are two important special cases:

(i) For a given mean service-time, $E(w)$ is least when $\sigma_v = 0$, that is for a *regular* service-time. In this case

$$E(w)/E(v) = \tfrac{1}{2}\, \varrho/(1 - \varrho) .$$

(ii) If the service-times are random, that is in the case of the queue $M/M/1$, $\sigma_v^2 = 1/\mu^2$ and (3) gives

$$E(w)/E(v) = \varrho/(1 - \varrho) .$$

Thus, for two queues $M/M/1$ and $M/D/1$, having the same mean service-time,

$$\frac{E(w) \text{ for } M/M/1}{E(w) \text{ for } M/D/1} = 2. \tag{4}$$

An analogous result, comparing random with regular *arrivals*, is due to Lindley (31). It is this:

$$\lim_{\mu \to \lambda} \frac{E(w) \text{ for } M/M/1}{E(w) \text{ for } D/M/1} = 2 . \tag{5}$$

It is a curious fact, from the mathematical point of view, that it is much more difficult to prove (5) than (4). We shall derive (5) in § 8. Apparently there is no elementary method available in this case.

6. The queue $M/M/1$: differential-difference equations for the queue length

In this section we introduce a method commonly used in the theory of queues. It had its origin in the mathematical theory of population dynamics. In the latter, an individual is born, has a life span, and dies; in the case of a queue, a customer arrives, has a service-time, and then leaves the system. The analogy is obvious and it is not surprising that the methods of one field are applicable to the other. We shall deal with what has been called the "birth and death" process.

Consider a single channel queueing system in which at some instant of time there are n members, including the customer being served. We shall say that the system is in a *state* E_n, and we denote by $P_n(t)$ the probability of the occurrence of this state at time t. The system may undergo a change of state, involving a transition, $E_n \to E_{n+1}$ or, in the case $n > 0$, $E_n \to E_{n-1}$. The latter arises when a customer leaves the system, the former when a customer arrives and joins the system. It is possible to envisage other transitions, such as $E_n \to E_{n \pm m}$ where $m > 1$, but we confine our attention here to the nearest neighbour transitions only, and we do this by assuming that the probability of a transition $E_n \to E_{n \pm m}$ for $m < 1$ is negligibly small compared with that for $m = 1$. In fact we shall make the following *fundamental assumption.* At any time t, when the queue length is n, the chance that a customer arrives in the interval $(t, t + \delta t)$ is $\lambda_n \delta t + O(\delta t^2)$; and the chance that a customer leaves in this interval is $\mu_n \delta t +$ $+ O(\delta t^2)$. The chance that more than one customer arrives or leaves in the interval is $O(\delta t^2)$. Under this assumption it is easy to set up a system of differential-difference equations for the state probabilities $P_n(t)$ $(n = 0, 1, 2, ...)$.

We seek the probability that the system is in a state E_n at time

$t + \delta t$, that is $P_n(t + \delta t)$. This situation may arise as the result of any one of the three following mutually exclusive events:

(i) The system is in state E_{n-1} at time t, and there is an arrival but no departure in time δt,

(ii) The system is in state E_n at time t, and there is no arrival nor departure in time δt,

(iii) The system is in state E_{n+1} at time t, and there is a departure but no arrival in time δt.

The probabilities of these events are

$$P_{n-1}(t)\lambda_{n-1}\delta t(1 - \mu_{n-1}\delta t), \quad P_n(t)\,(1 - \lambda_n\delta t)\,(1 - \mu_n\delta t)$$

and $P_{n+1}(t)(1 - \lambda_{n+1}\delta t)\mu_{n+1}\delta t$ respectively.†

It follows that $P_n(t + \delta t)$ is the sum of these three probabilities. By neglecting powers of δt beyond the first we obtain

$$P_n(t + \delta t) = P_{n-1}(t)\lambda_{n-1}\delta t + P_n(t)[1 - (\lambda_n + \mu_n)\delta t] + P_{n+1}(t)\mu_{n+1}\delta t\,.$$

Thus, since

$$P_n'(t) = \frac{\mathrm{d}}{\mathrm{d}t}\,P_n(t) = \lim_{\delta t \to 0} \frac{P_n(t+\delta t) - P_n(t)}{\delta t}$$

we obtain

$$P_n'(t) = \lambda_{n-1}P_{n-1}(t) - (\lambda_n + \mu_n)\,P_n(t) + \mu_{n+1}P_{n+1}(t) \tag{6}$$

and this equation holds for $n > 0$. For $n = 0$, the event (i) is not possible, and the equation in this case is

$$P_0'(t) = -\,\lambda_0 P_0(t) + \mu_1 P_1(t) \tag{7}$$

The initial conditions depend on the state of the system at some given time, say $t = 0$. It there are N customers present at zero time the conditions are

$$P_N(0) = 1, \quad P_n(0) = 0 \quad (n \neq N)\,. \tag{8}$$

---

† Note that the event in which the system is in state E_n at time t, and there is an arrival and a departure in δt, has a negligible chance of occurring, namely $P_n(t)\,\lambda_n\mu_n\delta t^2$.

Thus we have an infinite system (6) and (7) of differential-difference equations for the state probabilities. There is a considerable mathematical theory covering the solution of this system of equations and its properties. The reader interested in the theory may care to consult the book by Feller (19), and the paper by Ledermann and Reuter (29) on the spectral theory. Here we shall confine our attention to the simplest case, $\lambda_n = \lambda$, $\mu_n = \mu$ for all n, which applies to the queue $M/M/1$. In the next chapter we shall solve the equations in the case where λ_n and μ_n are functions of n applicable to the queue $M/M/s$, with several parallel channels. Also in Chapter VI the equations are used in the study of machine interference problems.

The Queue $M/M/1$. When

$$\lambda_n = \lambda, \quad \mu_n = \mu \quad (\text{all } n)$$

the fundamental assumption asserts that in *every* interval δt the chances of an arrival and a departure are $\lambda \delta t + O(\delta t^2)$ and $\mu \delta t + O(\delta t^2)$ respectively. Thus the queue possesses distribution functions $A(u)$ and $B(v)$ where

$$A(u) = 1 - e^{-\lambda u}, \quad B(v) = 1 - e^{-\mu v}.$$

Then we have the queue $M/M/1$ and in this case it is possible to solve the equations (6) and (7) completely, that is to find $P_n(t)$ explicitly as a function of t. The mathematics is rather heavy and is deferred until § 9. But the important case of statistical equilibrium may be treated now. In this case $P_n(t)$ approaches a limiting value, say p_n, as $t \to \infty$, and $P_n'(t) \to 0$. The equations (6) and (7) reduce then to the form

$$p_{n+1} = (1 + \varrho)p_n - \varrho p_{n-1} \, (n > 0)$$

$$p_1 = \varrho p_0 ,$$

where $\varrho = \lambda/\mu$. It is easy to show that $p_n = \varrho^n p_0$ for $n > 0$. Then, since $\sum_{i=0}^{\infty} p_i = 1$, it follows that $p_0 = 1 - \varrho$. Hence the solution is $p_n = (1 - \varrho)\varrho^n$ $(n = 0, 1, 2, ...)$, and the queue length n follows a geometric distribution. Note that since $p_0 = 1 - \varrho$, *the chance that there is no queue (the system is empty) is* $1 - \varrho$.

For the queue $M/M/1$ we can now find directly the mean $E(n)$ and variance var n of the queue length n, and also the frequency distribution $p(w)$ of the waiting time w. We have

$$E(n) = \sum_{n=0}^{\infty} np_n = p_0 \sum_{n=1}^{\infty} n\varrho^n = \varrho/(1-\varrho),$$

$$\operatorname{var} n = \sum_{n=0}^{\infty} n^2 p_n - \{E(n)\}^2 = \varrho/(1-\varrho)^2.$$

Let $\pi_n(w)\,\mathrm{d}w$, where $n > 0$, be the chance that a customer A, arriving at a time when there are $(n-1)$ customers waiting and 1 being served, waits for a time between w and $w + \mathrm{d}w$ before his service commences. The chance that a customer completes service in time $\mathrm{d}w$ is $\mu \mathrm{d}w$, and the chance that $(n-1)$ customers complete service in time w is $(\mu w)^{n-1}\mathrm{e}^{-\mu w}/(n-1)!$. Hence

$$\pi_n(w)\mathrm{d}w = \frac{\mu \mathrm{e}^{-\mu w}(\mu w)^{n-1}}{(n-1)!}\,\mathrm{d}w. \qquad (n = 1, 2, 3, \ldots)$$

Now when A arrives there may be any number, $n = 1, 2, 3, \ldots$, of customers in front of A. Hence

$$\begin{aligned} p(w)\mathrm{d}w &= \sum_{n=1}^{\infty} \pi_n(w) p_n \mathrm{d}w \\ &= \sum_{n=1}^{\infty} \frac{\mu \mathrm{e}^{-\mu w}(\mu w)^{n-1}}{(n-1)!}(1-\varrho)\varrho^n \mathrm{d}w \\ &= \mu\varrho(1-\varrho)\mathrm{e}^{-\mu w}\mathrm{d}w \sum_{n=1}^{\infty} \frac{(\mu\varrho w)^{n-1}}{(n-1)!} \\ &= \mu\varrho(1-\varrho)\mathrm{e}^{-\mu w(1-\varrho)}\mathrm{d}w. \end{aligned}$$

Hence

$$p(w) = \varrho\nu \mathrm{e}^{-\nu w}, \tag{9}$$

where

$$\nu = \mu(1-\varrho) = \mu - \lambda.$$

Note that the integral of $p(w)$ from 0 to ∞ is ϱ, not 1 as it should be. The explanation is that we did not consider the case $n = 0$.

In this case customer A on arrival finds no queue and hence his waiting time is zero. The chance of this is $1 - \varrho$; hence we must regard $p(w)$ as consisting of

(i) a δ-function component of magnitude $1 - \varrho$ at $w = 0$,

(ii) a continuous component $\varrho \nu \mathrm{e}^{-\nu w}$ for $w > 0$.

Then the total integral of $p(w)$ becomes $\varrho + (1 - \varrho)$, that is unity as it should be.

7. Use of the Laplace transform and probability generating function

There are several instances in the theory of queues where it is considerably easier to find the Laplace transform of a distribution function rather than the function itself directly. Having found the transform it is a simple matter of expansion, as explained in § 15 of Chapter I, to find the mean and variance of the distribution (and higher moments). Also, the distribution itself may be found, if desired, by the usual techniques of inversion. In illustration of the position we shall derive an important formula, due to Pollaczek (38) expressing the Laplace transform of the waiting-time distribution, $F(w)$, in terms of the transform of the service-time distribution, $B(v)$, in the case of the queue $M/G/1$, having random input. We begin with two lemmas.

LEMMA I: For the queue $M/G/1$, where the mean rate of arrival is λ, and the service-time distribution is $B(v)$, let r be the random variable equal to the number of customers that arrive while a customer is being served. Then the probability generating function $\Pi_r(z)$ of r is given by†

$$\Pi_r(z) = E(z^r) = \beta\{\lambda(1 - z)\},$$

where $\beta(x)$ is the Laplace transform of $B(v)$, that is

$$\beta(x) = \int_0^\infty \mathrm{e}^{-xv} \, \mathrm{d}B(v).$$

---

† In particular, if $B(v) = 1 - \mathrm{e}^{-\mu v}$, $\Pi_r(z) = b/(1 - az)$ where $a = \lambda/(\lambda + \mu)$, and $a + b = 1$, that is, r follows the geometric distribution, $p_s = ba^s$ $(s = 0, 1, 2, \ldots)$.

PROOF: The chance that s customers arrive in the service time v is $(\lambda v)^s \mathrm{e}^{-\lambda v}/s!$ and the chance that the service time is in the interval $(v, v+\mathrm{d}v)$ is $\mathrm{d}B(v)$. Hence the chance that $r=s$ is p_s, where

$$p_s = \int_0^\infty \frac{(\lambda v)^s \mathrm{e}^{-\lambda v}}{s!} \mathrm{d}B(v).$$

Thus the probability generating function of r is $\Pi_r(z)$ where

$$\Pi_r(z) = E(z^r) = \sum_{s=0}^\infty p_s z^s = \int_0^\infty \mathrm{e}^{-\lambda v} \sum_{s=0}^\infty \frac{(\lambda v z)^s}{s!} \mathrm{d}B(v)$$

$$= \int_0^\infty \mathrm{e}^{-\lambda v(1-z)} \mathrm{d}B(v) = \beta\{\lambda(1-z)\}.$$

LEMMA II. For the queue $M/G/1$, the probability generating function $\Pi_n(z)$ of the queue length n is given by $\Pi_n(z) = \beta(\vartheta)\,\gamma(\vartheta)$, where $\vartheta = \lambda(1-z)$ and $\gamma(x)$ is the Laplace transform of $F(w)$, that is

$$\gamma(x) = \int_0^\infty \mathrm{e}^{-xw}\, \mathrm{d}F(w).$$

PROOF: The queue length n, at the moment of completion of service of a customer C, is equal to the number of customers that arrive during the time $v+w$, the sum of the service time and waiting time of C. Hence $\Pi_n(z)$, by Lemma I, applied to $v+w$ instead of v, is equal to $T\{\lambda(1-z)\}$, where $T(x)$, the Laplace transform of the convolution of $B(v)$ and $F(w)$, is given by (Chapter I, § 15)

$$T(x) = \beta(x)\,\gamma(x).$$

Thus

$$\Pi_n(z) = T(\vartheta) = \beta(\vartheta)\,\gamma(\vartheta).$$

Another expression is now found for $\Pi_n(z)$. On equating this to that given by Lemma II, the formula of Pollaczek follows for the Laplace transform $\gamma(x)$ of $F(w)$. Consider the situation in § 5, where n_0 and n_1 are the queue lengths just after two consecutive customers have been served. We recall that the chance that there is no queue ($n_0 = 0$) is $1 - \varrho$. Thus, considering the queue size just after C_0 has been served we have

$$\Pi_n(z) = E(z^n) = (1 - \varrho) + \varrho E^*(z^n) ,$$

where E^* denotes an average over values of $n > 0$. Next, considering the queue size just after C_1 has been served, and remembering that $n = r$ if $n_0 = 0$ and $n = n_0 + r - 1$ if $n_0 \neq 0$, we have

$$\Pi_n(z) = E(z^n) = (1 - \varrho)E(z^r) + \varrho E^*(z^{n+r-1})$$

$$= \left\{(1 - \varrho) + \frac{\varrho}{z} E^*(z^n)\right\} E(z^r).$$

On elimination $E^*(z^n)$ from these two expressions for $\Pi_n(z)$ we obtain

$$\Pi_n(z) = \frac{(1 - \varrho)(1 - z)}{1 - z/E(z^r)} .$$

Now by Lemma I, $E(z^r) = \beta(\vartheta)$ where $\vartheta = \lambda(1 - z)$. Hence

$$\Pi_n(z) = \frac{(1 - \varrho)\vartheta/\lambda}{1 - (1 - \vartheta/\lambda)/\beta(\vartheta)} . \tag{10}$$

Using the result of Lemma II, we now have

$$\beta(\vartheta)\gamma(\vartheta) = \frac{(1 - \varrho)\vartheta/\lambda}{1 - (1 - \vartheta/\lambda)/\beta(\vartheta)} ,$$

that is

$$\gamma(\vartheta) = \frac{1 - \varrho}{1 - \lambda\{1 - \beta(\vartheta)\}/\vartheta} . \tag{11}$$

This is the formula of Pollaczek. It reduces the determination of the waiting time distribution, $F(w)$, in terms of the service time distribution, to the standard problem of inverting a Laplace transform. The mean and variance of w may be found directly from (11) by expansion. We have

$$\beta(\vartheta) = \int_0^\infty e^{-\vartheta v} dB(v) = 1 - m_1\vartheta + \frac{1}{2} m_2\vartheta^2 - \frac{1}{6} m_3\vartheta^3 + \ldots,$$

where $m_1 = E(v) = 1/\mu$, $m_2 = \sigma_v^2 + 1/\mu^2$ and $m_3 = \int_0^\infty v^3 \mathrm{d}B(v)$.

Let $$\gamma(\vartheta) = \int_0^\infty \mathrm{e}^{-\vartheta w} \mathrm{d}F(w) = 1 - \mu_1\vartheta + \frac{1}{2}\mu_2\vartheta^2 - \ldots,$$

where $\mu_1 = E(w)$ and $\mu_2 = \sigma_w^2 + \mu_1^2$. On expanding (11) into a power series in ϑ and equating coefficients we easily derive the results

$$E(w) = \frac{\lambda}{2(1-\varrho)}\left\{\frac{1}{\mu^2} + \sigma_v^2\right\},$$

$$\sigma_w^2 = \frac{\lambda}{12(1-\varrho)^2}\left\{4(1-\varrho)m_3 + 3\lambda\left(\frac{1}{\mu^2} + \sigma_v^2\right)^2\right\}.$$

The first result is, of course, essentially (3) of § 5.

In a similar way the mean and variance of the queue length n may be easily derived, from formula (10). We use the result (§ 15 of Chapter I) relating $\Pi_n(\mathrm{e}^{-s})$, when expanded into a power series in s, to the moments of n. Putting $\mathrm{e}^{-s} = z = 1 - \vartheta/\lambda$ it follows from (10) that

$$\Pi_n(\mathrm{e}^{-s}) = \frac{(1-\varrho)(1-\mathrm{e}^{-s})}{1 - \mathrm{e}^{-s}/\beta\{\lambda(1-\mathrm{e}^{-s})\}}.$$

Hence, if ν_t is the tth moment of n, that is $\sum_{r=0}^{\infty} p_r r^t$, this last expression equals $\sum_{t=0}^{\infty} (-)^t \nu_t s^t/t!$. Expanding into a power series in s and equating coefficients we derive expressions for the ν_t in terms of the moments of the service-time distribution. In particular, it is found that

$$\nu_1 = E(n) = \varrho + \frac{\varrho^2 + \lambda^2\sigma_v^2}{2(1-\varrho)},$$

which is formula (2) of § 5, and an expression may be derived for the variance of n (this involving the third moment of $B(v)$).

Remark on the Queue $M/E_k/1$ (k integral). If we define the *total* waiting time, τ, of a customer to be $v + w$, the sum of the service time and the waiting time prior to service, then (see the proof of Lemma II) the Laplace Transform $T(\xi)$ of the distribution of τ is given by $T(\xi) = \beta(\xi)\gamma(\xi)$, that is, from the formula (11) of Pollaczek,

$$T(\xi) = \frac{(1-\varrho)\xi/\lambda}{1-(1-\xi/\lambda)/\beta(\xi)} \,.$$

In the case of the queue $M/E_k/1$, where the service time frequency distribution (with mean $1/\mu$) is given by $(\mu k)^k v^{k-1} e^{-\mu k v}/(k-1)!$,

we have $$\beta(\xi) = \frac{(\mu k)^k}{(k-1)!}\int_0^\infty v^{k-1}e^{-(\xi+\mu k)v}dv = \left(\frac{\mu k}{\mu k+\xi}\right)^k.$$

Thus $$T(\xi) = \frac{(1-\varrho)\xi/\lambda}{1-\left(1-\dfrac{\xi}{\lambda}\right)\left(\dfrac{\xi+\mu k}{\mu k}\right)^k} \,.$$

Notice that ξ is a factor of the denominator and hence $T(\xi)$ is the reciprocal of a polynomial (of degree k). By locating the roots $\alpha_1, ..., \alpha_k$ of this polynomial† and expanding $T(\xi)$ in partial fractions, it is a simple matter to invert $T(\xi)$ and so obtain the frequency distribution of τ. This will clearly be of the form $\sum A_i e^{\alpha_i \tau}$.

Example: When $k = 2$, the roots α_1, α_2 are given by

$$2\alpha_1 = -(4\mu-\lambda)+\sqrt{(\lambda^2+8\lambda\mu)}, \quad 2\alpha_2 = -(4\mu-\lambda)-\sqrt{(\lambda^2+8\lambda\mu)}.$$

In the case of stability ($\lambda < \mu$), α_1 and α_2 are negative and the frequency function $f(\tau)$ of τ is given by

$$f(\tau) = \frac{4\mu^2(1-\varrho)}{\sqrt{(\lambda^2+8\lambda\mu)}}\,(e^{\alpha_1\tau}-e^{\alpha_2\tau})\,.$$

† The reader who wishes to go into more detail may care to note the following result on the location of $\alpha_1, ..., \alpha_k$. Write $1 + \xi/\mu k = z$. Then the denominator of $T(\xi)$ becomes $\vartheta z^{k+1} - (1+\vartheta)z^k + 1$, where $\vartheta = \mu k/\lambda$. Since $(z-1)$ is a factor this may be written $(z-1)\,E(z)$ where $E(z) = \vartheta z^k - (1 + z + z^2 + ... + z^{k-1})$. Note that in the case of stability ($\lambda < \mu$), $\vartheta > k$.

The result referred to is this.

The roots of $E(z) = 0$ *are all distinct, and, if* $\vartheta > k$, *there is a single root, say* z_0, *in the interval* $(0, 1)$; *the other* $k-1$ *roots all lie within the circle* $|z| = z_0$, *when* $\vartheta < k$.

Since the roots of $E(z) = 0$ are all inside the unit circle it follows that $R(\alpha_i) < 0$ $(i = 1, ..., k)$, which is a necessary condition in the case of a stable queue.

For further remarks on the case where $T(\xi)$ is the reciprocal of a polynomial see p. 113.

The Laplace transform has proved useful in various other queueing problems, such as the theory of the queue $M/M/1$ in the case where equilibrium is not attained, and the theory of queueing with bulk-service (§ 10). The former includes results on the distribution of the length of busy periods and on the time taken to reach certain states ("rush hour" theory), and some results are given in § 9.

8. Use of integral equations

In this section a general method, due to Lindley (31), is described for finding the distribution of waiting times, w. It involves the solution of an integral equation of the Wiener-Hopf type. The solution of this equation will be outlined in the case of the queue $D/E_k/1$, and the details given for the case $D/M/1$.

Let the waiting time of two successive customers C_r and C_{r+1} be w_r and w_{r+1}, and let v_r be the service time of C_r. Suppose that u_r is the time that elapses between the arrivals of C_r and C_{r+1}. It is clear that $w_{r+1} = 0$ if $u_r \geqslant w_r + v_r$, for in this case C_{r+1} arrives after C_r has departed. But if $u_r < w_r + v_r$, then $u_r + w_{r+1} = w_r + v_r$; for $u_r + w_{r+1}$ is the time from the arrival of C_r up to the commencement of servicing of C_{r+1} while $w_r + v_r$ is time from the arrival of C_r up to the departure of C_r. Write $\xi_r = v_r - u_r$. It is evident that $\xi_1, \xi_2, \ldots$, are particular values of the continuous random variable ξ, where $\xi = v - u$, that is the difference between the service time of a customer and the inter-arrival time between that customer and the next. Let $g(x)$ be the frequency distribution† of ξ, and note that $g(x)$ is defined over the interval $(-\infty < x < \infty)$.

---

† $g(x)$ is given, in terms of the frequency distributions $a(x)$ and $b(x)$ of u and v, by the formulae,

$$\text{(i)} \quad x > 0, \quad g(x) = \int_0^\infty b(u + x)\, a(u)\, \mathrm{d}u = \int_x^\infty a(v - x)\, b(v)\, \mathrm{d}v,$$

$$\text{(ii)} \quad x < 0, \quad g(x) = \int_{-x}^\infty b(u + x)\, a(u)\, \mathrm{d}u = \int_0^\infty a(v - x)\, b(v)\, \mathrm{d}v.$$

The relations between w_r and w_{r+1} may now be written in the form

$$\begin{aligned} w_{r+1} &= 0 \ (\xi_r + w_r \leqslant 0) \\ &= w_r + \xi_r \ (\xi_r + w_r > 0) \,. \end{aligned}$$

Denote by $F_r(x)$ the distribution function of w_r, that is

$$F_r(x) = P(w_r \leqslant x) = P(w_r = 0) + P(0 < w_r \leqslant x) \,.$$

Then $$\begin{aligned} F_{r+1}(x) &= P(w_{r+1} = 0) + P(0 < w_{r+1} \leqslant x) \\ &= P(w_r + \xi_r \leqslant 0) + P(0 < w_r + \xi_r \leqslant x) \\ &= P(w_r + \xi_r \leqslant x) \,. \end{aligned}$$

Thus $F_{r+1}(x)$ is the distribution function of the *sum* of the two variables w_r and ξ_r, and since $g(x)$ is the frequency distribution of each ξ_r, it follows that

$$F_{r+1}(x) = \int_0^\infty F_r(y) g(x-y) dy \,.$$

Lindley has shown that when $\lambda < \mu$ (that is $E(\xi) < 0$) $F_r(x)$ tends to a limit as $r \to \infty$.

Let $$F(x) = \lim_{r \to \infty} F_r(x) \,.$$

Then we have this important result.†

For the queue G/G/1, with arbitrary frequency functions a(u) and b(v) for the inter-arrival time u and service-time v, the distribution function F(x) of the waiting time (not including service) depends not on a(u) and b(v) individually, but only on the frequency distribution g(x) of v − u; F(x) is the solution of the integral equation

$$F(x) = \int_0^\infty F(y) g(x-y) dy \,.$$

† This result, published by Lindley in 1952, constitutes a landmark in the development of the theory of queues. It is one of the few results available for the general single-channel queue, with arbitrary (but "suitably respectable", as Lindley remarks) distributions for the arrival and service-times.

This is an equation of the Wiener-Hopf type (31). A general method for solving the equation is available but its application is not straightforward, and in practical cases other methods such as the one now to be described seem easier.

Application to the Queue $D/E_k/1$ (k integral). If customers arrive at regular intervals of time $1/\lambda$ then

$$A(u) = \begin{cases} 0 & (u < 1/\lambda) \\ 1 & (u \geqslant 1/\lambda) \end{cases}$$

and the frequency function $a(x)$ is given by $a(x) = \delta\{x - 1/\lambda\}$ where $\delta(x)$ is the Dirac delta function. For convenience we shall take $\lambda = 1$, which merely amounts to choosing the unit of time equal to the mean inter-arrival time. The frequency function $g(x)$ of $v - u$ is now given by

$$g(x) = \int b(u + x)\, \delta(u - 1)\, du = b(x + 1). \qquad (-1 < x < \infty)$$

Thus $F(x)$ satisfies

$$F(x) = \int_0^{x+1} F(y)\, b(x - y + 1)\, dy,$$

since $b(x) = 0$ for $x < 0$. It is easy to transform this equation into the form

$$F(x - 1) = \int_0^x F(x - y)\, b(y)\, dy\, .$$

For the queue $D/E_k/1$, with mean service time $1/\mu$, we have

$$b(y) = (\mu k)^k\, y^{k-1}\, e^{-\mu k y}/(k - 1)! \text{ and hence}$$

$$F(x - 1) = \frac{(\mu k)^k}{(k - 1)!} \int_0^x F(x - y)\, y^{k-1}\, e^{-\mu k y}\, dy.$$

A method for solving this equation has been given by Lindley. It depends on this

LEMMA: *The equation $(1 + z/\mu k)^k = e^z$ has k distinct roots occurring in conjugate pairs, with real negative parts.* For the proof of this lemma the reader may refer to Lindley's paper (31). It leads to the following real solution of the equation for $F(x)$:

$$F(x) = 1 + \sum_{i=1}^{k} c_i \, e^{z_i x},$$

where $c_1, \ldots, c_k$ (which are such that $c_j = \bar{c}_i$ if $z_j = \bar{z}_i$), are determined by the k linear equations

$$1 + \sum_{i=1}^{k} \frac{c_i}{(1 + z_i/\mu k)^r} = 0 \qquad (r = 1, 2, \ldots, k)$$

The case $k = 1$. This is the case of the queue $D/M/1$. The equation of the lemma is

$$1 + z/\mu = e^z$$

and there is one negative root, say $z = -\alpha$. Now

$$F(x) = 1 + ce^{-\alpha x},$$

where c is given by $1 + c/(1 - \alpha/\mu) = 0$, that is $c = \alpha/(\mu - 1)$. Thus,

$$F(x) = 1 - (1 - \alpha/\mu) \, e^{-\alpha x}.$$

Notice that the mean waiting time is given by

$$E(w) = \int_0^\infty t dF(t) = \frac{1}{\alpha} - \frac{1}{\mu},$$

and the variance by

$$\sigma_w^2 = \int_0^\infty t^2 dF(t) - \left(\frac{1}{\alpha} - \frac{1}{\mu}\right)^2 = \frac{1}{\alpha^2} - \frac{1}{\mu^2}.$$

We can now prove the relation

$$\lim_{\mu \to \lambda} \frac{E(w) \text{ for } M/M/1}{E(w) \text{ for } D/M/1} = 2,$$

which was mentioned at the end of § 5. Take $\lambda = 1$ and denote the ratio by $r(\mu)$. Notice that for equilibrium $\lambda < \mu$, so that we must let μ approach 1 *from above*. The mean waiting time for the queue $M/M/1$ is $1/\{\mu(\mu - 1)\}$.

Hence

$$r(\mu) = \frac{1}{\mu(\mu - 1)\left(\frac{1}{\alpha} - \frac{1}{\mu}\right)} = \frac{\alpha}{(\mu - 1)(\mu - \alpha)}.$$

Put $\mu = 1 + \varepsilon$, where $\varepsilon \ll 1$, and use this result:

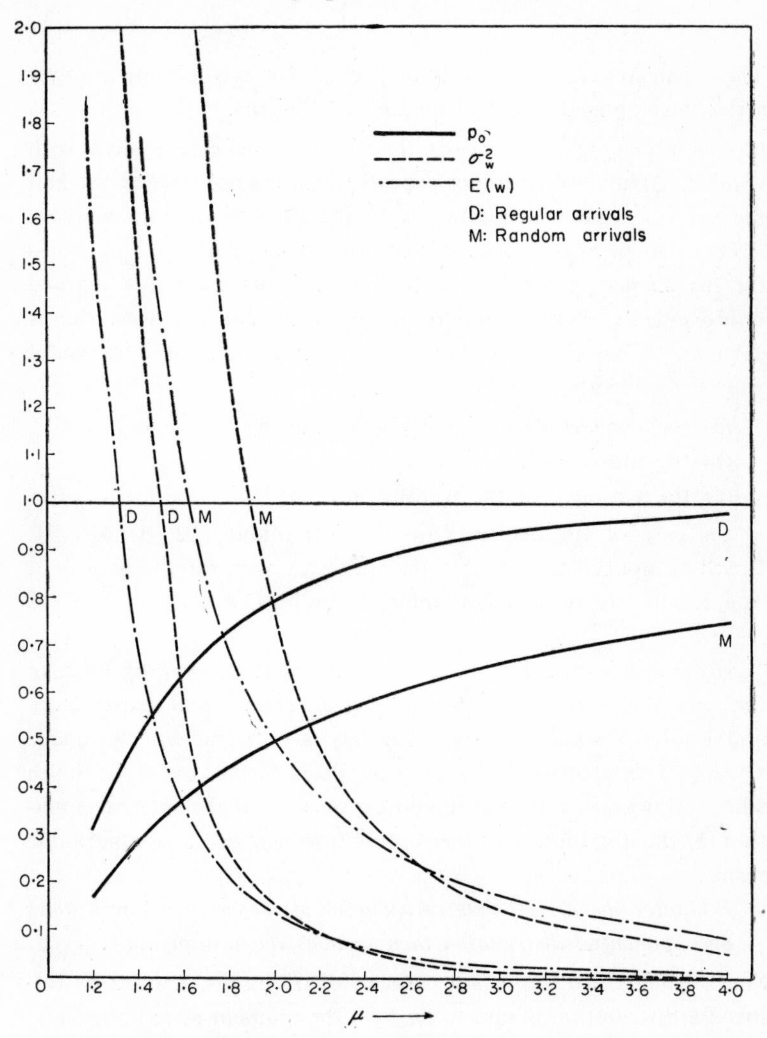

FIG. 4. Comparison between $D/M/1$ and $M/M/1$.

The root $z = -\alpha$ of the equation $1 + z/(1 + \varepsilon) = e^z$ is given by

$$\alpha = 2\varepsilon - \tfrac{1}{2}\varepsilon^2 + O(\varepsilon^3).$$

Then

$$r(\mu) = \frac{2\varepsilon + O(\varepsilon^2)}{\varepsilon[1 - \varepsilon + O(\varepsilon^2)]} \to 2 \text{ as } \varepsilon \to 0.$$

The expansion of α may easily be proved, for example, by a power series development and by equating coefficients.

The above relation means that in the queueing system with regular arrivals the customer expects to experience only about half the waiting time which attaches to the case of random arrivals. It can also be shown that this improvement of about 2 : 1 holds for the chance of not having to queue. Thus there is a marked improvement when customers arrive at regular intervals. Some calculations were carried out by Lindley giving, for a range of values of μ (with $\lambda = 1$),

(a) the chance of not having to queue, p_0,
(b) the mean waiting time, $E(w)$,
(c) the variance of the waiting time, σ_w^2,

in the case of the queues $D/M/1$, $M/M/1$ and $D/E_2/1$, $M/E_2/1$. It will be noticed that $E(w)$ and σ_w^2 increase very rapidly as $\mu \to 1$. The results are presented graphically in Figs. 4 and 5.

General Remark. In § 6, it was found that the waiting time, in the case of the queue $M/M/1$, follows an exponential distribution, and Lindley's solution shows that this is also true for the queue $D/M/1$. This property has been generalized further by W. L. Smith who, following a thorough investigation (43) of the integral equation for the distribution of the waiting time deduced this remarkable result:

Whatever the arrival-time distribution, if the service time follows an exponential distribution then so does the waiting time.

Smith isolated an important class of distributions, defined as follows: a distribution is said to be K_n if the moment generating function (or equivalently the Laplace transform of the distribution function) is the reciprocal of a polynomial of degree n. An example, noted in § 7, p. 106, is the distribution of the *total* waiting time in the case of the queue $M/E_k/1$. The above result on the distri-

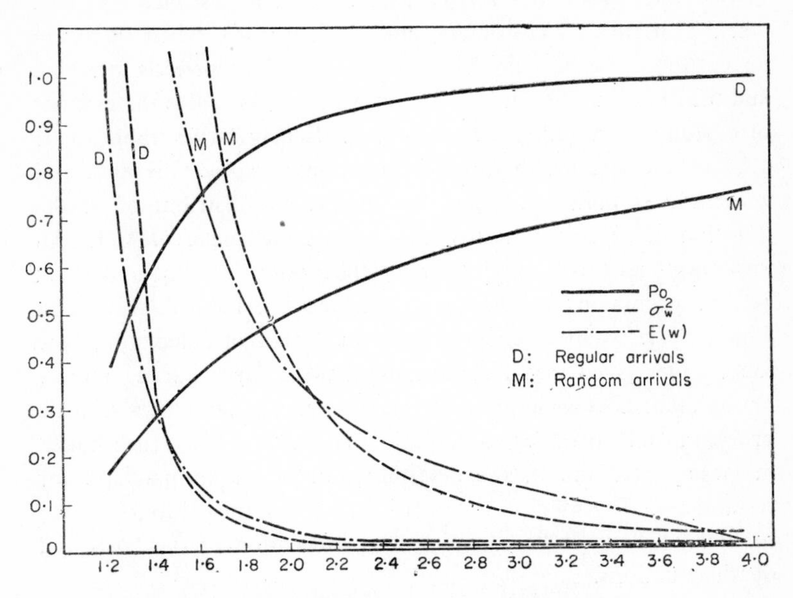

FIG. 5. Comparison between $D/E_2/1$ and $M/E_2/1$.

bution of the waiting time is a special case of the following [(43), Theorem 4]: *If the service-time distribution is K_n, then so also is the total waiting-time distribution.* The reader who is interested in further results on distributions which are K_n is referred to Smith's paper.

9. Analysis of transient behaviour

We have so far been concerned in this chapter with equilibrium properties of queues, that is properties which are attained only after a long time, and independently of the initial conditions. The mathematical investigation of the behaviour prior to the attainment of statistical equilibrium is considerably more difficult and for the most part is beyond the scope of this book. However, in the case of the queue $M/M/1$ we shall show briefly how various results of practical importance concerning the transient behaviour may be derived.

For any queue the service facility experiences busy periods, when it attends to customers, and slack periods, when there are no customers to be served. The busy and slack periods alternate and the duration of each is a random variable, as is also the number of customers served in a busy period. It may be desirable to be able to calculate the distribution functions of these variables, and a method is indicated below for finding the distribution of the duration of a busy period in the case of the queue $M/M/1$. An important industrial application of the notion of busy and slack periods occurs in the theory of machine interference, treated in Chapter VI. A more general problem is that of calculating how long, under given initial conditions, it takes for a queue to grow or to diminish to some pre-determined size. This may be a realistic problem, and arises for example in the study of the "rush-hour" in large cities, and in the determination of an optimal size for restaurants. The method described for solving this problem is due to Bailey (3) and is based on a neat application of the birth and death equations.

The Formula for $P_n(t)$. It was remarked in § 4 that p_n, where $p_n = \lim_{t\to\infty} P_n(t)$, exists when $\lambda < \mu$, and the formula for p_n, namely $p_n = (1 - \varrho)\, \varrho^n$ was found in § 6. But it is possible to derive an explicit formula for $P_n(t)$ itself. This has been done by a number of authors as follows:

(1) Clarke (9) solved a hyperbolic partial differential equation for the probability generating function,

(2) Ledermann and Reuter (29) used the spectral theory of birth and death processes,

(3) Bailey (3) used a standard generating function technique,

(4) Champernowne (8) used an "elementary" method involving the solution of a random walk problem.

The methods of Clarke and of Ledermann and Reuter are advanced and cover more general cases than the queue $M/M/1$; those of

Bailey and of Champernowne are a good deal simpler and involve, so to speak, more statistics and less mathematics.†

For the queue $M/M/1$, with $\mu = 1$ and the initial condition $n = a$ at $t = 0$, the formula for $P_n(t)$ is

$$P_n(t) = e^{-(1+\lambda)t} [\lambda^{\frac{1}{2}(n-a)} I_{n-a}(2t\sqrt{\lambda}) + \lambda^{\frac{1}{2}(n-a+1)} I_{n+a+1}(2t\sqrt{\lambda})]$$

$$+ (1 - \lambda)\lambda^n \sum_{r=a+n+2}^{\infty} \lambda^{-\frac{1}{2}r} I_r(2t\sqrt{\lambda})$$

where $I_r(x)$ is the modified Bessel function of the first kind, that is

$$I_r(x) \equiv \sum_{s=0}^{\infty} \frac{(\frac{1}{2}x)^{r+2s}}{s!(r+s)!} = i^{-r} J_r(ix) \quad (i = \sqrt{(-1)}).$$

The reader may care to verify that, when $\lambda < 1$, $\lim_{t\to\infty} P_n(t) = (1 - \lambda)\lambda^n$. The verification is carried out in detail by Saaty (42), using the asymptotic form of $I_r(x)$ and the standard expansion of exp. $\{\frac{1}{2}x(y + y^{-1})\}$ into a series of Bessel functions. This formula for $P_n(t)$ permits the calculation of stochastic means and variances. Bailey (4) carried out these calculations and also developed asymptotic formulae useful for numerical computation.

† Luchak (32), using essentially the method of Ledermann and Reuter found formulae for $P_n(t)$ in the case of a general class of queues with random input and a service-time characterized by a number of 'phases', in the sense used by Gaver (21). A particular case is the queue $M/E_k/1$, and for this the formula for $P_n(t)$ involves the function $I_r^k(x)$ where

$$I_r^k(x) = \sum_{s=0}^{\infty} \frac{(\frac{1}{2}x)^{r+(k+1)s}}{s!(r+ks)!}.$$

This reduces to $I_r(x)$ when $k = 1$. According to Luchak the function $I_r^k(x)$ is new to applied mathematics, but it may be transformed simply into the function $\varphi(\alpha, \beta, z)$ of Wright (48) used in 1933 in the asymptotic theory of partitions.

Morse (35) developed quite a different formula for $P_n(t)$. It is

$$P_n(t) = \frac{\lambda^{\frac{1}{2}(n-a)}}{\pi} \int_0^{2\pi} \{\sin a\vartheta - \lambda^{\frac{1}{2}} \sin (a+1)\vartheta\} \{\sin n\vartheta - \lambda^{\frac{1}{2}} \sin (n+1)\vartheta\} w^{-1} e^{-wt} d\vartheta ,$$

where $w = \lambda + 1 - 2\lambda^{\frac{1}{2}} \cos \vartheta$. This solution was used to obtain the auto-correlation function for the queue length $n(t)$ and hence the frequency spectrum of the fluctuations about the mean length L. The transient behaviour of the queue may be measured by the 'relaxation time', τ, of the fluctuations. This is defined as the mean time required for a deviation δ of $n(t)$ from L to return an amount δ/e towards L. Morse showed that as saturation is approached, that is as $\varrho \to 1$, where $\varrho = \lambda/\mu$, L increases as $1/(1-\varrho)$ but τ as $1/(1-\varrho)^2$. Thus, while the lengthening queue is a bad feature as saturation is approached, an even worse feature is the slowness with which the queue returns to its average when it undergoes some disturbance.

The Distribution of the Time Taken to Reach a Given State. Consider the queue† $M/M/1$, with $\mu = 1$ and $\lambda < 1$, and suppose that the queue length n is of size a at $t = 0$. The problem to be solved is this: find the frequency function $f(t)$ of the time τ required for n to reach, *for the first time*, the size b where $b < a$. This problem was solved by Bailey (4) using an elegant method based on the birth and death equations and involving the Laplace transform technique. It is interesting to observe at once the form of the answer, namely

$$f(t) = \alpha e^{-\beta t} I_{a-b}(\gamma t)/t ,$$

where α, β and γ are constants and I_{a-b} is the modified Bessel function. The problem of finding the duration of a busy period appears as a special case, for such a period commences with one

†Results for a more general type of queue have been obtained by Luchak (32). See the footnote on p. 115.

customer and finishes when all customers have departed. Thus $a = 1$, $b = 0$ in this case.

We begin with this

LEMMA: Let the queue $M/M/1$ have an initial size a and an average service-time $1/\mu$, and let τ be the time taken for the queue length n to fall, for the first time, to the size $b(b < a)$. The frequency function $f(t)$ of τ is given by

$$f(t) = \mathrm{d}\, p_b(t)/\mathrm{d}t,$$

where $p_b(t)$ is the chance that $n = b$ for the first time at time t.

There are two steps in the proof of this lemma. Firstly, $f(t)\,\mathrm{d}t$ being the chance that n *first* equals b in the interval $(t, t + \mathrm{d}t)$ given that it does not equal b at time t, equals the chance that $n = b + 1$ at time t and a customer departs in $\mathrm{d}t$.

Thus

$$f(t)\,\mathrm{d}t = p_{b+1}(t)\,\mu \mathrm{d}t.$$

Secondly, $n = b$ at $t + \mathrm{d}t$ if either $n = b + 1$ at t and a customer departs in $\mathrm{d}t$, or if $n = b$ at time t and there is no arrival and departure in $\mathrm{d}t$.† Hence $p_b(t + \mathrm{d}t) = p_b(t) + p_{b+1}(t)\,\mu\,\mathrm{d}t$, that is

$$\mathrm{d}p_b(t)/\mathrm{d}t = \mu\, p_{b+1}(t).$$

From these two equations the result of the lemma follows.

The equations describing the behaviour of the queue length during the period t stretching from the initial state $n = a$ at $t = 0$, to the final state, $n = b$ at $t = \tau$, are, in the case $\mu = 1$, as follows:

$$p_r'(t) = \lambda p_{r-1}(t) - (\lambda + 1)p_r(t) + p_{r+1}(t) \quad (r \geqslant b + 2)$$

$$p_{b+1}'(t) = - (\lambda + 1)p_{b+1}(t) + p_{b+2}(t)$$

$$p_b'(t) = p_{b+1}(t).$$

The third equation was derived in the proof of the lemma and the second equation follows by a similar argument. From these

† The case where there is an arrival and a departure in $\mathrm{d}t$ would mean either that n falls momentarily below b or rises momentarily to $b + 1$ and then falls back to b. Both these possibilities are ruled out since we are concerned with the time at which n *first* reaches b.

equations it is easy to derive an equation for the probability generating function $\Pi(z, t)$ of n, defined by

$$\Pi(z, t) = \sum_{r=b}^{\infty} p_r(t)\, z^r,$$

where it is to be noted that the summation starts at $r = b$ (and not $r = 0$) since n never takes on a value less than b during the period τ. Multiplying the equations by z^r, z^{b+1} and z^b respectively and adding, it is found that

$$z\,(\partial/\partial t)\,\Pi(z, t) = (1 - z)\,(1 - \lambda z)\,[\Pi(z, t) - p_b(t)\, z^b], \qquad (12)$$

and the problem is to solve this equation for $\Pi(z, t)$ subject to the initial condition, $n = a$ at $t = 0$, that is $\Pi(z, 0) = z^a$. The usual Laplace transform method is used. This method depends for its success upon the connection between the transforms of $\Pi(z, t)$ and $\partial\,\Pi(z, t)/\partial t$. Write

$$\Pi^*(z, st) = \int_0^{\infty} \mathrm{e}^{-st}\, \Pi(z, t)\, \mathrm{d}t.$$

Then

$$\int_0^{\infty} \mathrm{e}^{-st}\,(\partial/\partial t)\,\Pi(z, t)\,\mathrm{d}t = \Big[\mathrm{e}^{-st}\,\Pi(z, t)\Big]_0^{\infty} + s\int_0^{\infty} \mathrm{e}^{-st}\,\Pi(z, t)\,\mathrm{d}t$$
$$= s\,\Pi^*(z, s) - z^a,$$

on using the initial condition, that $\Pi(z, 0) = z^a$. Thus, on multiplying equation (12) by e^{-st} and integrating we obtain

$$z\{s\,\Pi^*(z, s) - z^a\} = (1 - z)\,(1 - \lambda z)\,[\Pi^*(z, s) - z^b\, p_b^*(s)],$$

where $p_b^*(s)$ is the transform of $p_b(t)$. From this the formula for $\Pi^*(z, s)$ follows, namely

$$\Pi^*(z, s) = \frac{z^{a+1} - z^b(1 - z)(1 - \lambda z)\, p_b^*(s)}{zs - (1 - z)(1 - \lambda z)}\,.$$

It is to be noticed that the denominator is quadratic in z. One of the roots, ξ, is given by

$$2\lambda\xi = (\lambda + 1 + s) - \{(\lambda + 1 + s)^2 - 4\lambda\}^{\frac{1}{2}} = \lambda + 1 + s - \{\Theta(s)\}^{\frac{1}{2}}$$

where

$$\Theta(s) = (\lambda + 1 + s)^2 - 4\lambda,$$

and that value of the square root is taken for which $R\{\sqrt{\Theta(s)}\} > 0$. In terms of this root it is possible to show that $sp_b^*(s) = \xi^{a-b}$. This follows from the fact that the numerator and denominator in the formula for $\Pi^*(z, s)$ must have the same zero in the region $R(s) > 0$. The full argument is too advanced to present here and the reader particularly interested in this mathematical aspect may care to consult Bailey's earlier paper (3) for the detail.

It is now easy to proceed to the finish. We require $f(t)$ and by the lemma this is $dp_b(t)/dt$. Now the transform $f^*(s)$ of $f(t)$ is given by

$$f^*(s) = \int_0^\infty e^{-st} p_b'(t) dt = sp_b^*(s) - p_b(0) = \xi^{a-b},$$

since $p_b(0) = 0$. The problem is to invert this transform. Success here depends on the following formula:†

$$r \int_0^\infty e^{-vt} I_r(t) \frac{dt}{t} = \frac{1}{\{v + \sqrt{(v^2 - 1)}\}^r},$$

where r is (for our purpose) a positive integer, and $I_r(t)$ is the modified Bessel function. By a simple transformation and the use of the identity $\{v - \sqrt{(v^2 - 1)}\}\{v + \sqrt{(v^2 - 1)}\} = 1$, the inverse of $f^*(s)$ is finally found to be

$$f(t) = \frac{(a - b)e^{-(1+\lambda)t} I_{a-b}(2t\sqrt{\lambda})}{t\, \lambda^{\frac{1}{2}(a-b)}}.$$

Following the remarks made in § 7 on the use of the transform to obtain the mean and variance of a distribution, the method may be applied here to $f^*(s)$. We obtain these results:

$$E(\tau) = (a - b)/(1 - \lambda),$$

$$\sigma_\tau^2 = (a - b)(1 + \lambda)/(1 - \lambda)^3.$$

Two observations may be made. The formula for $E(\tau)$ is just what one would expect, if the queue length decreased at a uniform rate from a to b. And, as saturation is approached, that is $\lambda \to 1$,

† See Erdélyi (16).

while the mean time for n to drop from a to b becomes very large, in any sample of observations the fluctuations about $E(\tau)$ are also very large and increase much faster than $E(\tau)$ itself. Thus it is very undesirable to operate the queueing system at a point somewhere near saturation.

The Length of a Busy Period. This is the special case when $a = 1$, $b = 0$. Then

$$f(t) = e^{-(1+\lambda)t} I_1 (2t\sqrt{\lambda})/t\sqrt{\lambda},$$

and

$$E(\tau) = 1/(1 - \lambda),\ \sigma_\tau^2 = (1 + \lambda)/(1 - \lambda)^3.$$

The formula for $f(t)$ was derived also by Kendall (25), and by Ledermann and Reuter (29).

The Growth of a Queue. The method used above for studying the decay of the queue size is also available in the case where the queue length increases over a period of time. The problem here is this: find the frequency function, $f(t)$, of the time, τ, required for n to reach, *for the first time*, the value c, given that $n = a$ at $t = 0$. This problem is slightly more complicated than the problem of decay, primarily because of the extra finiteness condition, that is that n is bounded above by c as well as below by 0. The equations for the process are:

$$p_c'(t) = \lambda p_{c-1}(t),$$
$$p_{c-1}'(t) = \lambda p_{c-2}(t) - (\lambda + 1) p_{c-1}(t),$$
$$p_r'(t) = \lambda p_{r-1}(t) - (\lambda + 1) p_r(t) + p_{r+1}(t) \quad (1 \leqslant r \leqslant c - 2)$$
$$p_0'(t) = - \lambda p_0(t) + p_1(t).$$

The probability generating function is $\Pi(z, t)$ where

$$\Pi(z, t) = \sum_{r=0}^{c} p_r(t) z^r,$$

and it is found that the transform $\Pi^*(z, s)$ is given by

$$\Pi^* (z, s) = \frac{z^{a+1} - (1 - z) \{p_0^*(s) + (1 - \lambda z) z^c p_c^*(s)\}}{z s - (1 - z) (1 - \lambda z),},$$

where $p_0^*(s)$ and $p_c^*(s)$ are the transforms of $p_0(t)$ and $p_c(t)$. Thus we have, in this case, to find both $p_0^*(s)$ and $p_c^*(s)$. To do this it is essential to observe that $\Pi(z, t)$ is a *polynomial* (not a power series) in z, and hence the numerator of $\Pi^*(z, s)$ must vanish at *both* zeros of the denominator. This makes the analysis somewhat heavy. But it may be carried through and Bailey obtained the following formula for the transform $f^*(s)$ of $f(t)$:

$$f^*(s) = \frac{\lambda(\xi^{a+1} - \eta^{a+1}) - (\xi^a - \eta^a)}{\lambda(\xi^{c+1} - \eta^{c+1}) - (\xi^c - \eta^c)},$$

where $\xi(s)$ and $\eta(s)$ are the zeros of the denominator of $\Pi^*(z, s)$. This leads to the formula for $E(\tau)$, the expected time taken for n to reach the value c, namely

$$E(\tau) = \frac{c-a}{\lambda - 1} - \frac{\lambda^c - \lambda^a}{\lambda^{a+c}(\lambda-1)^2} \quad (\lambda \neq 1)$$

$$= \tfrac{1}{2}(c-a)(c+a+1) \quad (\lambda = 1).$$

10. Queue disciplines: random selection, bulk service and priority

In the theory so far presented we have assumed (although it was not always necessary) the commonest form of queue discipline, 'first-come, first-served', where customers are served in the order of arrival. But there are various other types of discipline which are important in practical operations and some of these are considered now. They include random selection, which has been the subject of much study by those engaged in the analysis of telephone traffic, bulk service, where customers are dealt with not individually but in batches, and various forms of priority. However, before going into detail, it will prepare the way if we make a general observation on variation of the discipline.

If we consider a queue with a single server, where the customers are served individually, the number of customers served over a long period of time does not depend on the order in which those customers receive service. Thus a variation in the order in which customers are served has no effect on the state probabilities p_n, that is, the chance that the queue has length n, and hence no effect on quantities derived from these, such as the mean and variance of n. The chance that a customer will not have to queue, for example, does not depend on the order of service. Similarly there will be no change in the average waiting time of a customer (this may also be seen by reference to formula (3) of § 5). However, the waiting time distribution does depend on the order in which customers are served. The case of random service is discussed below, and the queue with a 'last-come, first-served' discipline was studied by Vaulot (45).

The chief result of varying the order of service is that, compared with the 'first-come, first-served' discipline, a higher proportion of customers receive quick service and, to compensate (since the mean service time is the same in both cases), a higher proportion wait longer. Thus the 'first-come, first-served' discipline is the most equitable, which is, of course, clear on intuitive grounds. What the mathematical study reveals, and intuition not, is, so to speak, the degree to which other forms of discipline are unfair. In addition, it must be remembered that priority is often a necessity; and the mathematical treatment of priority has already been developed far enough to yield results of practical use.

Random Selection. The case of random selection, with random arrivals and exponential service times, is of great importance in the study of telephone traffic, and in estimating the size of telephone exchanges. One important question is clearly that of relating the number of channels, c, to the waiting time experienced by customers wishing to make a call. The existing literature in this field is extensive and outside the scope of this book, but the interested reader may care to consult the review article by Cohen (12), and the references mentioned in § 2. Here we shall confine our attention to some basic theory in the case of a single channel ($c = 1$), so that a comparison may be made with the queue $M/M/1$.

Let the average service time be unity, so that $\mu = 1$. For the queue $M/M/1$, the frequency function of the waiting time is then given by (see § 6)

$$p(w) = \lambda(1-\lambda)\,\mathrm{e}^{-(1-\lambda)w}.$$

Thus the chance of a delay at least t is P where

$$P = \int_t^\infty p(w)\mathrm{d}w = \lambda \mathrm{e}^{-(1-\lambda)t}.$$

But the chance of a delay is ϱ and hence the *conditional* probability, $F(t)$, of a delay at least t, that is, the chance that a customer who is definitely delayed waits for a time at least t is given by

$$F(t) = P/\varrho = \mathrm{e}^{-(1-\lambda)t}. \tag{13}$$

For comparison with (13) we need the function $F(t)$ in the case of random service. An explicit formula is not available (at least in closed form) in this case and it is perhaps surprising that the mathematics is of a different order of complexity. An outline of the position follows.

Let $F_n(t)$ be the conditional probability of a delay at least t to a customer who on arrival finds n other customers waiting. An enumeration of the possible events, during a short interval $\mathrm{d}t$, and their probabilities, leads to the equation (see Refs 40, 44),

$$F_n'(t) = \frac{n}{n+1} F_{n-1}(t) - (1+\lambda)F_n(t) + \lambda F_{n+1}(t). \tag{14}$$

The boundary conditions are

$$F_n(0) = 1 \text{ (all } n\text{)},\ F_n(\infty) = 0,\ \lim_{n\to\infty} F_n(u) = 1 \text{ (all } u\text{)}.$$

Now $F(t)$, the chance of a delay at least t to a customer who is certainly delayed, is given by

$$F(t) = \sum_n p_n F_n(t), \tag{15}$$

where p_n, being the chance of a queue length n, is given by $p_n = (1-\varrho)\varrho^n$.

It is formula (15) which is to be compared with (13). But the difficulty is to solve Vaulot's equation (14) for $F_n(t)$. As remarked earlier, a direct solution in closed or simple form, does not seem possible. Mellor (33), observing the boundary condition, $\lim_{n\to\infty} F_n(t)=1$ (all t), noted that for large n, $F_{n-1}(t)$, $F_n(t)$ and $F_{n+1}(t)$ are all approximately equal. By making these strictly equal and substituting in (14) we obtain the equation

$$F_n'(t) + F_n(t)/(1+n) = 0$$

which has the solution $F_n(t) = e^{-t/(n+1)}$. Riordan (40) improved on this by developing a Maclaurin series for $F_n(t)$ and noticed that this series is given by

$$F_n(t) = \{1 - t(1-\lambda)/(1+n)\}^{1/(-\lambda)}$$

It is easily seen that this expression approaches Mellor's solution as $\lambda \to 1$. Apart from this, and one or two other approximations, the theory of the solution of (14) is in an unsatisfactory state.† Riordan (40) has given perhaps the best discussion, including calculation of the moments of the frequency function, $-F'(t)$, of the waiting time (all these moments, other than the first, are higher than in the case of service in the order of arrival); and Le Roy (30) has developed some matrix formulae for computation

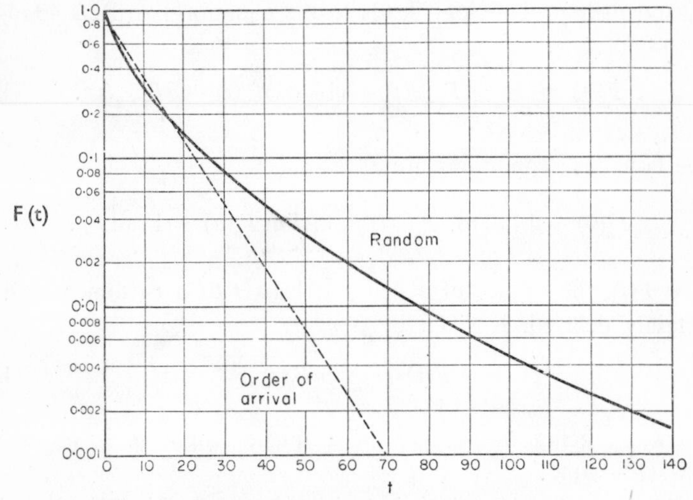

FIG. 6. Comparison delay curves for order of arrival and random service $\lambda = 0 \cdot 9$.

† In an interesting recent paper (*Proc. Cambridge Phil. Soc.*), **58** (1962), 79–91) a real step forward has been made by Kingman who has found a generating function for the Laplace transform of $F_n(t)$.

of the moments. Fig. 6 shows the delay curves, plotted on semi-logarithmic paper, for the two cases of random service and order of arrival service, in the case $\lambda = 0 \cdot 9, \mu = 1$. The curves are based on numerical calculations by Riordan, and show clearly that with random service a higher proportion of customers receive quick service and also a higher proportion receive slow service (the latter being those who are so unlucky as to miss their turn, so to speak).

Before leaving the subject of random service it is interesting to note that the case of impatient customers may also be treated mathematically. Thus, suppose we have the above case of random arrival and service, and exponential service times. Suppose also that a customer, if delayed for a time τ, decides to wait no longer but to leave the system. The steady state probability equations may then be written in the form

$$-\lambda p_0 + (\mu + c_1)p_1 = 0\,,$$

$$\lambda p_{n-1} - (\lambda + \mu + c_n)p_n + (\mu + c_{n+1})p_{n+1} = 0\,,$$

where c_n is the average rate at which customers leave the system when there are n customers waiting, (including the one being served). These equations follow, in the usual way, on noting that the chance of a departure in time dt, when the queue is of length n is $(\mu + c_n)\,dt$. They may easily be solved to give

$$p_n = \lambda^n p_0 \prod_{i=1}^{n} (\mu + c_i)^{-1} \quad (n = 1, 2, \ldots)\,,$$

where p_0 is found from the usual condition that $\sum_{n=0}^{\infty} p_n = 1$. The real problem here is to calculate the value of $c_n (n = 1, 2, \ldots)$. Barrer (5) has shown that

$$c_n = \frac{\mu e^{-\mu\tau/n}}{1 - e^{-\mu\tau/n}}\,.$$

Bulk Service. In practical queueing situations it frequently happens that the server deals with customers not individually but in batches. One example is a ferry service, and another, mentioned by Downton (14), occurs in the factory railway marshalling yard. Bailey (1) considered this type of service in a study of the problem of estimating the sizes and frequencies of clinic sessions in a hospital outpatient department, where the important items are the patient's waiting time and, on the part of the consultants, the desire to avoid idle periods. In cases such as these we use the term "*bulk-service*" to denote that the server deals with customers in groups.

The theory of bulk service is due to Bailey (2) and Downton (14, 15). It is concerned mainly with the determination on of the customer's waiting time, and is based largely on the use of probability generating functions and Laplace transforms. The theory is in various respects too advanced for inclusion here and we shall restrict our attention to the main result—the formula for the Laplace transform of the waiting time distribution—and its use in special cases.

Suppose that customers arrive at random, the mean inter-arrival time being unity (so that $\lambda = 1$), and let the distribution of the service time, v, be $B(v)$. It is supposed that customers form a single queue and that the server deals with batches of size s. If the queue length is less than s, when the server becomes free, he may or may not wait until a batch of size s has formed. The customers within a batch are supposed to be served in the order of arrival. The service time v is the time to service a batch so that, in the case where the server deals only with batches of size s, and not less, the mean service time per customer is $E(v)/s$. Thus the condition for statistical equilibrium is, since $\lambda = 1$,

$$\varrho = E(v)/s < 1 .$$

Let the Laplace transform of $\mathrm{d}B(v)/\mathrm{d}v$ be $\beta(t)$, so that

$$\beta(t) = \int_0^\infty \mathrm{e}^{-tv}\, \mathrm{d}B(v) .$$

Then Downton (14) has shown that $\gamma(t)$, the transform of the waiting time distribution, is given by

$$\gamma(t) = \frac{\Pi(1-t)}{tE(v)} \left\{ \frac{1}{\beta(t)} - 1 \right\},$$

where $\Pi(z)$ is the probability generating function of the queue length. Bailey (2) derived a general formula for $\Pi(z)$ and the use of this leads to an explicit formula for $\gamma(t)$. We consider the case of Erlangian service. Then, $dB(v)/dv = b(v)$, where

$$b(v) = (\mu k)^k v^{k-1} e^{-\mu k v}/(k-1)!\,,$$

and $$E(v) = 1/\mu\,, \quad \varrho = E(v)/s = 1/\mu s\,.$$

The formula for $\gamma(t)$ involves the roots of certain algebraic equations and we use the following lemma, proved by Bailey (2).

LEMMA: Apart from the root $z = 1$, the equation

$$z^s[1 + (1-z)/\mu k]^k - 1 = 0$$

has $s-1$ simple zeros $z_1, \ldots, z_{s-1}$ within the unit circle and k zeros $z_s, \ldots, z_{s+k-1}$, outside this circle. This remains true if $k \to \infty$ in which case the equation becomes $z^s e^{(1-z)/\mu} - 1 = 0$. In terms of the roots $z_s, \ldots, z_{s+k-1}$ the formula for $\gamma(t)$ may be written

$$\gamma(t) = \frac{(\mu/t)\,[(1 + t/\mu k)^k - 1]}{\prod_{i=s}^{s+k-1} [1 + t/(z_i - 1)]}$$

Since the Laplace transform is a moment generating function we may expand into a power series in t and obtain the mean and variance of the waiting time w. The results are

$$E(w) = \sum_{i=s}^{s+k-1} \frac{1}{z_i - 1} - \frac{k-1}{2\mu k}\,, \tag{16}$$

$$\sigma_w^2 = \sum_{i=s}^{s+k-1} \frac{1}{(z_i - 1)^2} + \frac{(k-1)(k-5)}{12\mu^2 k^2}\,. \tag{17}$$

Regular Bulk Service. This is the above case when $k \to \infty$. Then the formula for $\gamma(t)$ involves an infinite product, and the formulae for $E(w)$ and σ_ω^2 are infinite series. These may be avoided by transforming, before taking the limit as $k \to \infty$, the expression for $\gamma(t)$ into one involving the roots $z_1, \ldots, z_{s-1}$ which are *inside* the unit circle. We proceed as follows.

By writing $x = 1 + t/(z - 1)$ the equation of the lemma may be transformed into the equation,

$$(x + t - 1)^s [x - (1 + t/\mu k)]^k - (x - 1)^{k+s} = 0\,.$$

The $s + k - 1$ roots of this equation are given by

$$x_i = 1 + t/(z_i - 1) \qquad (i = 1, 2, ..., s + k-1)$$

Now the coefficient of x^{k+s-1} and the constant term in this equation are A and B respectively, where

$$A = t(s - 1/\mu), \quad B = (-)^{k+s} \quad [(1 - t)^s (1 + t/\mu k)^k - 1]\,.$$

Thus

$$\prod_{i=1}^{s+k-1} x_i = (-)^{s+k-1} B/A = -\frac{(1 - t)^s (1 + t/\mu k)^k - 1}{t(s - 1/\mu)}\,,$$

and from this follows an expression for $x_s x_{s+1} \ldots x_{s+k-1}$, involving of course $x_1\, x_2 \ldots x_{s-1}$. If we substitute this expression into the formula for $\gamma(t)$ we obtain

$$\gamma(t) = \frac{(1 - \mu s)\,[(1 + t/\mu k)^k - 1]}{(1 - t)^s (1 + t/\mu k)^k - 1}\, x_1\, x_2 \ldots x_{s-1}\,.$$

Then, taking the limit as $k \to \infty$, we obtain the result that the transform of the waiting time distribution in the case of regular service is given by

$$\gamma(t) = \frac{(1 - \mu s)\,(e^{t/\mu} - 1)}{(1 - t)^s\, e^{t/\mu} - 1} \prod_{i=1}^{s-1} \{1 + t/(z_i - 1)\}\,,$$

where $z_1, ..., z_{s-1}$, are the roots, *inside* the unit circle of the equation

$$z^s e^{(1-z)/\mu} - 1 = 0\,.$$

From this formula follow expressions for $E(w)$ and σ_ω^2 namely

$$E(w) = \frac{s(1 + \mu - \mu s)}{2(\mu s - 1)} - \sum_{i=1}^{s-1} \frac{1}{z_i - 1}\,,$$

$$\sigma_w^2 = \frac{s(6\mu + 2 - \mu s)}{12\mu} - \frac{\mu s(5\mu s - 8)}{12(\mu s - 1)^2} - \sum_{i=1}^{s-1} \frac{1}{(z_i - 1)^2}\,.$$

Downton used these formulae and also (16) and (17) to obtain numerical results,† and graphs based on these results are shown in Figs. 7 and 8, where the value of $E(w)/s$ and σ_w^2/s^2 are plotted against s for $\varrho = 1/\mu s = 0 \cdot 8$, and for $k = 1, 2, 3$ and ∞.

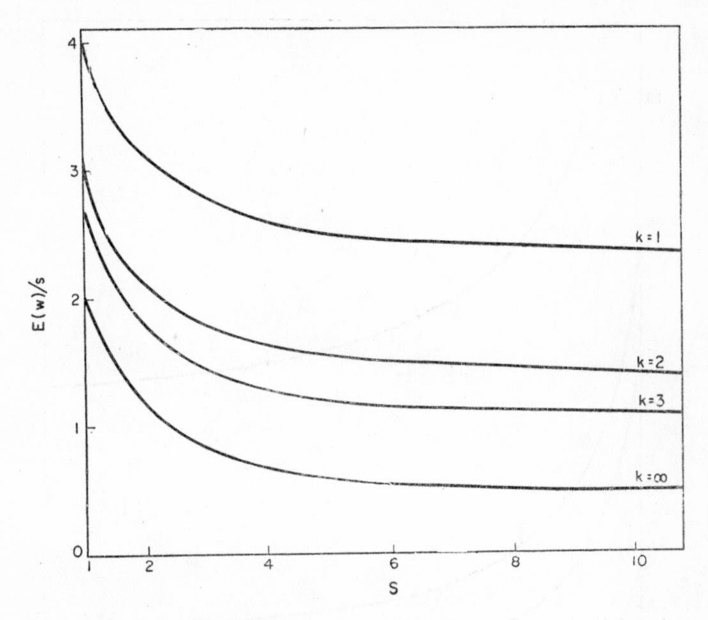

FIG. 7. Average waiting time when $\varrho = 0 \cdot 8$ ($k = 1$, random service; $k = \infty$, regular service).

Priority. Priority arises in a queueing system when, as regards the order of service, some sort of preferential treatment is given to some customers by the server. The purpose of priority is to reduce the expected waiting times of certain customers, it being realized, in a qualitative way, that this implies an extension of the expected waiting times of other customers; and the aim in attempting a mathematical analysis of priority is to determine, if possible, how the introduction of priority changes the experience of customers as regards waiting time. It must be stated

† Asymptotic formulae for $E(w)/s$ and σ_w^2/s^2, as $s \to \infty$, are necessary for purposes of calculation, when s is large. For these formulae see (16).

at the outset that we envisage a *fixed* form of priority, that is a form in which there is given a definite number of priority classes, and each customer on arrival is placed in one of these classes. Anyone who has experienced systems of priority in practice will

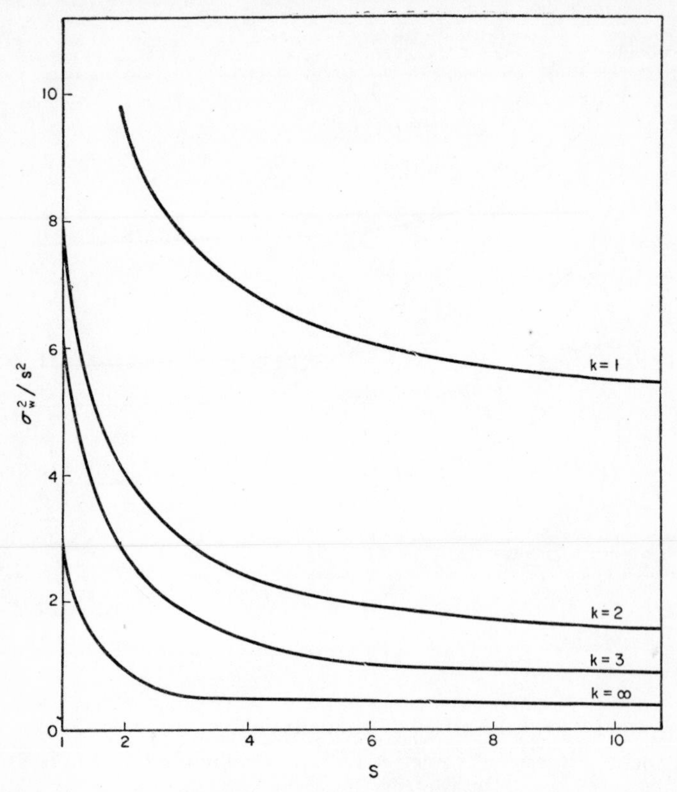

FIG. 8. Variance of waiting time when $\varrho = 0 \cdot 8$.

know how it frequently happens that the number of priority classes is not fixed, but so far the mathematical treatment has not been applied to situations of this type. A degree of discipline arises here and it is assumed that management has arranged a definite number of priority classes, and knows that this number will remain fixed.

The mathematical theory relates to the following situation. Each customer is placed in one of r priority classes, and priority

1 is the highest, priority r the lowest. A customer C of priority r will be served before a customer C' of priority r' if $r < r'$, but if C' is actually being served when C arrives then C does not displace C', that is C waits until the servicing of C' is completed†. In each class customers arrive at random, the mean rate of arrival for those of priority p being λ_p; as a result the combined arrival is also random with a rate λ where $\lambda = \lambda_1 + ... + \lambda_r$. It is supposed that the customers of a given priority are served in the order of arrival, and that the service time distribution, for customers of priority p, is some arbitrary distribution, $F_p(t)$. It is important to observe the combined service time distribution, $F(t)$. When servicing is taking place, the chance that a customer of priority p is being served is λ_p/λ. Hence, if the service time is v, and the service time of customers of priority p is v_p, then

$$F(t) = P(v \leqslant t) = \sum_{p=1}^{r} (\lambda_p/\lambda) P(v_p \leqslant t) = (1/\lambda) \sum_{p=1}^{r} \lambda_p F_p(t) \quad (18)$$

The problem we shall consider is that of finding the mean waiting time, W_p, of a customer of priority p, who for the sake of brevity, will be called a p-customer. We commence with this

LEMMA: Let a customer A arrive while another customer B is being served. If T_0 is the time that A waits until the servicing of B is completed, the mean value of T_0 is given by

$$E(T_0) = \tfrac{1}{2}\lambda \int_0^\infty t^2 \mathrm{d}F(t)\,.$$

To see this note that the chance that the service time of B lies between t and $t + \mathrm{d}t$ is $\mathrm{d}F(t)$, and the chance that a customer A arrives during the interval $(\tau, \tau + \mathrm{d}\tau)$ is $\lambda \mathrm{d}\tau$. Now, if τ is measured from the start of service of B, then $T_0 = t - \tau$; and τ ranges from 0 to t, and t from 0 to ∞. Thus

$$E(T_0) = E(t - \tau) = \int_0^\infty \Big(\int_0^t (t - \tau)\, \lambda \mathrm{d}\tau \Big) \mathrm{d}F(t) = \tfrac{1}{2}\lambda \int_0^\infty t^2 \mathrm{d}F(t)\,.$$

---

† If C does displace C', so that C' is sent back to the queue, we speak of *pre-emptive* service. The theory of this type of service has only appeared recently (46) and is not discussed here.

Let T_p be the waiting time, not including the service time, of a p-customer A arriving when there are $n_k k$-customers awaiting service where $k = 1, 2, ..., r$. Note that we are seeking W_p where $W_p = E(T_p)$, and that n_k is a random variable whose mean value will be required. Let

T_0 = the time required to complete the service of the customer being served when A arrives,

T_k = the time required to service the n_k k-customers, where $k = 1, 2, ..., p$,

T'_k = the time required to service the n'_k k-customers who arrive during the total waiting time T of A, where $k = 1, 2, ..., p - 1$.

Then, since a k-customer is served before a p-customer for $k = 1, ..., p - 1$, and those p-customers present when A arrives are served before A, it follows that

$$T_p = T_0 + \sum_{k=1}^{p} T_k + \sum_{k=1}^{p-1} T'_k . \tag{19}$$

In averaging this equation we clearly need the values of $E(T_0)$, $E(T_k)$ and $E(T'_k)$. The former is given by the lemma. For $E(T_k)$ note that $E(T_k) = E(n_k)/\mu_k$ where $1/\mu_k$, the mean service time of a k-customer, is given by

$$\frac{1}{\mu_k} = \int_0^\infty t \mathrm{d}F_k(t) .$$

But $E(n_k)$ is the expected number of k-customers arriving in time W_k, and since the mean arrival rate is λ_k we have

$$E(n_k) = \lambda_k W_k .$$

Similarly $E(T'_k) = E(n'_k)/\mu_k$ and $E(n'_k)$, the expected number of k-customers arriving during the expected waiting time W_p of A is given by $E(n'_k) = \lambda_k W_p$. Thus, writing

$$\varrho_k = \lambda_k/\mu_k , \quad \sigma_k = \sum_{i=1}^{k} \varrho_i \quad (k = 1, ..., p) ,$$

we have

$$E(T_k) = \varrho_k W_k, \quad E(T'_k) = \varrho_k W_p .$$

On averaging equation (19) we obtain

$$W_p = E(T_p) = E(T_0) + \sum_{k=1}^{p} \varrho_k W_k + \sigma_{p-1} W_p ,$$

and this equation is true for $p = 2, 3, ..., r$ and also for $p = 1$, if we put $\sigma_0 = 0$.

Thus $\quad (1 - \sigma_{p-1}) W_p = E(T_0) + \sum_{k=1}^{p} \varrho_k W_k \quad (p = 1, 2, ..., r)$

It is easy to show that the solution of this set of equations is

$$W_p = \frac{E(T_0)}{(1 - \sigma_p)(1 - \sigma_{p-1})} = \frac{\lambda}{2(1 - \sigma_p)(1 - \sigma_{p-1})} \int_0^\infty t^2 \mathrm{d}F(t) , \tag{20}$$

and this is the formula for the mean waiting time of a customer of priority p. Notice that if a customer wishes to determine the relative improvement he is likely to achieve by getting into a class of higher priority, he will find that it depends not on the *form* of the individual distributions, $F_1(t), ..., F_r(t)$, but only on the mean rates of arrival and service; for

$$W_p/W_q = (1 - \sigma_q)(1 - \sigma_{q-1})/(1 - \sigma_p)(1 - \sigma_{p-1}) .$$

From the formula for W_p it is easy to derive an expression for the mean length L of the queue, that is the mean number of customers waiting for service, not including the customer being served. For in time W_p the expected number of arrivals is $\lambda_p W_p$. Hence

$$L = \sum_{p=1}^{r} \lambda_p W_p = E(T_0) \sum_{p=1}^{r} \{\lambda_p/(1 - \sigma_p)(1 - \sigma_{p-1})\} . \tag{21}$$

This may be simplified if all priority classes have the same arrival rate λ_0 and same mean service time, μ_0. Then

$$\lambda_0 = \lambda_1 = ... = \lambda_r ; \quad \mu_0 = \mu_1 = ... = \mu_r ,$$

and we have

$$\varrho_k = \varrho_0 (k = 1, ..., r), \quad \sigma_p = p\varrho_0 \, (p = 1, ..., r) .$$

Thus

$$L = \lambda_0 E(T_0) \sum_{p=1}^{r} 1/(1 - p\varrho_0)(1 - (p-1)\varrho_0)$$

$$= \mu_0 E(T_0) \, [1/(1 - r\varrho_0) - 1] = \frac{r\lambda_0 E(T_0)}{1 - r\varrho_0}$$

Now, from (18)

$$F(t) = \frac{1}{r} \sum_{p=1}^{r} F_p(t) .$$

Thus

$$E(T_0) = \tfrac{1}{2} r\lambda_0 \int_0^\infty \frac{t^2}{r} \sum_{p=1}^{r} F_p'(t) \, \mathrm{d}t = \tfrac{1}{2} \lambda_0 \sum_{p=1}^{r} \int_0^\infty t^2 F_p'(t) \, \mathrm{d}t$$

$$= \tfrac{1}{2} \lambda_0 \sum_{p=1}^{r} \left(\frac{1}{\mu_0^2} + \sigma_p^2 \right),$$

where σ_p^2 is the variance of the service time distribution for p-customers. It follows that

$$L = \frac{r}{2(1 - r\varrho_0)} (r\varrho_0^2 + \lambda_0^2 \sum_{p=1}^{r} \sigma_p^2) .$$

This is a generalization of the classical case of the $M/M/1$ queue, given by $r = 1$ (see equation (2) of § 5, where $E(n)$, being the average queue length, including the customer being served, is given by $E(n) = \varrho + L$).

Formula (20) is due to Cobham (10) who seems to have been the first to consider the theory of priority. He also obtained a formula for W_p in the case of a multi-channel system in which service in each channel follows the same exponential distribution.

Holley (22) simplified the method of Cobham and in the above development we have essentially followed Holley's method. It may be of interest to the reader to note that a formula for the Laplace transforms of the waiting time distributions for the various priority classes have recently been derived by Kasten and Runnenburg (41) of the Mathematisch Centrum in Amsterdam. These relate to the single channel case with random input and arbitrary service times discussed above.

Continuous Number of Priorities. In 1956, following Cobham's paper of 1954, there appeared an interesting paper by Phipps (37) in which waiting time experienced during the repair of a sequence of machines was treated as a queueing problem with a continuous number of priorities. The priority given to each repair job was determined by the average time required to carry out the repair (the time being either known or estimated), the shorter jobs receiving the higher priority. The theory developed above for the discrete case of r priority classes may be carried over to the continuous case. Instead of λ_p, we have $\lambda_t \mathrm{d}t$, the mean rate of arrival of jobs whose repair periods lie between t and $t + \mathrm{d}t$. Obviously, because of the way the priority is determined the mean service time $1/\mu_p$ becomes the service time t itself. Let $F(t)$ be the job repair time distribution. Then, if λ is the combined arrival rate, that is $\lambda = \int_0^\infty \lambda_t \mathrm{d}t$, the chance of a job arriving with a repair time between τ and $\tau + \mathrm{d}\tau$ is $\mathrm{d}F(\tau)$ and also $\lambda_\tau \mathrm{d}\tau/\lambda$. Hence $\lambda_\tau \mathrm{d}\tau = \lambda \mathrm{d}F(\tau)$. It is now easy to see that the analogies, in the continuous case, of ϱ_k and σ_k are $\varrho_t \mathrm{d}t$ and σ_t where

$$\varrho_t \mathrm{d}t = t\lambda_t \mathrm{d}t, \quad \sigma_t = \int_0^t \varrho_\tau \mathrm{d}\tau = \int_0^t \tau\lambda_\tau \mathrm{d}\tau = \lambda \int_0^t \tau \mathrm{d}F(\tau)\,.$$

In the formula (20) for W_p, each of σ_p and σ_{p-1} therefore becomes $\lambda \int_0^t \tau \mathrm{d}F(\tau)$ and the formula for W_p becomes, in the continuous case,

$$W_t = E(T_0) \Big/ \Big(1 - \lambda \int_0^t \tau \mathrm{d}F(\tau)\Big)^2,$$

where $E(T_0)$ is as before. For the average number of jobs waiting in the queue the analogue of (21) is L where

$$L = \int_0^\infty \lambda_t W_t \mathrm{d}t = \lambda \int_0^\infty W_t \mathrm{d}F(t) = \lambda E(T_0) \int_0^\infty \frac{\mathrm{d}F(t)}{\left(1 - \lambda \int_0^t \tau \mathrm{d}F(\tau)\right)^2} .$$

As an example of the use of these formulae take the case of exponential repair times, where $F(t) = 1 - \mathrm{e}^{-\mu t}$, and where the arrival rate of (all) jobs is λ. Then

$$E(T_0) = \tfrac{1}{2} \lambda \int_0^\infty t^2 \mu \mathrm{e}^{-\mu t} \mathrm{d}t = \frac{\lambda}{\mu^2} ,$$

and it is found that W_t, the mean waiting time of jobs whose repair times are about t, and L, the mean number of jobs awaiting repair, are given by

$$W_t = \frac{\lambda}{\mu^2 D^2} , \quad L = \frac{\lambda^2}{\mu} \int_0^\infty \frac{\mathrm{e}^{-\mu t}}{D^2} \mathrm{d}t ,$$

where

$$D = 1 - \lambda[1 - (1 + \mu t)\, \mathrm{e}^{-\mu t}]/\mu .$$

In Fig. 9 graphs are shown of L, plotted against ϱ, both for the case of priority (the solid curve) where the shorter the job the higher the priority, and the case of 'first-come, first-served' (the dotted curve). The effectiveness of priority in reducing the expected queue length is evident.

It is necessary to notice that the above account only applies to stable conditions, where all jobs have a finite chance of repair. If this is not the case there is a critical repair time t', such that all jobs with repair times t, where $t > t'$ will not be repaired. This case of 'saturation' is analysed by Phipps, who also gives a method of evaluating the critical repair time t'. In the continuous case the traffic intensity of jobs whose repair times are t or less is σ_t where

$$\sigma_t = \lambda \int_0^t \tau \mathrm{d}F(\tau) .$$

Thus the critical repair time t' is given by

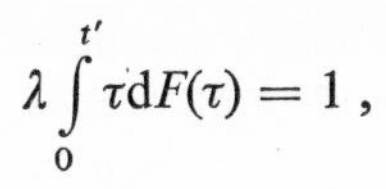

$$\lambda \int_0^{t'} \tau \mathrm{d}F(\tau) = 1 ,$$

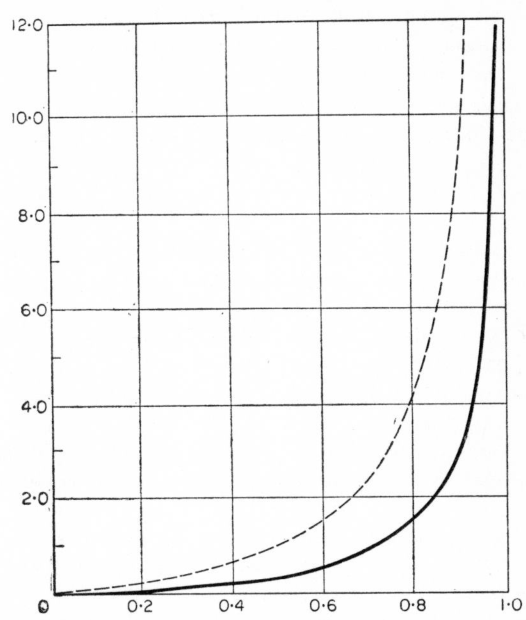

FIG. 9. Comparison of the mean queue length, L, for the cases of priority (———), and 'first — come, first — served' (------).

and in the particular case above where $F(t) = 1 - \mathrm{e}^{-\mu t}$, it is found that t' is the root, $\tau = t'$, of the equation

$$\lambda[1 - (1 + \mu\tau)\,\mathrm{e}^{-\mu\tau}] = \mu .$$

REFERENCES

For a more extensive list of references see the bibliography by Alison Doig in *Biometrika*, **44** (1957), 490.

1. N. T. J. BAILEY, "A study of queues and appointment systems in outpatient departments with special reference to waiting times", *J. R. Statist. Soc.*, B, **14** (1952), 185.

2. N. T. J. BAILEY, "On queueing processes with bulk service", *J. R. Statist. Soc.*, B, **16** (1954), 80.
3. N. T. J. BAILEY, "A continuous time treatment of a simple queue using generating functions", *J. R. Statist. Soc.*, B, **16** (1954), 288.
4. N. T. J. BAILEY, "Some further results in the non-equilibrium theory of a simple queue", *J. R. Statist. Soc.*, **19** (1957), 326.
5. D. Y. BARRER, "Queueing with impatient customers and indifferent clerks", *Operations Res.*, **5** (1957), 644.
6. E. BROCKMEYER, H. L. HALSTROM, and A. JENSEN, *The Life and Works of A. K. Erlang*, Danish Academy of Technical Science, Copenhagen, 1948.
7. P. J. BURKE, "The output of a queueing system", *J. Operations Res.*, **4** (1956), 699.
8. D. G. CHAMPERNOWNE, "An elementary method of solution of the queueing problem with a single server and constant parameters", *J. R., Statist. Soc.*, B, **18** (1956), 125.
9. A. B. CLARKE, "A waiting line process of Markov type", *Ann. Math. Statist.*, **27** (1956), 452.
10. A. COBHAM, "Priority assignment in waiting line problems", *J. Operations Research Soc. Amer.*, **2** (1954), 70; *ibid.* **3** (1955), 547.
11. J. W. COHEN, "Certain delay problems for a full availability trunk group loaded by two traffic sources", *Commun. News*, **16** (1956), 105.
12. J. W. COHEN, A Survey of Queueing Problems Occurring in Telephone and Telegraph Traffic Theory, *Proc. of the First International Conference on Operational Research*, Oxford, 1957, p. 132, Eng. Uni. Press, London, 1957.
13. R. E. COX, "Traffic flow in an exponential delay system with priority categories", *Proc. Inst. Elect. Engrs.*, B, **102** (1955), 815.
14. F. DOWNTON, "Waiting time in bulk service queues", *J. R. Statist. Soc.*, B, **17** (1955), 256.
15. F. DOWNTON, "On limiting distributions arising in bulk service queues". *J. R. Statist. Soc.*, B, **18** (1956), 265.
16. A. ERDELYI, *Tables of Integral Transforms*, McGraw-Hill, N. Y., 1954.
17. A. K. ERLANG, "Sandsynlighedsregning og telefonsamtaler", *Nyt Tidsskr. Mat.*, B, **20** (1909), 33.
18. A. K. ERLANG, "Losning af nogle problemer fra sandsynlighedsregningen af betydning for de automatiske telefoncentraler", *Elektroteknikeren*, **13** (1917), 5.
19. W. FELLER, *An Introduction to Probability Theory and its Applications*, John Wiley, (N. Y., 1957).
20. T. C. FRY, *Probability and its engineering uses*, van Nostrand, N. Y., 1928.
21. D. P. GAVER, "The influence of servicing times in queueing processes", *J. Operat. Res. Soc. Amer.*, **2** (1954), 139.

22. J. L. HOLLEY, "Waiting line subject to priorities", *J. Operations Research Soc. Amer.*, **2** (1954), 341.
23. G. C. HUNT, "Sequential arrays of waiting lines", *Operations Res.*, **4** (1956), 674.
24. J. R. JACKSON, "Networks of waiting lines", *Operations Res.*, **5** (1957), 518.
25. D. G. KENDALL, "Some problems in the theory of queues", *J. R. Statist. Soc.*, B, **13** (1951), 151.
26. A. JA. KHINTCHINE, "Mathematisches über die Erwartung vor einem öffentlichen Schalter", *Mat. Sborn.*, **39** (1932), 73.
27. A. JA. KHINTCHINE, "Über die mittlere Dauer des Stillstandes von Maschinen", *Mat. Sborn.*, **40** (1933), 119.
28. A. KOLMOGOROV, "Sur le problème d'attente", *Mat Sborn.*, **38** (1931), 101.
29. W. LEDERMANN and G. E. H. REUTER, "Spectral theory for the differential equations of simple birth and death processes", *Phil. Trans. Roy. Soc.*, A, **246** (1954), 321.
30. J. LE ROY, "Formules matricielles du calcul du délai d'attente dans le cas des appels desservis au hasard", *Ann. Télé-comm.*, **12** (1957), 2.
31. D. V. LINDLEY, "The theory of queues with a single server", *Proc. Camb. Phil. Soc.*, **48** (1952), 277.
32. G. LUCHAK, "The solution of the single-channel queueing equations characterized by a time-dependent Poisson-distributed arrival rate and a general class of holding times", *Operations Res.*, **4** (1956), 711.
33. J. W. MELLOR, "Delayed call formulae, when calls are served in random order", *P. O. Elect. Engrgs' J.*, **35** (1942), 53.
34. E. C. MOLINA, "Application of the theory of probability to telephone-trunking problems", *Bell Syst. Tech. J.*, **6** (1926), 461.
35. P. M. MORSE, "Stochastic properties of waiting lines", *J. Operat. Res. Soc. Amer.*, **3** (1955), 255.
36. C. PALM, "Bidrag till teorin för wäntsystem", *Tekn. Medd. Teleg.*, **104** (1946).
37. T. E. PHIPPS JR., "Machine repair as a priority waiting line problem", *Operations Res.*, **4** (1956), 76.
38. F. POLLACZEK, "Über eine Aufgabe der Wahrscheinlichkeitstheorie", *Math. Z.*, **32** (1930), 64 and 729.
39. E. REICH, "Waiting times when queues are in tandem", *Ann. Math. Stat.*, **28** (1957), 768.
40. J. RIORDAN, "Delay curves for calls at random", *Bell Syst. Tech. J.*, **32** (1953), 100.
41. J. T. RUNNENBURG and H. KESTEN, "Priority in waiting problems", *Proc. Koninkl. Nederl. Akad. van Wetenschappen Amsterdam*, A, **60** (1957), 312.
42. T. L. SAATY, *Mathematical Methods of Operations Research*, McGraw-Hill, N. Y., 1959, p. 340.

43. W. L. SMITH, "On the distribution of queueing times", *Proc. Camb. Phil. Soc.*, **49** (1953), 449.
44. E. VAULOT, "Délais d'attente des appels téléphoniques traités au hasard", *C. R. Acad. Sci. Paris*, **222** (1946), 268.
45. E. VAULOT, "Délais d'attente des appels téléphoniques dans l'ordre inverse de leur arrivée", *C. R. Acad. Sci. Paris*, **238** (1954), 1188.
46. H. WHITE and L. L. CHRISTIE, Queueing with pre-emptive priorities or with breakdown", *Operations Res.*, **6** (1958), 79.
47. R. I. WILKINSON, "Working curves for delayed exponential calls served in random order", *Bell Syst. Tech. J.*, **32** (1953), 360.
48. E. M. WRIGHT, "On the coefficients of power series having exponential singularities", *J. Lond. Math. Soc.*, **8** (1933), 71.

CHAPTER V

QUEUEING THEORY: CHANNELS IN SERIES OR PARALLEL

1. Introduction

In this chapter the theory of compound queues is developed where the queue consists of a number of single channel queues arranged in series or parallel as indicated in § 2 of the previous chapter. In practice compound queues are frequently encountered. An industrial production line, for example, generally involves several distinct processes, $P_1, ..., P_r$, and the material being processed may encounter delays at the input to one or more of the processing operations. It is envisaged that the material flows in units or batches, and the delay experienced may be necessary (for example, P_i may be operated only on one shift and P_{i+1} on two shift working) or it may be accidental in the sense that unsmooth production will obviously cause temporary accumulations of material at various points. This situation gives rise to the problem of *process stocks*† and the queueing problem involved is, in its simplest form, one where a number of single channel queues are arranged in series.

Problems involving channels in parallel arise, for example, in the study of telephone traffic. This field has been explored a great deal, and in fact is the original subject in which a theory of queueing was first developed. Erlang, Fry, Vaulot and others all contributed to the development of the theory, which is treated in a recent book by Syski (15). As a result we shall not

† The problem is to determine a "reasonable" level for the stocks, since excessive stock results in the use of unnecessary working capital, which may be quite high if the material processed is expensive.

deal with much of the theory of telephone traffic in this book; attention will be confined to the calculation of the steady state probabilities in the case of a number of parallel channels and to various quantities expressible in terms of these.

It is convenient to remark here on what has been called a 'network' of queues. Practical flow problems are frequently more complicated than either of the above cases of series and parallel channels. There are many possibilities. Customers may branch out from a single queue into several parallel service channels and then converge again into a single channel or several channels in series. Customers may even return, after service, to the input to the queue and await service again, and this may be repeated thus giving rise to a closed operation involving several cycles. It may even happen that over a period of time some channels normally open are closed for certain intervals, so that the network itself may change its structure with time. Very little, in the way of a theory, has so far been developed for networks of queues, but an indication of the direction in which research is moving is given in Refs. 2, 7 and 14.

2. Channels in parallel with random input

In this section it will be assumed that customers arrive at random at an average rate λ, for attention at one of a number of service channels in parallel. In each channel service is supposed to follow the same exponential distribution, $B(v)$, where $B(v) = 1 - e^{-\mu v}$, v being the service time. The number, c, of channels may be finite or infinite and both cases will be discussed below. When a customer arrives he receives service at once if there is a free channel. Otherwise he either joins a queue and waits for service, or decides to leave the system in which case he is said to be 'lost'. In the case of telephone traffic a customer is, of course, a call on the exchange.

It is particularly important to make a clear distinction between the number, n_0, of customers in the queue proper, that is definitely waiting for service to commence, and the number n, of customers in the system. It is clear that $n_0 = 0$ if $n \leqslant c$, and that $n_0 = n - c$, if $n \geqslant c$. We shall call n the 'length of the queue' and n_0 the 'length of the waiting line', that is, we shall use the term 'waiting line' to refer to the collection of customers waiting for service to start. Let

$$L = E(n), \quad L_0 = E(n_0),$$

and let p_n, for $n = 0, 1, 2, \ldots, \ldots$, be the chance that, in the case of statistical equilibrium, there are n customers in the system. Further let c_0 be the mean number of free service channels. Then

$$L_0 = L - c + c_0 .$$

To see this note that $L = \sum_{n=0}^{\infty} np_n$, $L_0 = \sum_{n=c}^{\infty} (n - c)\, p_n$, and that

$$c_0 = cp_0 + (c-1)\,p_1 + \ldots + p_{c-1}$$
$$= c\,(p_0 + p_1 + \ldots + p_{c-1}) - (p_1 + 2p_2 + \ldots + (c-1)\,p_{c-1}) .$$

Then

$$L_0 = \sum_{n=c}^{\infty} np_n - c \sum_{n=c}^{\infty} p_n = L - (p_1 + 2p_2 + \ldots$$
$$+ (c-1)\,p_{c-1}) - c[1 - (p_0 + p_1 + \ldots + p_{c-1})] = L - c + c_0 .$$

(i) *The Case of a Finite Number, c, of Channels.* Let $P_n(t)$ be the chance that the queue length is n at time t. The chance of an arrival in time dt is λdt. The chance of a departure in a single channel is μdt, and thus, since the channels are supposed to operate independently, the chance of a departure from the system in time dt is $n\mu dt$ for $n < c$ and $c\mu dt$ for $n \geqslant c$. The equations (6) of § 2 of the previous chapter apply, where

$$\lambda_n = \lambda, \quad \mu_n = c\mu \quad \text{for} \quad n \geqslant c,$$
$$\lambda_n = \lambda, \quad \mu_n = n\mu \quad \text{for} \quad n < c,$$

that is

$$P_n'(t) = \lambda P_{n-1}(t) - (\lambda + n\mu)P_n(t) + (n+1)\,\mu P_{n+1}(t) \qquad (0 < n < c)$$
$$P_n'(t) = \lambda P_{n-1}(t) - (\lambda + c\mu)P_n(t) + c\mu P_{n+1}(t) \qquad (n \geqslant c)$$

and

$$P_0'(t) = -\,\lambda P_0(t) + \mu P_1(t) .$$

If we assume that a state of statistical equilibrium is ultimately reached as $t \to \infty$, then the probabilities $p_0, p_1, \ldots,$ satisfy the equations

$$\lambda p_0 = \mu p_1$$
$$(\lambda + n\mu)\, p_n = \lambda p_{n-1} + (n+1)\,\mu p_{n+1} \quad (1 \leqslant n < c)$$
$$(\lambda + c\mu)\, p_n = \lambda p_{n-1} + c\mu p_{n+1} \quad (n \geqslant c)\,.$$

It may easily be verified that the solution of this system is given by

$$p_n = p_0 \sigma^n / n! \quad (0 \leqslant n < c)$$
$$p_n = p_0 \sigma^n / c!\, c^{n-c} \quad (n \geqslant c)$$

where $\sigma = \lambda/\mu$ and p_0 is found from the condition $\sum_{n=0}^{\infty} p_n = 1$, that is,

$$p_0 = 1 \bigg/ \left[\sum_{n=0}^{c-1} \frac{(c\varrho)^n}{n!} + \frac{(c\varrho)^c}{c!(1-\varrho)} \right],$$

the constant ϱ being given by $\varrho = \sigma/c = \lambda/c\mu$.

From this solution the value of L_0, and hence L, follows easily. It is given by

$$L_0 = \frac{p_0}{c!} \sum_{n=c}^{\infty} (n-c) \frac{\sigma^{n-c}}{c^{n-c}} = \frac{p_0 (\varrho c)^c \varrho}{c!(1-\varrho)^2}\,.$$

An expression can also easily be obtained for the chance P of waiting, namely

$$P = p_c + p_{c+1} + \ldots = \frac{p_0\, (c\varrho)^c}{c!(1-\varrho)}\,.$$

Note that when $c = 1$ this reduces to the correct result, $P = \varrho$ for a single channel. The condition that a state of statistical equilibrium be reached can be derived by noting that the service rate μc of the whole system, must be greater than the arrival rate λ. Thus the condition is $\mu c > \lambda$ that is $\varrho < 1$.

The Number of Busy Channels. This number may have any value in the range 0 to c. Let $P_n^*(t)$ be the chance that n channels are busy at time t. The equations for $P_n^*(t)$ are as before, for $n = 0, 1, 2, ..., c-1$ but for $n = c$ there is a modification. In this case, we have

$$P_c^*(t + \mathrm{d}t) = P_{c-1}^*(t)\lambda \mathrm{d}t + P_c^*(t)\,(1 - c\mu \mathrm{d}t)\,,$$

there being no factor $\lambda \mathrm{d}t$ in the last term, since there are c channels and not more. Thus we obtain

$$P_c^{*\prime}(t) = \lambda P_{c-1}^*(t) - c\mu P_c^*(t)\,.$$

The equations in the case of statistical equilibrium are now given by

$$- \lambda p_0^* = \mu p_1^*\,,$$

$$(\lambda + n\mu)\,p_n^* = \lambda p_{n-1}^* + \mu(n+1)\,p_{n+1}^*\,, \qquad (n = 1,2, ..., c-1)$$

$$\lambda p_{c-1}^* = c\mu p_c^*\,,$$

where $p_n^* = \lim_{t\to\infty} P_n^*(t)$. The solution, which was first given by Erlang in 1918, is

$$p_n^* = k\varrho^n/n! \qquad (n = 0, 1, ..., c)\,,$$

where k is given by $\sum_{n=0}^{c} p_n^* = 1$, that is

$$k = 1/\sum_{r=0}^{c} \varrho^r/r!$$

This applies to the case of random input and exponential service times. An explicit formula has recently been found for p_n^* in the more general case of an arbitrary input and exponential service time by Takács (16). Erlang's formula itself holds under more general conditions. Pollaczek (13), Palm (12) and others have proved that it is valid for an arbitrary distribution of service times, provided the input is random. In the case of random input and constant service time, formulae for the p_n and for P were found by Crommelin (5).

It is of interest to note that the mean waiting time for a finite number of priority classes in the case of a number of parallel channels was solved by Cobham (3), when all channels have the same exponential service time, with mean $1/\mu$, and the input to the kth priority class is random with a mean rate λ_k. The formula for W_k, the mean waiting time for k-customers, is similar to (20) of §10 in the previous chapter, namely

$$W_k = \frac{E(T_0)}{1 - \frac{1}{c\mu}\sum_{i=1}^{k-1}\lambda_i} = \frac{\pi/\mu c}{\left(1 - \frac{1}{c\mu}\sum_{i=1}^{k-1}\lambda_i\right)\left(1 - \frac{1}{c\mu}\sum_{i=1}^{k}\lambda_i\right)},$$

where the value of π was found by Molina (11) to be given by

$$\pi = \frac{\sigma^c}{c!(1-\sigma/c)\left[\sum_{i=0}^{c-1}\frac{\sigma^i}{i!} + \sum_{i=c}^{\infty}\frac{\sigma^i}{c!c^{i-c}}\right]}.$$

(ii) *The Case of an Infinite Number of Channels.* This is case (i) with $c = \infty$. Then there is no queue proper. The equations for $P_n(t)$ $(n = 0, 1, 2, \ldots)$ then become simply

$$P_0'(t) = -\lambda P_0(t) + \mu P_1(t),$$
$$P_n'(t) = \lambda P_{n-1}(t) - (\lambda + n\mu) P_n(t) + (n+1)\mu P_{n+1}(t) \quad (n \geqslant 1)$$

From these it is easy to derive the equation for the generating function $\Pi(z, t)$, defined by

$$\prod(z, t) = \sum_{n=0}^{\infty} P_n(t) z^n .$$

Multiplying the second equation by z^n and summing over n from 0 to ∞ the equation is found to be

$$\frac{\partial \Pi}{\partial t} - \mu(1-z)\frac{\partial \Pi}{\partial z} + \lambda(1-z)\Pi = 0,$$

and the solution of this equation, subject to the initial condition,

$$P_n(0) = \begin{cases} 0 \ (n \neq a) \\ 1 \ (n = a) \end{cases}$$

is

$$\prod(z, t) = e^{\theta(z,t)}\varphi(z, t),$$

where

$$\theta(z, t) = -\lambda(1-z)(1-e^{-\mu t})/\mu, \qquad \varphi(z, t) = \{1 - (1-z)e^{-\mu t}\}^a.$$

The formula for $P_n(t)$ now follows by a standard procedure, since

$$P_n(t) = \frac{1}{n!}\left[\frac{\partial^n \Pi(z, t)}{\partial z^n}\right]_{z=0}$$

The use of Leibnitz theorem for evaluating the nth derivative gives, for $n < a$,

$$P_n(t) = \frac{e^{-\sigma f(t)}}{n!}\sum_{r=0}^{n}\binom{n}{r}\frac{a!}{(a-r)!}\,\sigma^{n-r}\{f(t)\}^{n+a-2r}e^{-\mu rt},$$

where $\sigma = \lambda/\mu$ and $f(t) = 1 - e^{-\mu t}$. The formula for the case $n > a$ may be obtained in a similar manner.

For the mean number, L, of busy channels in the transient case the formula can be easily derived from $\Pi(z, t)$ itself. For

$$L = \sum_{n=0}^{\infty} nP_n(t) = \left(\frac{\partial \Pi}{\partial z}\right)_{z=1} = \left(e^{\theta}\frac{\partial \varphi}{\partial z} + \varphi e^{\theta}\frac{\partial \theta}{\partial z}\right)_{z=1}$$

But $e^{\theta} = 1$ and $\varphi(1, t) = 1$ when $z = 1$. Hence

$$L = \sigma(1 - e^{-\mu t}) + ae^{-\mu t}.$$

The case $a = 0$. If at time $t = 0$ there are no customers in the system, that is $a = 0$, the formula for $\Pi(z, t)$ simplifies to $\Pi(z, t) = e^{\theta(z,t)}$, since $\varphi(z, t) = 1$ when $a = 0$. Now $\theta(z, t) = -m(1 - z)$ where $m = \sigma(1 - e^{-\mu t})$. Thus $\Pi(z, t) = e^{-m(1-z)}$, showing that the $P_n(t)$ follow a Poisson distribution with a mean m.

In the case of statistical equilibrium the equations for the p_n become

$$\lambda p_0 = \mu p_1,$$

$$(\lambda + n\mu)p_n = \lambda p_{n-1} + (n + 1)\mu p_{n+1} \qquad (n \geqslant 1)$$

and the solution of these is

$$p_n = e^{-\sigma}\sigma^n/n!$$

Thus the number of busy channels follows a Poisson distribution, with a mean λ/μ.

(iii) *The Case of a Limited Source.* In cases (i) and (ii) it is tacitly assumed that there is an infinite supply of potential customers.

This is not always so and the case is now considered where there is a strictly finite number of customers or units which may require attention. Consider, as shown in Fig. 1, a closed system consisting of a reservoir R containing units which do not require

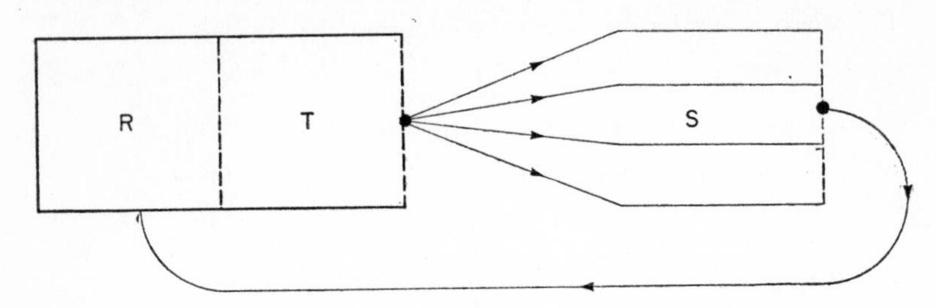

FIG. 1. R is a reservoir, T a waiting line, S a set of c parallel service channels. Customers return to R after service.

attention, a waiting line T, and a set S of c parallel service channels. It is assumed that

(a) in time δt there is a chance $\lambda \delta t$ that a unit in R will require service, in which case the unit moves to T, or, if there is a free channel, to S,

(b) all channels in S have the same exponential service time distribution, $B(v) = 1 - e^{-\mu v}$,

(c) units return to the reservoir R after service.

Before proceeding further it may help to give two practical illustrations of this situation:

(A) *A problem of power-supply.* The unit is a welder and the channels of S are power-supply lines, so numerous that a welder is never kept waiting when he requires power, that is $c > m$, where m is the total number of welders. Then there is no waiting line T and the problem is to determine the probability $P_n(t)$ that n of the power-supply lines will be occupied at time t, where $n = 0, 1, 2, \ldots, m$. We deal with this problem below. The original treatment is due to Adler and Miller (1).

(B) *A Machine Repair Problem.* Here a unit is a machine, normally in working order, that is not requiring service (or repair) and hence in R. When it fails it is either serviced at once by one of c operators, where $c < m$ (m being the total number of machines), or else joins a waiting line T, which will not always be empty since $c < m$. The problem is to determine the probability that $m - n$ machines will be in working order, for $n = 0, 1, ..., m$. This is the central problem in the theory of Machine Interference, treated in the next chapter (see especially § 5).

To return to the power-supply problem note that when n channels are busy, that is n welders are receiving power, there are $m - n$ welders in R, each being a potential customer for a power line. The chance that an individual welder completes service, that is no longer requires power, in time δt is $\mu \delta t$, so the chance of a departure from S in time δt is $n\mu\delta t$. Similarly, if $\lambda\delta t$ is the chance that a welder in R requires service during δt, then $(m - n)\lambda\delta t$ is the chance that another power line will be required in time δt. It follows that if $P_n(t)$ is the chance that n of the m welders are receiving power at time t, then

$$P_n'(t) = (m - n + 1)\lambda P_{n-1}(t) - [(m - n)\lambda + n\mu] P_n(t) + (n + 1)\mu P_{n+1}(t) \quad (1 \leqslant n \leqslant m - 1),$$

while the equations for $P_0'(t)$ and $P_m'(t)$ are

$$P_0'(t) = -m\lambda P_0(t) + \mu P_1(t),$$
$$P_m'(t) = -m\mu P_m(t) + \lambda P_{m-1}(t).$$

For this system of equations the generating function $\Pi(z, t)$, given by $\Pi(z, t) = \sum_{n=0}^{m} P_n(t) z^n$ satisfies the equation

$$\frac{\partial \Pi}{\partial t} - (1 - z)(\mu + \lambda z)\frac{\partial \Pi}{\partial z} = -m\lambda(1 - z)\Pi.$$

The solution of this equation, subject to the condition that there are no welders using power lines at $t = 0$, that is, $P_0(0) = 1$, $P_i(0) = 0$ $(i > 0)$, is

$$\Pi(z, t) = \{(\mu + \lambda e^{-kt}) + \lambda z(1 - e^{-kt})\}^m / k^m,$$

where $k = \lambda + \mu$. Thus $P_n(t)$, being the coefficient of z^n in the expansion of $\Pi(z, t)$, is given by

$$P_n(t) = \binom{m}{n} \lambda^n(1 - e^{-kt})^n(\mu + \lambda e^{-kt})^{m-n}/k^m \qquad (n = 0, 1, ..., m)$$

and, for the steady state, we have

$$p_n = \lim_{t \to \infty} P_n(t) = \binom{m}{n} \lambda^n \mu^{m-n}/k^m .$$

Notice that in this problem since m, and hence n, is finite, there is no condition on λ and μ for statistical equilibrium.

3. Parallel channels with general input: the queue $G/M/c$

In § 2 a basic assumption was that the input was random. With a view to applications of the theory it is obviously desirable to relax this assumption, if possible. A survey of the literature reveals that this was not achieved for at least two decades. Then, in 1953, an outstanding paper by D. G. Kendall (10) presented a penetrating analysis of the many-server queue, $G/M/c$, using a new method called 'the method of the imbedded Markov chain', based on Feller's theory of denumerable Markov chains. The treatment is too advanced for inclusion in this book, but the results achieved are so important that an outline of the position is now given.

Suppose that, as before, there are c channels, each having an exponential service time distribution, $1 - e^{-\mu v}$, and that the inter-arrival time, u, follows a general distribution $A(u)$ with mean $1/\lambda$. The traffic intensity is ϱ where $\varrho = \lambda/c\mu$ and the condition for statistical equilibrium is $\varrho < 1$. Denote by $\mathbf{p}$ the vector $(p_0, p_1, ...)$, where the ith component, p_i, is the chance that the queue is of length i, just before the arrival of a customer. Then we have this

Theorem of Kendall. For the queue $G/M/c$, where $c > 1$ and $\varrho = \lambda/c\mu < 1$, the state probability vector $\mathbf{p}$ is given by

$$\mathbf{p} = (a_0, a_1, ..., a_{c-2}, 1, x, x^2, x^3, ...)/D,$$

where

(i) $a_0, ..., a_{c-2}$ are certain constants,

(ii) x is the unique root, in the range $0 < x < 1$ of the equation

$$x = \int_0^\infty exp[-(1-x)\, c\, \mu u]\, dA(u), \tag{1}$$

(iii) D, chosen so that $\sum_{i=0}^{\infty} p_i = 1$, has the value

$$D = \sum_{i=0}^{c-2} a_i + 1/(1-x).$$

From this theorem we deduce the following results regarding the length Q of the waiting line (the customers actually waiting and not being served).

(a)
$$P(Q=0) = (\sum_{i=0}^{c-2} a_i + 1 + x)/D\,.$$

For $Q = 0$ if 0, 1, 2, ..., or c channels only are occupied.

(b) The mean, L_0, of Q is given by

$$L_0 = E(Q) = \{x^2 \cdot 1 + x^3 \cdot 2 + x^4 \cdot 3 + ...\}/D = x^2/\{D(1-x)^2\}\,.$$

(c) Given that $Q > 0$, the conditional probability that $Q = n$ is $(1-x)\, x^{n-1}$ $(n = 1, 2, ...)$.
To see this note that

$$P(Q > 0) = (x^2 + x^3 + ...)/D = x^2/\{D(1-x)\}\,,$$

and the unconditional probability that $Q = n$ is x^{n+1}/D. Hence, the conditional probability that $Q = n$ is given by

$$P(Q = n | Q > 0) = \frac{x^{n+1}}{D} \Big/ \frac{x^2}{D(1-x)} = (1-x)x^{n-1}\,.$$

Similar results are obtainable for the waiting time, w. Thus

(a1)
$$P(w=0) = (1 + \sum_{i=0}^{c-2} a_i)/D\,,$$

(b1)
$$E(w)/E(v) = x/\{cD(1-x)^2\}\,.$$

(c1) Given that $w > 0$, the conditional probability density of w is $\nu e^{-\nu w}$ where $\nu = \mu c(1-x)$.

Before these formulae can be used it is necessary to know the value of x, given by equation (1) and also the values of $a_0, a_1, \ldots, a_{c-2}$. In the case of random input, where $dA(u) = \lambda e^{-\lambda u} du$, equation (1) becomes

$$x = \lambda \int_0^\infty exp\{-u[\lambda + (1-x)c\mu]\} du = \frac{1}{1+(1-x)/\varrho}.$$

Thus

$$x^2 - (1+\varrho)x + \varrho = 0,$$

and the root in (0, 1) is $x = \varrho$. For regular input, where

$$A(u) = \begin{cases} 0 & (u < 1/\lambda) \\ 1 & (u \geqslant 1/\lambda) \end{cases}$$

the equation for x becomes

$$x = e^{-(1-x)c\mu/\lambda} = e^{-(1-x)/\varrho}.$$

The solution x, is plotted in Fig. 2 as a function of ϱ.

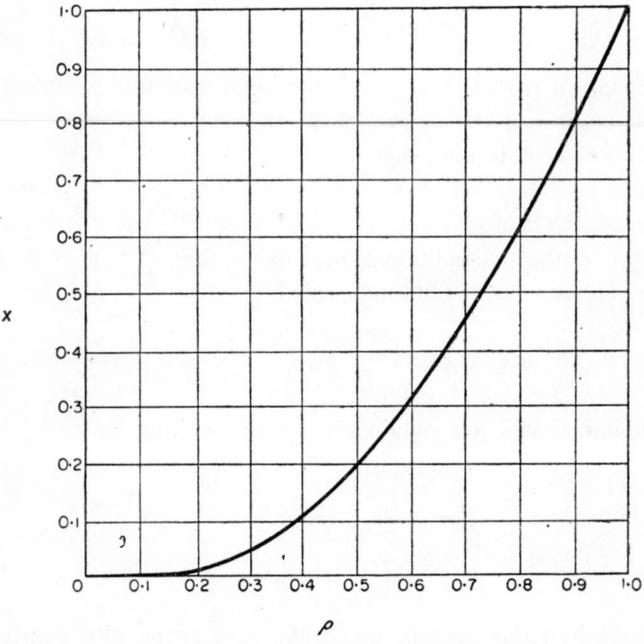

FIG. 2. The solution, x, of the equation $x = e^{-(1-x)/\varrho}$

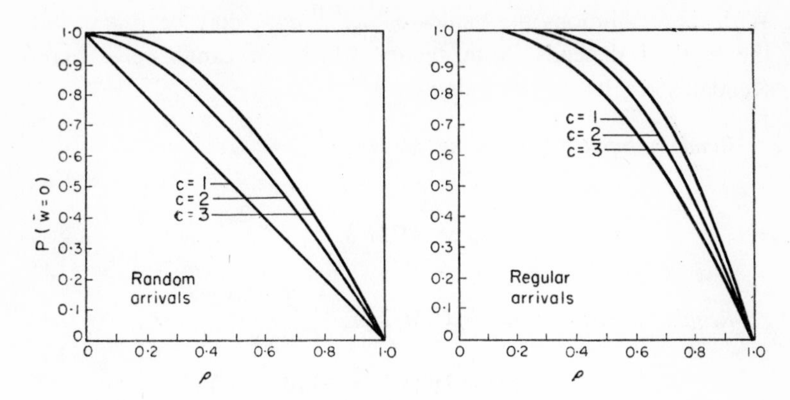

FIG. 3. The probability, $P(w = 0)$, of not having to wait.

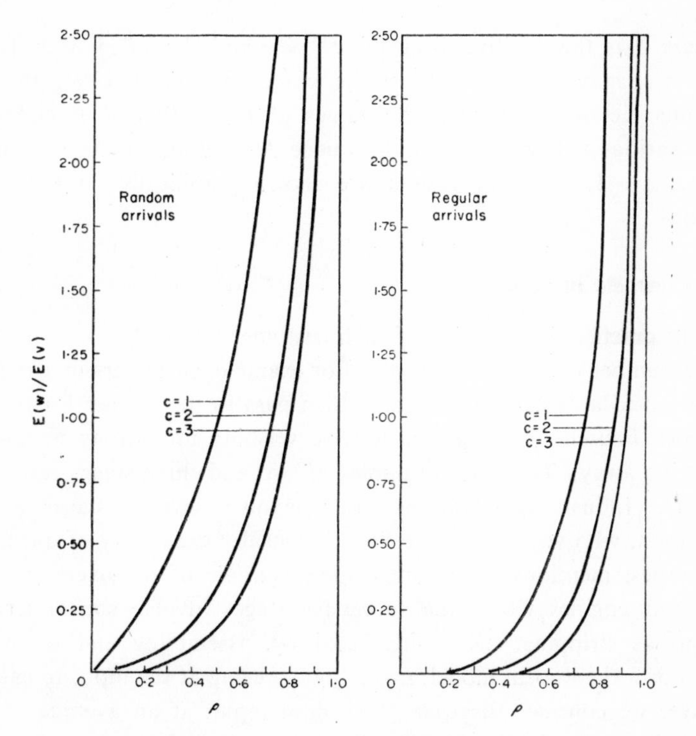

FIG. 4. The ratio of the mean waiting time, $E(w)$, to the mean service time, $E(v)$.

With these solutions the values of $a_0, \ldots, a_{c-2}$ may be found, but the method depends upon theory which we cannot give here. Kendall's results are as follows:

Random Input. The queue $M/M/2$: $a_0 = \frac{1}{2\varrho}$,

The queue $M/M/3$: $a_1 = \frac{2}{3\varrho}$, $a_0 = \frac{2}{(3\varrho)^2}$.

Regular Input. The queue $D/M/2$: $a_0 = \frac{2 - e^{1/(2p)}}{2x - 1}$,

The queue $D/M/3$: $a_1 = (3 - \vartheta^2)/(3x - 1)$,

$$a_0 = \frac{2(3 - 2\vartheta)}{3x - 2} - (2 - \vartheta)\, a_1,$$

where ϑ is the positive root of $\vartheta^{3\varrho} = e$ and the value of x, for given ϱ, may be derived from the curve in Fig. 2. Using these results Kendall calculated the values of $P(w = 0)$ and $E(w)/E(v)$ for various values of ϱ, for the queue $M/M/c$ and $D/M/c$ in the cases $c = 1, 2, 3$. The results are shown graphically in Figs. 3 and 4.

4. Channels in series

In practice the servicing of each customer frequently takes place in a number of successive stages. For example, customers in a shop are served at a counter and may then pass to the cashier for payment; household operations involve washing up, wiping up and putting away. These are examples of two and three stages respectively. Industrial operations often involve several stages and Jackson, who was one of the first to consider the theory of queues in series, mentions (8) the interesting example of the overhaul of aircraft engines where the successive stages involve such operations as stripping, inspecting, repairing, assembling and testing.

For a theoretical model, involving queueing at the input to each stage, we consider the case of random input, at an average rate λ, and exponential service time distribution at each stage, the mean service time at the ith stage being $1/\mu_i$. Following the nomenclature set up by Gaver (6) and Jackson (9) we refer to each stage as a *phase*, and we shall assume that every customer is served at each of the phases. Denote the phases by $S_1, ..., S_k$. When a customer emerges from one phase he joins a queue to wait for service at the next phase, unless the latter can accept him at once. Thus the input to each queue, after the first, is the output from the previous phase and the question arises as to whether this input is random. The answer is YES for the condition assumed, of initial random input and exponential service, and a proof has been given by Burke (2) and, more generally, by Reich (14). It is essential for what follows that the input to each phase be random, and this is the reason for making the assumption on initial input and service-time.

For the model just introduced the algebra becomes rather heavy for several phases, and for this reason we confine attention to the case of two phases, since this illustrates the method. Let $P(n_1, n_2, t)$ be the chance that at time t there are n_1 customers in the phase S_1, and n_2 in phase S_2. It is easily seen that there are *four* possible events occurring between t and $t + dt$, which give rise to n_1 customers at S_1 and n_2 at S_2 at time $t + dt$, namely

(i) n_1 in S_1 and n_2 in S_2 at time t, no arrival and no departure in dt,

(ii) $n_1 + 1$ in S_1 and $n_2 - 1$ in S_2 at time t, a departure from S_1 (into S_2) in dt,

(iii) n_1 in S_1 and $n_2 + 1$ in S_2 at time t, a departure from S_2 in dt,

(iv) $n_1 - 1$ in S_1 and n_2 in S_2 at time t, an arrival at S_1 in dt.

The probabilities of these events are respectively

$$P(n_1, n_2, t)\,(1 - \lambda dt)\,(1 - \mu_1\, dt)\,(1 - \mu_2 dt),$$
$$P(n_1 + 1,\ n_2 - 1,\ t)\,\mu_1 dt,$$
$$P(n_1,\ n_2 + 1,\ t)\,\mu_2 dt,$$
$$P(n_1 - 1,\ n_2,\ t)\,\lambda dt.$$

It follows that when $n_1, n_2 > 0$, the equation for $P(n_1, n_2, t)$ is

$$P'(n_1, n_2, t) = \lambda P(n_1 - 1, n_2, t) + \mu_1 P(n_1 + 1, n_2 - 1, t) + \mu_2 P(n_1, n_2 + 1, t) - (\lambda + \mu_1 + \mu_2) P(n_1, n_2, t).$$

We also have

$$n_1 > 0,\ n_2 = 0: \quad P'(n_1, 0, t) = \lambda P(n_1 - 1, 0, t) + \mu_2 P(n_1, 1, t) - (\lambda + \mu_1) P(n_1, 0, t),$$

$$n_1 = 0,\ n_2 > 0: \quad P'(0, n_2, t) = \mu_1 P(1, n_2, t) + \mu_2 P(0, n_2 + 1, t) - (\lambda + \mu_2) P(0, n_2, t),$$

$$n_1 = n_2 = 0: \quad P'(0, 0, t) = -\lambda P(0, 0, t) + \mu_2 P(0, 1, t).$$

For the state of statistical equilibrium, assuming one is reached as $t \to \infty$, the difference-equations obtained by equating all the derivatives to zero may easily be solved. Write

$$P(n_1, n_2) = \lim_{t \to \infty} P(n_1, n_2, t).$$

Then, if $\varrho_1 = \lambda/\mu_1$, $\varrho_2 = \lambda/\mu_2$, it is found that

$$P(n_1, n_2) = \varrho_1^{n_1} \varrho_2^{n_2} P_0, \tag{2}$$

where $P_0 = P(0, 0)$ and P_0 is found from the fact that $\sum_{n_1, n_2} P(n_1, n_2) = 1$. It is easy to show that $P_0 = (1 - \varrho_1)(1 - \varrho_2)$.

Having found the state probabilities (2) it is a simple matter of summation to compute various averages. Thus, for example,

(a) The average number of customers in the complete system

$$= \sum_{n_1, n_2} (n_1 + n_2) P(n_1, n_2) = \frac{\varrho_1}{1 - \varrho_1} + \frac{\varrho_2}{1 - \varrho_2},$$

(b) The average number of customers strictly waiting for service in phase $S_1 = \sum_{n_1=1}^{\infty} \sum_{n_2=0}^{\infty} (n_1 - 1) P(n_1, n_2) = \dfrac{\varrho_1^2}{(1 - \varrho_1)}$,

(c) The chance that there are n customers in phase S_2

$$= P_2(n) = \sum_{n_1=0}^{\infty} P(n_1, n) = \varrho_2^n (1 - \varrho_2),$$

(d) The chance that there are n customers in the complete system

$$= P(n) = \sum_{n_1 + n_2 = n} P(n_1, n_2) = (1 - \varrho_1)(1 - \varrho_2)(\varrho_2^{n+1} - \varrho_1^{n+1}) // (\varrho_2 - \varrho_1).$$

These results indicate that each phase, in the state of statistical equilibrium, behaves independently of the other, and this, of course, is in conformity with the statement made earlier that the output from each phase is random.

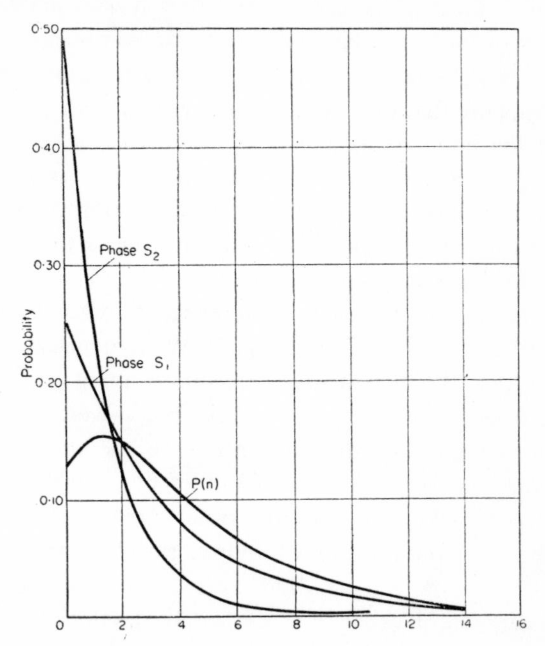

FIG. 5. Probabilities $P_1(n)$, $P_2(n)$ and $P(n)$, where $\varrho_1 = 3/4$, $\varrho_2 = 1/2$.

The respective probabilities $P_1(n)$, $P_2(n)$ and $P(n)$, that there are n customers in phase S_1, phase S_2 and the complete system are graphed in Fig. 5 in the case where $\varrho_1 = \frac{3}{4}$, $\varrho_2 = \frac{1}{2}$. This graph is due to Jackson (8), who first carried out the above analysis. The case of a limited source, where no more customers arrive when the total number in the system is N, was also analysed by Jackson, and the interested reader is referred to his paper for details. The analysis is simple but the formulae somewhat complicated. Jackson also derived some results for the case of three phases and a limited source, and in a later paper (9) extended the results to k phases, where k is any positive integer.

5. Channels in series: various restricted cases

Let a queueing system consist of k phases $S_1, ..., S_k$. In § 4 it was assumed that a waiting line of any length is permissible at the input to each phase. This may not be even approximately true in some practical situations, and thus it is desirable to have an analysis of the case where only finite waiting lines are allowed. The effect of a finite waiting line is to increase congestion in the system. Suppose that the maximum allowable length of the waiting line $\mathcal{L}$ at the input to S_i is $q - 1$. Then when $q - 1$ customers are waiting to be served at S_i, a customer whose service at S_{i-1} has been completed cannot join $\mathcal{L}$ but must remain at S_{i-1} so preventing this phase from proceeding with the service of the next customer, until the length of $\mathcal{L}$ falls to $q - 2$. This phenomenon is called *blocking*, and its immediate effect is to reduce the effective service rate of the phase blocked. While a phase is blocked the chance that the immediately preceding waiting line will reach its maximal length is greater than if the phase were not blocked; and if the maximal length is reached then the preceding phase also becomes blocked. Thus the effect of blocking is cumulative as we proceed backwards along the system from the final towards the initial phase, there being, of course, no blocking at the final phase.

The theory of blocking is inadequately developed at present. Published results to date suggest that the mathematical development, while conceptually simple enough, would lead to rather complicated expressions for a system containing only a moderate number, k, of phases. We shall, therefore, confine attention to the simplest case, $k = 2$, and no waiting line allowed before the second phase, and, for the cases $k = 3$ and $k = 4$, quote a few results of Hunt (7). There are apparently no known results of an asymptotic nature for large values of k.

Consider a system of two phases S_1 and S_2, each having the same average rate of service, μ, when there is no limitation on the size of the waiting line $\mathcal{L}$ before S_2. If now the system is restricted so that no waiting line is allowed before S_2 (that is $\mathcal{L} = 0$) then S_1 will undergo periods of blocking and the effective rate of service of S_1 will be reduced to some value $\mu^*(< \mu)$. Thus the maximum permissible arrival rate, in order that a state of equilibrium be reached, will be reduced from μ to μ^*, and hence the maximum servicing factor ϱ will be not unity but ϱ_{max} where

$$\varrho_{max} = \mu^*/\mu.$$

One problem is to find ϱ_{max}. Another is to find the various state probabilities. The method now to be described solves both of these problems. The differential-difference equations for the state probabilities will be written down for the general case where S_1 and S_2 have different service rates μ_1 and μ_2. Then, to simplify the algebra, the solution will be derived for the case $\mu_1 = \mu_2$.

Denote by $\mathcal{L}_1$ the initial waiting line, that is, at the input to S_1, and suppose that at time t there are $n - 1$ customers in $\mathcal{L}_1$ and 1 in the phase S_1. Then there are, for given n, *three* distinct states possible at time t, namely:

(i) $n - 1$ customers in $\mathcal{L}_1$, a customer at S_1, no customer at S_2,

(ii) $n - 1$ customers in $\mathcal{L}_1$, a customer, A, at S_1, a customer, B, at S_2, A and B each receiving service at time t,

(iii) $n - 1$ customers in $\mathcal{L}_1$, A at S_1, B at S_2, A having completed service at time t or before.

When the system is in state (iii), phase S_1 is, of course, blocked. Let $P(n, 0, t)$, $P_1(n, 1, t)$ and $P_2(n, 1, t)$ denote the probabilities of these respective states at time t. Note that P and P_1 are defined for $n \geqslant 0$, but P_2 only for $n > 0$. The equations for these probabilities follow in the usual way by considering the appropriate events in time $\mathrm{d}t$, and taking the limit. Thus

$$\begin{aligned} P(n, 0, t + \mathrm{d}t) = {} & P(n, 0, t)(1 - \lambda \mathrm{d}t)(1 - \mu_1 \mathrm{d}t) \\ & + P(n - 1, 0, t)\lambda \mathrm{d}t(1 - \mu_1 \mathrm{d}t) \\ & + P_1(n, 1, t)\mu_2 \mathrm{d}t(1 - \lambda \mathrm{d}t)(1 - \mu_1 \mathrm{d}t), \end{aligned}$$

where, for example, the last of the three terms on the right is the probability that

(a) A and B are each being served at time t, when there are $n - 1$ customers in $\mathcal{L}_1$,

(b) B completes service in time $\mathrm{d}t$,

(c) A does not complete service in time dt,

(d) there is no arrival in time dt.

This and similar expressions lead to the equations,

$$P'(n, 0, t) = -(\lambda + \mu_1)P(n, 0, t) + \lambda P(n-1, 0, t) + \mu_2 P_1(n, 1, t)$$

$$P_1'(n, 1, t) = -(\lambda + \mu_1 + \mu_2)P_1(n, 1, t) + \lambda P_1(n-1, 1, t) + \mu_1 P(n+1, 0, t) + \mu_2 P_2(n+1, 1, t)$$

$$P_2'(n, 1, t) = -(\lambda + \mu_2)P_2(n, 1, t) + \mu_1 P_1(n, 1, t) + \lambda P_2(n-1, 1, t),$$

where, in the first two equations $n > 0$, and in the third equation $n > 1$. The initial equations are

$$P'(0, 0, t) = -\lambda P(0, 0, t) + \mu_2 P_1(0, 1, t),$$

$$P_1'(0, 1, t) = -(\lambda + \mu_2) P_1(0, 1, t) + \mu_2 P_2(1, 1, t) + \mu_1 P(1, 0, t),$$

$$P_2'(1, 1, t) = -(\lambda + \mu_2) P_2(1, 1, t) + \mu_1 P_1(1, 1, t).$$

Now assume that a state of statistical equilibrium is possible. Then equating the derivatives to zero we obtain, on writing small letters instead of capitals for the probabilities, as $t \to \infty$,

$$\left.\begin{aligned} &-(\lambda + \mu_1) p(n, 0) + \lambda p(n-1, 0) + \mu_2 p_1(n, 1) = 0, \\ &-(\lambda + \mu_1 + \mu_2) p_1(n, 1) + \lambda p_1(n-1, 1) + \mu_1 p(n+1, 0) \\ &+ \mu_2 p_2(n+1, 1) = 0., \\ &-(\lambda + \mu_2) p_2(n, 1) + \mu_1 p_1(n, 1) + \lambda p_2(n-1, 1) = 0, \end{aligned}\right\} \quad (3)$$

with appropriate initial equations. We shall indicate how the solution to this set of difference equations may be obtained in the case $\mu_1 = \mu_2 = \mu$ (the method is still available, when $\mu_1 \neq \mu_2$, but the analysis cannot be carried through explicitly). Then, writing $\varrho = \lambda/\mu$ the equations (3) become

$$\left.\begin{aligned} &-(1 + \varrho) p(n, 0) + \varrho p(n-1, 0) + p_1(n, 1) = 0, \\ &-(2 + \varrho) p_1(n, 1) + \varrho p_1(n-1, 1) + p(n+1, 0) + p_2(n+1, 1) \\ &\quad = 0, \\ &-(1 + \varrho) p_2(n, 1) + \varrho p_2(n-1, 1) + p_1(n, 1) = 0. \end{aligned}\right\} \quad (4)$$

For a solution write

$$p(n, 0) = A\, w^n,\; p_1(n, 1) = B\, w^n,\; p_2(n, 1) = C\, w^n,$$

where A, B, C and w are to be determined. Then the equations (4) lead to the system of equations

$$M\begin{pmatrix}A\\B\\C\end{pmatrix} \equiv \begin{pmatrix}\varrho-(1+\varrho)w & w & 0\\ w^2 & \varrho-(2+\varrho)w & w^2\\ 0 & w & \varrho-(1+\varrho)w\end{pmatrix}\begin{pmatrix}A\\B\\C\end{pmatrix} = 0.$$

Thus, for a solution it is necessary that $|M| = 0$. But

$$|M| = [\varrho-(1+\varrho)\,w]\,[\{\varrho-(1+\varrho)\,w\}\,\{\varrho-(2+\varrho)\,w\} - \\ - 2w^3] = 0.$$

The four roots of this equation are

$$w_1 = 1, \quad w_2 = \varrho/(1+\varrho),$$

$$w_3 = \tfrac{1}{4}\varrho\,[(\varrho+3)-Q], \quad w_4 = \tfrac{1}{4}\varrho\,[(\varrho+3)+Q],$$

where $Q = (\varrho^2+6\varrho+1)^{\frac{1}{2}}$. For each root, w_i, the appropriate values of A_i, B_i, C_i, may be determined, using the initial equations, and then, remembering that for convergence only those roots such that $w_i < 1$ are taken, the solutions are

$$p(n, 0) = A_2 w_2^n + A_3 w_3^n + A_4 w_4^n,$$

$$p_1(n, 1) = B_2 w_2^n + B_3 w_3^n + B_4 w_4^n,$$

$$p_2(n, 1) = C_2 w_2^n + C_3 w_3^n + C_4 w_4^n.$$

We have assumed, of course, that $w_i < 1$ for $i = 2, 3, 4$. It is clear that $w_2 < 1$ but the inequality $w_4 < 1$ leads to the restriction $\varrho < \frac{2}{3}$. Thus we have the result sought that the maximum servicing factor is given by $\varrho_{max} = \frac{2}{3}$.

The mean number, L, of customers in the complete system is given by

$$L = \sum_{n=0}^{\infty} [np(n, 0) + (n+1)p_1(n, 1) + (n+2)p_2(n+1, 1)].$$

Hunt (7) calculated the value of L, as a function of the servicing factor ϱ, and the result is shown graphically in Fig. 6 (see p. 164).

The value of ϱ_{max}. When $\mu_1 \neq \mu_2$ Hunt found that the value of ϱ_{max} is given by

$$\varrho_{max} = \mu_2(\mu_1 + \mu_2)/(\mu_1^2 + \mu_1\mu_2 + \mu_2^2),$$

and the corresponding expression for a system of three phases ($k = 3$) was obtained. When the service rates for all phases are equal the values of ϱ_{max} are as follows:

k	2	3	4
ϱ_{max}	0.667	0.564	0.512

The case of a finite waiting line. Another case studied by Hunt is that of the two-phase system where a waiting line of length $q - 1$ but not more is permissible before the second stage. The value found for ϱ_{max} is

$$\varrho_{max} = \frac{x^{q+2} - x}{x^{q+2} - 1},$$

where $x = \mu_1/\mu_2$. In the limiting case, where $\mu_2 \to \mu_1$, the value of ϱ_{max} is easily obtained by the standard procedure. Thus

$$\varrho_{max} = \lim_{x \to 1} \left(\frac{x^{q+2} - x}{x^{q+2} - 1} \right) = \lim_{x \to 1} \left(\frac{(q+2)\, x^{q+1} - 1}{(q+2)^{q+1}} \right) = \frac{q+1}{q+2}.$$

For the three-phase system with equal mean service times in each phase, where waiting lines of maximum length unity are allowed before phases two and three, the value of ϱ_{max} is approximately 0.6705 (fifteen state probabilities are involved).

The belt production line. Consider a production line consisting of N stages where the service times at each stage are exponentially distributed, with mean $1/\mu$, and where each stage of the line is occupied by a single unit, or customer. Suppose there is a restriction whereby the line moves on one step, only when service has been completed on *all* of the existing N units on the line. The only waiting line allowed, and this of infinite capacity, is that at the input to the production line. Because of the restriction a type of blocking occurs, and the problem is to calculate the average time, τ_N, required for a unit to be processed through all N stages. If the line is working to capacity, that is at a rate such that an infinite waiting line just does not develop at the input, then the mean arrival rate is equal to the mean throughput rate, which is $1/\tau_N$. Thus the maximum servicing factor, $\varrho_{\max}$, is given by $\varrho_{\max}$ = (mean arrival rate) × (mean service time) = $(1/\tau_N)$ $(1/\mu)$ $= 1/\mu\tau_N$.

The time τ taken for the production line to move on one step equals the maximum of the times taken to service the N units on the line. Thus the chance, $R_N(t)\,\mathrm{d}t$, that τ lies between t and $t + \mathrm{d}t$ equals the chance that

(i) the unit at a given stage is serviced in a time between t and $t + \mathrm{d}t$, and

(ii) each of the times taken to service the units at the other $N - 1$ stages does not exceed t.

The probabilities of (i) and (ii) are $\mu\,\mathrm{e}^{-\mu t}$ and $(1 - \mathrm{e}^{-\mu t})^{N-1}$ respectively. Hence

$$R_N(t)\,\mathrm{d}t = \mu \mathrm{e}^{-\mu t}\,(1 - \mathrm{e}^{-\mu t})^{N-1}\,\mathrm{d}t.$$

Now

$$E(\tau) = \int_0^\infty tR_N(t)\,\mathrm{d}t,$$

and clearly the average time, τ_N, required for a unit to be processed through all N stages is given by $\tau_N = NE(\tau)$. Thus

$$\tau_N = N\mu \int_0^\infty t\mathrm{e}^{-\mu t}(1 - \mathrm{e}^{-\mu t})^{N-1}\mathrm{d}t.$$

This integral may be evaluated in terms of the derivative of the beta function $B(u, v)$ defined by

$$B(u, v) = \int_0^1 x^{u-1}(1 - x)^{v-1}\,\mathrm{d}x.$$

It is evident that

$$\frac{\partial B}{\partial u} = \int_0^1 x^{u-1}(1 - x)^{v-1} \log x\,\mathrm{d}x,$$

and, putting $x = \mathrm{e}^{-\mu t}$, the formula for τ_N becomes

$$\tau_N = -\frac{N}{\mu}\int_0^1 (1 - x)^{N-1} \log x\mathrm{d}x = -\frac{N}{\mu}\left[\frac{\partial}{\partial u} B(u, N)\right]_{u=1}$$

For small values of N the integral may, of course, be evaluated directly. Thus $\tau_2 = 3/(2\mu)$, $\tau_3 = 11/(6\mu)$, $\tau_4 = 25/(12\mu)$. These values give the values of ϱ_{max} as follows:

N	2	3	4
ϱ_{max}	$\frac{2}{3}$	$\frac{6}{11}$	$\frac{12}{25}$

It should be noted that the analysis of the belt production line may be carried out in terms of the equations describing the state probabilities. Hunt solved completely the case $N = 2$ and calculated the mean number L of units in the system, as a function of the servicing factor ϱ. The graphs in Fig. 6 show L plotted against ϱ for the following cases:

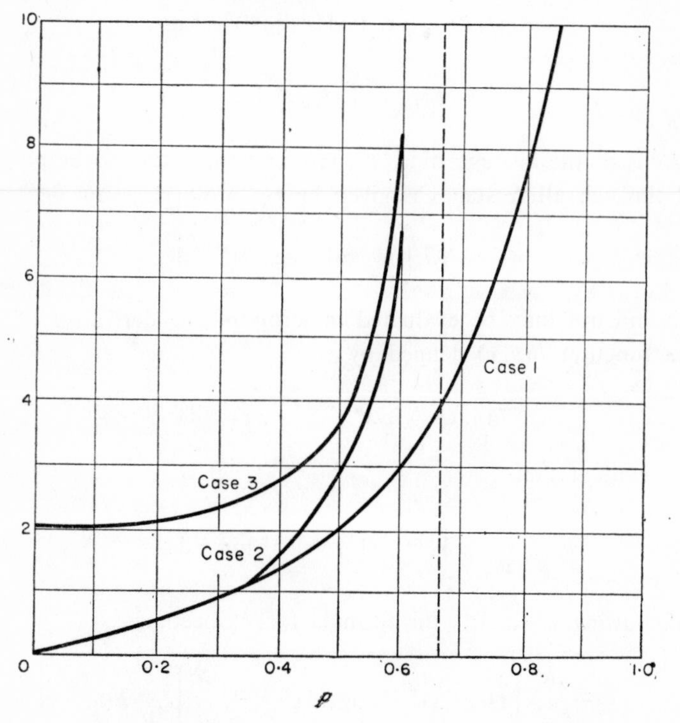

FIG. 6. The mean number, L, of units in the system.

Case 1: Two phases in series, infinite waiting lines possible,
Case 2: Two phases in series, no waiting line between the phases, so that blocking occurs,
Case 3: The belt production line, for two stages.

The latter, by definition, involves always two units in the line, so that the graph in this case is asymptotic to the line $L = 2$.

REFERENCES

1. H. A. ADLER and K. W. MILLER, "A new approach to probability problems in electrical engineering", *Trans. Amer. Inst. Elect. Engrs*, **65** (1946), 630–2.
2. P. J. BURKE, "The output of a queueing system", *Operations Res.*, **4** (1956), 699–704.
3. A. COBHAM, "Priority assignment in waiting line problems", *J. Operat. Res. Soc. Amer.*, **2** (1954), 70–6.
4. C. D. CROMMELIN, "Delay probability formulae when the holding times are constant", *P. O. Elect. Engrs. J.*, **25** (1932), 51.
5. C. D. CROMMELIN, "Delay probability formulae", *P. O. Elect. Engrs J.*, **26** (1934), 266.
6. D. P. GAVER, "The influence of servicing times in queueing processes", *J. Operat. Res. Soc. Amer.*, **2** (1954), 139–49.
7. G. C. HUNT, "Sequential arrays of waiting lines", *Operations Res.*, **4** (1956), 674–83.
8. R. R. P. JACKSON, "Queueing systems with phase-type service", *Operations Res. Quart.*, **5** (1954), 109–20.
9. R. R. P. JACKSON, "Random queueing processes with phase-type service", *J. R. Statist. Soc.*, B, **18** (1956), 129–32.
10. D. G. KENDALL, "Stochastic processes occurring in the theory of queues and their analysis by the method of the imbedded Markov chain", *Ann. Math. Statist.*, **24** (1953), 338–54.
11. E. C. MOLINA, "Applications of the theory of probabilities to telephone trunking problems", *Bell Syst. Tech. J.*, **6** (1927), 461.
12. C. PALM, "Analysis of the Erlang traffic formulae for busy-signal arrangements", *Ericsson Tech.*, **4** (1938), 39–58.
13. F. POLLACZEK, "Lösung eines geometrischen Wahrscheinlichkeitsproblem", *Math. Z.*, **35** (1932), 230–78.
14. E. REICH, "Waiting times when queues are in tandem", *Ann. Math. Statist.*, **28** (1957), 768.
15. R. SYSKI, *Congestion Theory in Telephone Systems*, Oliver and Boyd, Edinburgh, 1960.
16. L. TAKÁCS, "On the generalization of Erlang's formula", *Acta Math. Hung.*, **7** (1957), 419–33.

CHAPTER VI

MACHINE INTERFERENCE

1. Introduction

In this chapter we consider the following situation. There is a group of m machines, assumed to be all of the same type, subject to failure at irregular times. There is a group of $r(< m)$ repairmen, called operators, who attend to the repair of these machines. As soon as a machine becomes idle (that is, fails) it is attended to by an operator, *if available*. And as soon as an operator finishes servicing a machine he attends to another machine, if one needing repair is waiting. It is clear that at any instant there may be some idle machines awaiting repair if all operators are occupied, or some idle operator if more than $m - r$ machines are working. From an economic point of view it is costly to have operators or machines idle. The former involves labour charges and the latter various costs such as the capital cost of the equipment and depreciation charges.

Various problems may now be seen to arise. For example, given m and r (and some other parameters to be specified later) it might be required to find the average time per day or per shift that a machine or an operator is idle; or, for given m, to determine the most economical number, r, of operators to have available for servicing the machines. These and other problems will be solved in the present chapter. We shall develop in some detail the theory in the case of *one* operator ($r = 1$). However, a "birth and death" process for dealing with the case $r > 1$ will be outlined and the main results stated.

2. The case of one operator ($r = 1$)

The theory of this section is due to Ashcroft (1). For each machine there is a sequence of working periods interlaced with a sequence of idle periods, as shown in Fig. 1. Let the lengths of successive working periods be $w_1, w_2, \ldots$. and consider n such periods where n is large. The total working time is $\sum_{j=1}^{n} w_j$. We define a number λ, which is of fundamental importance in the theory, as follows:

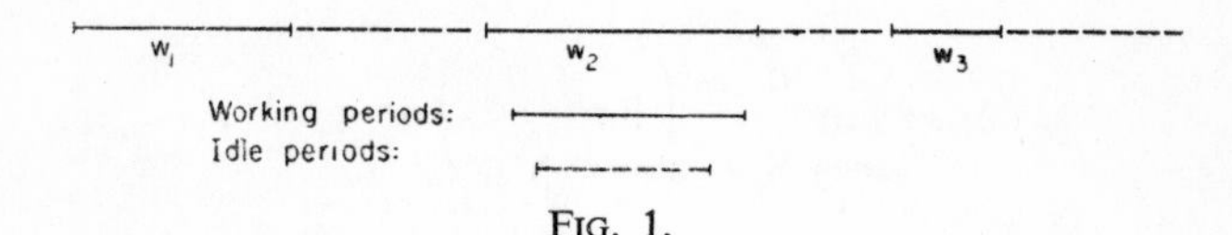

FIG. 1.

$\lambda =$ the average number of failures of each machine per unit of its working time.

Clearly,

$$\lambda = \lim_{n \to \infty} (n / \sum_{j=1}^{n} w_j),$$

and the average uninterrupted working time of a machine is $1/\lambda$.

Another important number is μ where

$\mu =$ the average number of repairs completed by the operator per unit of his repair time.

Clearly the average repair time is $1/\mu$.

A quantity which we shall use frequently, called the *servicing factor*, is ϱ where $\varrho = \lambda/\mu$.

Notice that the definition of λ involves these assumptions:

(i) All machines have the same average working times.

(ii) The system consisting of the machines and the operator is in a state of statistical equilibrium.

If (ii) is satisfied the above limit, which is essentially an average over a long period of time, exists.

In order to develop the theory it is necessary to make some assumption about the distributions of the working periods and repair periods. We shall assume that

(iii) The working periods $w_1, w_2, \ldots$ are independent random variables with an exponential distribution; that is

$$P(w_i \leqslant t) = 1 - e^{-\beta t}$$

where β is a constant.

With this form for the distribution function it may be shown that $\beta = \lambda$. To see this note that from the theory of the Poisson distribution the chance that a machine fails in a short time δt is $\beta \delta t$. But there are n failures in a working time of $\sum_{j=1}^{n} w_j$ and this time consists of N intervals δt, where $N\,\delta t = \sum_{j=1}^{n} w_j$. Thus

$$\beta\delta t = \lim_{n\to\infty} \frac{n}{N} = \left(\lim_{n\to\infty} \frac{n}{\sum_{j=1}^{n} w_j}\right) \delta t = \lambda\delta t\,,$$

and hence $\beta = \lambda$.

We shall assume that

(iv) The repair periods (u) follow the discrete distribution,

$$P(u = u_i) = \vartheta_i \qquad (i = 1, 2, ...)\,.$$

But later we shall convert the results to those for the exponential distribution.

Note that the average repair period is $1/\mu$ where

$$1/\mu = \sum_i u_i \vartheta_i\,.$$

Clear periods and repair periods. A clear period is a period of maximum length during which *all* machines are working. As soon as a machine fails the operator attends to it. At that instant a repair period commences. During the repair of this machine one or more other machines may fail, and thus a reservoir of machines *awaiting* repair may be set up. The repair period ends only when the reservoir is empty and the operator has finished servicing the last machine (see Fig. 2). Then, of course, another clear period begins. Thus we have an alternating cycle of clear and repair periods.

An important problem is to evaluate, in terms of m, λ and μ, the quantities x_m, v_m and x'_m, v'_m where

x_m = the average length of a repair period,

v_m = the average number of machine running hours per repair period,

x'_m, v'_m are similar quantities for a clear period. These latter quantities are easily evaluated. Since all machines run for the whole of a clear period, we have

$$v'_m = mx'_m .$$

Also, at the end of a clear period there is one failure. Thus

$$1 = \lambda v'_m .$$

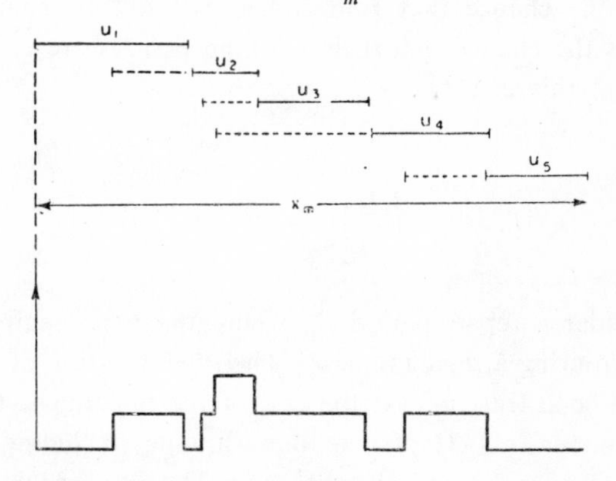

FIG. 2. Structure of a repair period and the corresponding variation in the size of the reservoir.

From these equations it follows that

$$v'_m = 1/\lambda, \quad x'_m = 1/m\lambda . \tag{1}$$

Now consider a repair period. Since the average repair time is $1/\mu$, the average number of repairs in a repair period is μx_m. This exceeds by one the number of failures in the repair period (the *first* failure being regarded as occurring in the clear period preceding the repair period). Also the average number of failures in this period is λv_m. Hence

$$\mu x_m = 1 + \lambda v_m . \tag{2}$$

This equation determines v_m in terms of λ, μ and x_m.

3. Determination of the average length (x_m) of a repair period

A recurrence relation for x_m will be obtained, using an elementary method due to Ashcroft. As a preliminary result we need a formula for $p_{s,r}(\tau)$ where

$p_{s,r}(\tau)$ = the chance that if, at some instant, s machines are running, there will be exactly r still running after a time τ.

The chance that $(s - r)$ machines will have stopped after a time τ is the chance that their working periods are each less than τ, and this, by assumption (iii) is $(1 - e^{-\lambda\tau})^{s-r}$.
Similarly, the chance that r machines will still be running after a time τ is the chance that their working periods are each greater than τ, and this is $e^{-r\lambda\tau}$.
Hence

$$p_{s,r}(\tau) = \binom{s}{r} e^{-r\lambda\tau} (1 - e^{-\lambda\tau})^{s-r}.$$

Now consider a repair period P_i, where the *first* repair is definitely one requiring a repair time u_i. Then the duration of the repair period will be at least u_i. At the end of the first repair there may be any number $(r + 1)$ of machines running (including that just repaired) from $r = 0$ to $r = m - 1$. The chance that exactly $(r + 1)$ are running is $p_{m-1,r}(u_i)$. If $r = m - 1$, then P_i ends after the first repair, and in this case the duration of the repair period is given by $x_m = u_i$. If $r = m - 2$, then at the end of the first repair there is one (and only one) machine awaiting repair, so the position is as at the start of a repair period and an average further time x_m will be required.

Now consider the case $r = m - 3$. At the end of the first repair there are two machines awaiting repair. The operator must ignore one of these and then the position is that he is attending to $m - 1$ machines, with one awaiting repair. Thus after an average time, x_{m-1}, the $m - 1$ machines will all be running. The operator now attends to the machine previously ignored. It is the only machine, out of a total of m, awaiting repair and hence a further average time, x_m, will be required before all m machines are running. Thus in the case $r = m - 3$ an average time, $x_m + x_{m-1}$, will be required after the first repair to end the repair period P_i.

A similar argument holds for smaller values of r. Thus for the average total duration of the period P_i we obtain the expression

$$u_i + p_{m-1,\, m-2}(u_i)\, x_m + p_{m-1,\, m-3}(u_i)\,(x_m + x_{m-1}) + \ldots$$

that is

$$u_i + \sum_{r=0}^{m-2} (x_m + x_{m-1} + \ldots + x_{r+2})\, p_{m-1,\, r}(u_i)$$

$$= u_i + \sum_{r=0}^{m-2} \binom{m-1}{r} e^{-r\lambda u_i} \left(1 - e^{-\lambda u_i}\right)^{m-r-1} \left(x_m + \ldots + x_{r+2}\right).$$

Now the chance that P_i occurs, that is, that a repair period commences with a repair requiring a time u_i is ϑ_i. Thus by averaging the last expression over the values of u_i for $i = 1, 2, 3, \ldots$ we obtain (since $\sum_i u_i \vartheta_i = 1/\mu$)

$$x_m = \frac{1}{\mu} + \sum_{r=0}^{m-2} \sum_i \binom{m-1}{r} e^{-r\lambda u_i} \left(1 - e^{-\lambda u_i}\right)^{m-r-1} \vartheta_i\,(x_m + \ldots + x_{r+2})\,.$$

Now the coefficient of x_m on the right side

$$= \sum_i \vartheta_i \sum_{r=0}^{m-2} \binom{m-1}{r} e^{-r\lambda u_i} \left(1 - e^{-\lambda u_i}\right)^{m-r-1}$$

$$= \sum_i \{1 - exp[-(m-1)\,\lambda u_i\}\, \vartheta_i\,.$$

Thus, since $\sum_i \vartheta_i = 1$, we obtain

$$x_m = B_m / A_m \qquad (m > 2) \tag{3}$$

where

$$A_m = \sum_i \vartheta_i\, exp\,\{-(m-1)\,\lambda u_i\},$$

and

$$B_m = 1/\mu + \sum_{r=0}^{m-3} \sum_i \binom{m-1}{r} e^{-r\lambda u_i} \left(1 - e^{-\lambda u_i}\right)^{m-r-1} (x_{m-1} + \ldots + x_{r+2}).$$

This is the recurrence relation for x_m. In particular it may be noted that

$$x_1 = \frac{1}{\mu}, \; x_2 = \frac{1}{\mu \alpha_1}, \; x_3 = \frac{1}{\mu}\left(\frac{1}{\alpha_1 \alpha_2} + \frac{1}{\alpha_1} - \frac{1}{\alpha_2}\right)$$

where

$$\alpha_k = \sum_i \vartheta_i \, e^{-k\lambda u_i} \qquad (k = 1, 2, \ldots) \, .$$

The recurrence relation (3) is not very convenient for the calculation of successive values of x_m. If we write $y_m = \mu x_m$ ($m = 1, 2, 3, \ldots$) then (3) can clearly be written in the form

$$\alpha_{m-1} y_m = 1 + \sum_{r=0}^{m-3} \sum_i \binom{m-1}{r} e^{-r\lambda u_i} (1 - e^{-\lambda u_i})^{m-r-1} (y_{m-1} + \ldots + y_{r+2}) \, \vartheta_i \qquad (m > 2). \tag{4}$$

Based on this equation Ashcroft developed a difference equation which is convenient for the calculation of y_m, and the interested reader is referred to Ashcroft's paper (Ref. 1, p. 147) for the details.

In the particular case where all the repair times are equal, that is, where $u_i = 1/\mu$, (4) reduces to the equation

$$e^{-(m-1)\varrho} y_m = 1 + \sum_{r=0}^{m-3} \binom{m-1}{r} e^{-r\varrho} (1 - e^{-\varrho})^{m-r-1} (y_{m-1} + \ldots + y_{r+2}) \qquad (m > 2) \, . \tag{5}$$

It may be shown that the solution of this equation is

$$y_m = 1 + \binom{m-1}{1} (\vartheta - 1) + \binom{m-1}{2} (\vartheta - 1)(\vartheta^2 - 1) + \ldots + \binom{m-1}{m-1} (\vartheta - 1)(\vartheta^2 - 1) \ldots (\vartheta^{m-1} - 1) \tag{6}$$

where $\vartheta = e^{\varrho}$.

Another particular case, where an explicit expression for y_m may be found, occurs when the repair times (u) follow an exponential distribution, $1 - e^{-\mu u}$ so that the average repair time is still $1/\mu$. In this case the discrete frequency distribution

$$P(u = u_i) = \vartheta_i,$$

is replaced by the continuous distribution,

$$P(x < u < x + dx) = \mu\, e^{-\mu x}\, dx\,,$$

and the constants α_k, given in the discrete case by $\alpha_k = \sum_i \vartheta_i\, e^{-k\lambda u_i}$, become

$$\alpha_k = \mu \int_0^\infty \exp[-(\mu + k\lambda)u]\, du = 1/(1 + k\varrho) \qquad (k = 1, 2, \ldots).$$

In this case

$$\begin{aligned} y_m &= 1 + (m-1)\varrho + (m-1)(m-2)\varrho^2 + \ldots + (m-1)!\,\varrho^{m-1} \\ &= e^{1/\varrho}\varrho^{m-1}(m-1)!\,[1 - I\{1/\varrho\sqrt{m},\ m-1\}] \end{aligned} \qquad (7)$$

where

$$I(u, p) = \frac{1}{p!}\int_0^{u\sqrt{(p+1)}} e^{-x}x^p\, dx,$$

is the incomplete gamma function, as tabulated by Pearson (see Chapter I, § 7).

4. System characteristics

Let a_m, b_m, and c_m be the average number of machines which are running, being repaired, and awaiting repair respectively. Formulae for these quantities are derived below. It is to be noted that $b_m < 1$ since there is only one operator. Also a_m is a measure of the rate of production of the system.

The performance of the system may be judged in terms of three quantities defined as follows:

Machine efficiency $= \eta_m = a_m/m$,
Operator efficiency $= \eta_0 = b_m$,
Interference loss $= l = c_m/m$.

Note that η_m is an average measure of the fraction of the total number of machines which are running at any time. Also η_0 is a measure of the fraction of the operator's time spent on repair work. And l is a measure of the proportion of machines which are idle and awaiting repair. Since this last situation can only occur when two or more machines are simultaneously idle, l is appropriately called the interference loss.

The calculation of a_m, b_m, and c_m is now carried out.

Since each machine is either running, awaiting repair or being repaired it follows that

$$a_m + b_m + c_m = m. \tag{8}$$

Also, since a_m/b_m is the ratio of the average working time of a machine to the average repair time, we have

$$a_m/b_m = \mu/\lambda = 1/\varrho\,. \tag{9}$$

To evaluate a_m, consider the sequence of clear and repair periods. Since these periods alternate any long period of time contains equal numbers of clear and repair periods. Since the average durations of a repair period and a clear period are x_m, and x'_m, respectively, and the average number of machine hours per period are v_m and v'_m, it follows that

$$a_m = (v_m + v'_m)/(x_m + x'_m)\,.$$

On using the values given in (1) and (2) for v_m, v'_m and x'_m it is found that $a_m = 1/D$, where $D = \varrho + 1/(m\,y_m)$.

The value of b_m is given by (9), namely,

$$b_m = \varrho a_m = \varrho/D\,,$$

and the value of c_m, from (8), is

$$c_m = m - (1 + \varrho)\,a_m = [1/y_m + (m-1)\,\varrho - 1]/D\,.$$

The reader interested in numerical calculations may care to note that Ashcroft's paper (1) contains tables of a_m (the rate of production) for the case where all repair times are equal (to $1/\mu$). These tables cover the range $m = 1, 2, 3, \ldots, 20$, $0 < \varrho < 1$, and the graph of a_m shown in Fig. 3 is based on these.† They are useful in answering various questions on the productivity of a group of machines.

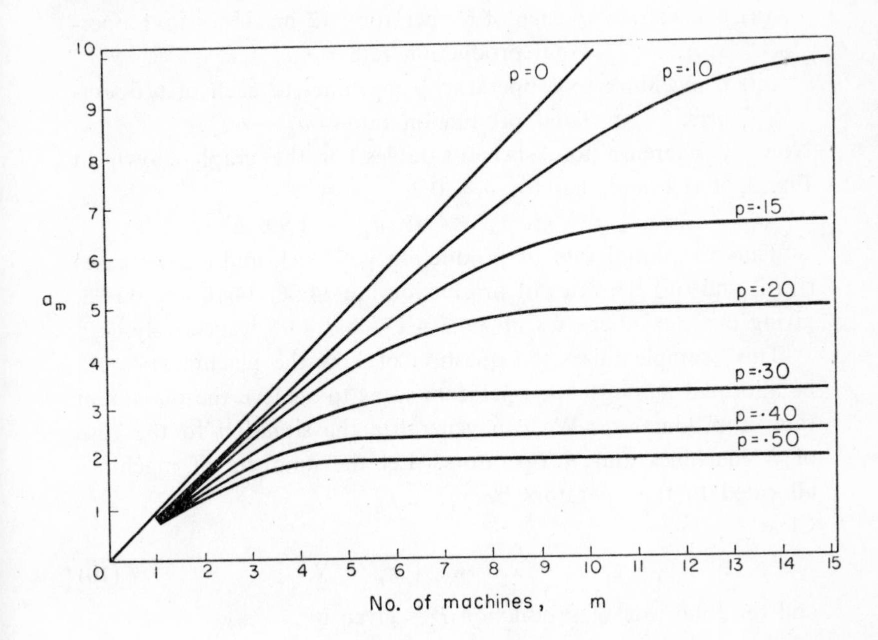

FIG. 3. Graph of a_m for various values of p.

Example: There are 6 operators, each in charge of 10 machines. It is desired to increase the total rate of production from the 60 machines, and for this purpose another operator is engaged. If the machines are all identical, with a servicing factor $\varrho = 0{\cdot}2$, what is the marginal increase in the rate of production when the extra operator is available?

The marginal increase clearly depends on how the 60 machines are allocated amongst the 7 operators. In the initial situation, of

† The graph is drawn for convenience as though m were a continuous variable.

6 groups of 10 machines per operator, the total rate of production is $6a_{10}$. In the case of 7 operators typical possibilities are:

(i) 8 machines to each of 3 operators, 9 machines to each of 4 operators.

Total production rate $= 3a_8 + 4a_9$,

(ii) 8 machines to each of 6 operators, 12 machines to 1 operator. Total production rate $= 6a_8 + a_{12}$,

(iii) 6 machines to 1 operator, 9 machines to each of 6 operators. Total production rate $= a_6 + 6a_9$.

Now by reference to Ashcroft's tables, or the graph shown in Fig. 3, it is found that for $\varrho = 0{\cdot}2$,

$$a_6 = 4{\cdot}26,\ a_8 = 4{\cdot}85,\ a_9 = 4{\cdot}95,\ a_{10} = 4{\cdot}99,\ a_{12} = 5{\cdot}00.$$

Thus the initial rate of production is 29·93, and for the cases (i) (ii) and (iii) the rates of production are 34·36, 34·10 and 33·98, giving marginal increases of 4·43, 4·17, and 4·05 respectively.

This example raises the question of how the machines should be allocated amongst the operators so as to achieve the maximum rate of production. We can generalize the situation to the case of N machines and R operators. Let the numbers of machines allocated to the operators be $x_1, ..., x_R$.

Clearly

$$x_1 + x_2 + ... + x_R = N, \tag{10}$$

and the total rate of production P is given by

$$P = a_{x_1} + a_{x_2} + ... + a_{x_R}.$$

The problem is to find $x_1, ..., x_R$ subject to (10) so that P is a maximum. Since a_x is not a linear function of x the problem is one of non-linear programming. It is intuitively clear that the solution consists of the allocation in which $x_1, ..., x_R$ are as nearly equal as possible (remembering that integral values only are involved). But it is instructive to consider the mathematics of the problem, for an interesting illustration is obtained of the use of the notion of convexity in problems of non-linear programming. A glance at the graph of a_x shows that a_x is a convex function of x.

Now suppose that the numbers $x_1, ... ,x_R$ are ordered so that

$$x_1 \leqslant x_2 \leqslant ... \leqslant x_R,$$

and let $S(x_1, x_2, ..., x_R)$ denote the allocation. We consider a modified allocation $S^*(x_1, ..., x_i + 1, ..., x_j - 1, ..., x_R)$, obtained from S by the transformation $x_i \to x_i + 1, x_j \to x_j - 1$, where $x_i < x_j$. Clearly the allocation numbers of S^* are "more nearly equal" than those of S. If $P(S)$ and $P(S^*)$ denote the production rates for the allocations S and S^*, we have

$$P(S^*) - P(S) = a_{x_i+1} + a_{x_j-1} - a_{x_i} - a_{x_j}.$$

It is clear from Fig. 4 that

$$a_{x_i+1} + a_{x_j-1} = 2AC, \quad a_{x_i} + a_{x_j} = 2BC,$$

where A and B are the mid-points of the chords shown. Since a_x is a convex function, we have $AC > BC$. Thus

$$P(S^*) - P(S) = 2(AC - BC) > 0 .$$

That is, S^* has a higher rate of production than S. This process may be repeated as much as possible. At each stage the

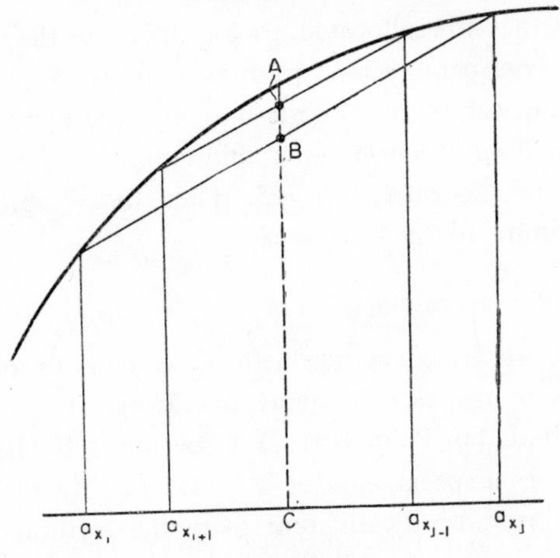

FIG. 4. Graph of a_x.

allocation numbers are more nearly equal than at the previous stage. Hence we have deduced the intuitively obvious optimal allocation. Our purpose in doing this has been to illustrate the use of convexity in proving the optimality of solutions to problems of non-linear programming.

Minimal Production Costs. In the practical operation of a system of machines subject to failure, it is clear that if a large number of machines are allocated to one operator then there will be a good deal of idleness of machines awaiting repair (a high interference loss). This will mean a high production cost per unit of time, especially when the machine cost per unit of time is high. On the other hand if a small number of machines are allocated to an operator, then for a given total number of machines, a relatively large number of operators will be required, and operator idleness will be high. This too will involve high production cost, particularly when operator time is expensive. We have here a typical conflict situation. The problem is this:

How many machines should be allocated to each operator in order to ensure minimal production cost?

Let the unit of time be 1 hour (say), and let

a = the cost per hour per operator

b = the cost per hour per machine.

If m machines are allocated to an operator the total labour and machine cost per machine running hour is $(a + bm)/a_m$.

Thus the answer to our question is m_0 where m_0 is the value of m for which $(a + bm)/a_m$ is a minimum.

Example: Let $\varrho = 0{\cdot}2$, $a/b = 5$. Then $(a/b + m)/a_m$ is found to be a minimum for $m = m_0 = 6$.

5. The case of r operators ($r > 1$)

In this section we are concerned with the calculation of the system characteristics in the case of many operators. The method used will be that initiated by Palm (14), and developed by Feller (5) and Naor (11). It is a special case of a "birth and death" process. In this respect it is radically different from the method of Ashcroft described in § 2, and the reader may be interested to compare the scope and limitations of the two approaches to the same general problem. The method of Palm, Feller and Naor applies to any number, r, of operators whereas Ashcroft's method is only available for the case $r = 1$. On the other hand the latter method involves no assumption about the form of the distribution of repair periods, whereas for the former method a basic assumption is that the repair periods, like the working periods, follow an exponential distribution.

The States of the System. Any number of the m machines of the system may be working at an arbitrarily chosen instant. If it is found that $m - n$ are working, the system is said to be in a *state* E_n. The possible states are thus $E_0, E_1, ..., E_m$; and the system is in state E_n, if

(i) $m - n$ machines are working, and either

(ii) $n > r$, r machines are under repair, $n - r$ are waiting, or

(iii) $n \leqslant r$, n machines are under repair.

Let $P_n(t)$ be the chance of finding the system in a state E_n at any instant, t, chosen at random. The theory to be presented depends on assumptions (i)–(iv) of § 2, and the additional assumption

(v) The repair periods (u) are independent random variables following the exponential distribution, $1 - e^{-\mu u}$.

Under these conditions differential-difference equations may be written down for the state probabilities $P_n(t)$.
For example, when $r = 1$, the equations are

$$P_n'(t) = (m - n + 1)\,\lambda\, P_{n-1}(t) - \{(m - n)\,\lambda + \mu\}\, P_n(t) + \mu\, P_{n+1}(t),$$

for $n = 1, 2, ..., (m - 1)$, together with the 'boundary' equations

$$P_0'(t) = - m\lambda P_0(t) + \mu P_1(t),$$

$$P_m'(t) = \lambda P_{m-1}(t) - \mu P_m(t),$$

and there are similar equations for $r > 1$. They follow from a consideration of the transitions $E_n \rightarrow E_{n+1}$, which occur if there is a breakdown, and $E_n \rightarrow E_{n-1}$, occurring if the repair to a machine is completed. No other transitions from E_n are possible in view of our assumptions that the working and repair periods are exponentially distributed. In the case of statistical equilibrium, where $p_n = \lim_{t\to\infty} P_n(t)$, the derivatives are zero and we obtain a set of difference equations for $p_0, ..., p_n$. For the case $r > 1$ these take the form

$$m\lambda p_0 = \mu p_1,$$

$$\{(m-n)\lambda + n\mu\} p_n = (m-n+1)\lambda p_{n-1} + (n+1)\mu p_{n+1} \quad (1 \leqslant n < r),$$

$$\{(m-n)\lambda + r\mu\} p_n = (m-n+1)\lambda p_{n-1} + r\mu p_{n+1} \quad (r \leqslant n \leqslant m).$$

From the last two equations it is easy to prove by induction that

$$(n+1)\mu p_{n+1} = (m-n)\lambda p_n \quad (1 \leqslant n < r),$$

$$r\mu p_{n+1} = (m-n)\lambda p_n \quad (r \leqslant n \leqslant m).$$

Calculation of the State Probabilities. Various calculations have been made, using the recursive equations for the p_n. Palm (14) in a pioneering paper gives tables and graphs useful in answering important practical questions, such as the optimal number of operators for a given set of machines. Feller (5) has shown that some surprising situations arise in the calculation of this optimal number; for example, with $\varrho = 0{\cdot}1$ it is much more economical to allocate 3 operators to 20 machines than 1 operator to 6 machines. Benson and Cox (4) derived explicit formulae for the p_n, in terms of the system parameters m, r and ϱ. Finally Naor (12, 13) in several recent papers, has shown how all calculations relating to the system and its characteristics may be carried out in terms of two Poisson functions, defined below. An outline of Naor's results is now given.

Fundamental for the solution of the recursive equations satisfied by $p_0, ..., p_n$ are the two Poisson functions

$$p(k, x) = \mathrm{e}^{-x} x^k/k!, \quad P(k, x) = \sum_{i=k}^{\infty} p(i, x),$$

where $k = 0, 1, 2, ...$. These are the frequency and cumulative distribution functions of the Poisson variate x. Extensive tables of $p(k, x)$ and $P(k, x)$ were published by Molina (10), and these are useful in calculations arising in problems of machine interference in view of the formulae given below. Let a third function $S(m, r, x)$ be defined by

$$S(m, r, x) = \sum_{i=0}^{r-1} (r^i/i!)\,p(m-i, rx) + \\ - \{r^{r-1}/(r-1)!\}\,[1 - P(m-r+1, rx)].$$

Write $\sigma = S(m, r, 1/\varrho)$. Then the equations for the p_n have the solution

$$\sigma p_n = (r^n/n!)\,p(m-n, r/\varrho) \qquad (n < r) \tag{11}$$

$$\sigma p_n = [r^{r-1}/(r-1)!]\,p(m-n, r/\varrho) \qquad (r \leqslant n \leqslant m) \tag{12}$$

Special case. For $r = 1$ the formula for p_n is

$$p_n = \frac{p(m-n, 1/\varrho)}{1 - P(m+1, 1/\varrho)}.$$

6. System characteristics in the case of several operators

As in the case of one operator, we have the three quantities a_m, b_m and c_m, each of which is now a function of r. In addition we define d_m as the average number of unoccupied operators. Clearly $b_m + d_m = r$ and a_m, b_m and c_m still satisfy equations (8) and (9). Thus, we have

$$a_m = b_m/\varrho,\ c_m = m - (1 + 1/\varrho)\,b_m,\ d_m = r - b_m, \tag{13}$$

so it is sufficient to calculate b_m. Now b_m is the average number of machines being repaired; and if the system is in state E_n there are r machines being repaired, if $n > r$, and n being repaired if $n \leqslant r$. Thus

$$b_n = \sum_{n=0}^{r} np_n + r \sum_{n=r+1}^{m} p_n.$$

Using the formulae (11) and (12) for the p_n we obtain

$$\sigma b_m = r\,S(m-1, r, 1/\varrho).$$

Thus we can calculate the system characteristics on using Molina's tables.

Asymptotic Results. Each of the quantites a_m, b_m, c_m and d_m are expressible in terms of S-functions, that is the functions

$S(m, r, 1/\varrho)$, and these are tabulated by Molina in terms of the parameter ϑ, where $\vartheta = r/\varrho$. Molina's tables stop at $\vartheta = 100$, and thus for values of r so large that $\vartheta < 100$ the tables are not available and an alternative method of computation is required. A method has recently been described by Naor (12), and the main result is recorded here. For large values of ϑ an approximate asymptotic formula for $S(m, r, 1/\varrho)$ is obtained. This is in terms of the normal distribution function,

$$\Phi[(x - \xi)/\sigma],$$

where $$\Phi(u) = (2\pi)^{-\frac{1}{2}} \int_{-\infty}^{u} e^{-\frac{1}{2}x^2} dx.$$

The result is that

$$S(m, r, 1/\varrho) \approx [r^{r-1}/(r - 1)!]\Phi[(x - \xi)/\sigma],$$

where $$x = m + \tfrac{1}{2} \text{ and, if } \vartheta = r/\varrho,$$

$$\xi \approx \vartheta + r - \tfrac{1}{2}(2\pi r)^{\frac{1}{2}} + \tfrac{1}{3},$$

$$\sigma^2 \approx \vartheta + r(2 - \tfrac{1}{2}\pi) - \tfrac{1}{6}(2\pi r)^{\frac{1}{2}} + \tfrac{2}{9}.$$

The approximation is accurate for $\vartheta \gg 1$ and m comparable to ϑ.

7. The case of an arbitrary distribution of repair periods

In this section we return to the case of *one* operator ($r = 1$). The machine efficiency of the system, as defined in § 4, is given by

$$\eta_m = a_m/m = y_m/(1 + m\varrho y_m),$$

and the other system characteristics are, on using equations (8) and (9) of § 4, expressible in terms of η_m, and hence y_m. It follows that the performance of the system is known, once y_m is known.

Consider again the case of a Poisson distribution of repair times, namely

$$P(x < u < x + dx) = p(x)dx = \mu e^{-\mu x}dx,$$

and assume that the time interval is chosen so that the average uninterrupted working time of a machine is unity (that is, $\lambda = 1$). Then formula (7) for y_m becomes

$$y_m = 1 + (m-1)\varrho + (m-1)(m-2)\varrho^2 + \ldots + (m-1)!\varrho^{m-1}$$

$$= 1 + \sum_{r=1}^{m-1} \binom{m-1}{r} r!\varrho^r$$

where $$\varrho = 1/\mu \, .$$

Now consider the Laplace Transform A_k of the repair-time frequency distribution, $p(x)$, namely

$$A_k = \int_0^\infty e^{-kx}p(x)dx = \mu \int_0^\infty exp[-(k+\mu)x]dx = \mu/(k+\mu)\,,$$

and define f_k by the relation $(1+f_k)\,A_k = 1$. In the case of the Poisson distribution $f_k = k/\mu$.

Now $$f_1 f_2 \ldots f_r = r!/\mu^r = r!\varrho^r \, .$$

Hence

$$y_m = 1 + \sum_{r=1}^{m-1} \binom{m-1}{r} f_1 f_2 \ldots f_r \, .$$

This formula holds true in the general case, but a *proof* of this result will not be given here. The general statement runs as follows:

In the case of one operator, let the chance that a repair period have a length between t and t + d*t be p(t)*d*t.*
Define A_k, f_k by the relations

$$A_k = \int_0^\infty e^{-kt}p(t)\,dt\,, \quad (1+f_k)A_k = 1\,.$$

Then the machine efficiency is $y_m/(1+m\varrho y_m)$ where

$$y_m = 1 + \sum_{r=1}^{m-1} \binom{m-1}{r} f_1 f_2 \ldots f_r \tag{14}$$

A variation of this formula has been given by Kronig and Mondria (7), whose result is

$$y_m = \sum_{i=0}^{m-2} \binom{m-2}{i} (1 + f_{i+1}) f_1 f_2 \dots f_i .$$

A third method was developed by Khintchine (6). All three methods are equivalent, although analytically different.†

Example: Let the repair periods follow a χ^2-distribution with $2n$ degrees of freedom, given by

$$p(t) = [(\mu n)^n/(n-1)!]t^{n-1}e^{-\mu nt} .$$

Prove that $$f_k = (1 + k/\mu n)^n - 1 .$$

If $n \to \infty$, the case where all repair periods are equal is obtained. Show that, in this case, $f_k = \vartheta^k - 1$,
where $\vartheta = e^{1/\mu}$ and hence, using formula (14) for y_m derive the formula (6) of § 3.

8. General remarks

The theory developed in the preceding sections has found useful application in various industries, including textiles, golf ball winding, automatic screw cutting and electrical cables. However, many practical situations involving machine interference either do not satisfy all the assumptions on which the preceding theory rests or else satisfy additional restrictions. In such cases it is necessary to construct a particular mathematical model to fit the case at hand. For example, the operators may have some additional form of work to perform at times when they are not busy on repair work; or it may be that priority is accorded to certain types of repair. Again, in a case where it takes an appreciable time to move from one machine to another, a method must be devised for incorporating such time in the theory. This is an example of

† For a comparison of the three methods, and a formal proof of the equivalence of the methods of Ashcroft and of Kronig and Mondria the reader may care to consult the thesis (1957) of Dr. F. Benson, of the University of Birmingham.

patrolling, and the reader interested in this topic may care to consult the paper of Anson (2), who treated the case of a patrol interval having an exponential distribution. A rather advanced theory of patrolling has recently been discussed by Runnenburg (15), and this theory is particularly interesting as it involves the notion of renewal.

For a treatment of *priority* in machine interference the papers by Benson and by Cox (4) may be consulted. Perhaps the most comprehensive treatment is to be found in Dr. Benson's thesis (3) where various models covering ancillary work are also discussed.

REFERENCES

1. H. ASHCROFT, "The productivity of several machines under the care of one operator", *J. R. Statist. Soc.*, B **12** (1950), 145.
2. C. J. ANSON, "Determining the number of machines to be attended by an operator in order to minimize the total cost per unit of production", *Time and Motion Study*, **6** (1957), No. 4, 13.
3. F. BENSON, "Machine Interference. A mathematical study of some congestion problems in industry", Thesis, Birmingham, (1957).
4. F. BENSON and D. R. COX, "The productivity of machines requiring attention at random intervals", *J. R. Statist. Soc.*, B **13** (1951), 65.
5. W. FELLER, *An Introduction to Probability Theory and its Applications*, vol. 1, 2nd ed., J. Wiley, N. Y., 1957, p. 416.
6. A. J. KHINTCHINE, "The average idle time of machines", *Mat. Sborn.*, **40** (1935), 2.
7. R. KRONIG and H. MONDRIA, "On time losses in machinery undergoing interruptions", *Physica*, **10** (1943), 215 and 331.
8. C. MACK, T. MURPHY and N. L. WEBB, "The efficiency of N machines uni-directionally patrolled by one operative when walking time and repair times are constant", *J. R. Statist. Soc.*, B **19** (1957), 166.
9. C. MACK, "The efficiency of N machines uni-directionally patrolled by one operative when walking time is constant and repair times are variable", *J. R. Statist. Soc.*, B **19** (1957), 173.
10. E. C. MOLINA, *Poisson's Exponential Binomial Limit*, 7th printing, van Nostrand, N. Y. 1942.
11. P. NAOR, "On machine interference", *J. R. Statist. Soc.*, B **18**, (1956), 280.
12. P. NAOR, "Normal approximation to machine interference with many repairmen", *J. R. Statist. Soc.*, B **19** (1957), 334.

13. P. NAOR, "Some problems of machine interference", *Proc. 1st International Conf. on Operat. Res.*, Oxford, 1957, English Universities Press, London, 1957, p. 147.
14. C. PALM, "Arbetskraftens fordelning vid betjaning av automatmaskiner" (The distribution of repairmen in servicing automatic machines), *Industritidn. Nord.*, **75** (1947), 75, 90, 119.
15. J. T. RUNNENBURG, *Machines Served by a Patrolling Operator*, Mathematisch Centrum, Amsterdam, 1957.

CHAPTER VII

PROBLEMS OF STOCK CONTROL

1. Introduction

In many industrial operations stocks of material goods are of fundamental importance. The entrepreneur who finds it necessary to hold a stock soon realizes that part of his capital, perhaps a large part, is tied up in the stock holdings; and he may find it very desirable to reduce the level of stock held, in order to free part of the capital for employment elsewhere in the business. The problem is to determine a reasonable stock level, having regard to the dynamic and psychological characteristics of the environment in which the stock is operating. Problems of this sort are, of course, solved every day by directors and managers, who must make a decision. Until relatively recently such decisions were based largely on general experience of the situation at hand and were made in a qualitative or semi-qualitative way. However, in an age where scientific method has found a place in management, it is now possible to provide a more rational and quantitative basis for making these decisions. Mathematical methods are available for answering some of the questions that arise in considering stock levels and stock control, and it is the purpose of this chapter to introduce the reader to these methods.

Stocks may be held for various reasons, and in any practical situation an operational research study prior to an analysis of the stock problem would certainly be desirable. The input and ouptut characteristics of the stock holding may depend, perhaps sensitively, on various forms of human behaviour as well as on purely physical or engineering or financial aspects; and a proper analysis of the problem of stock levels must take into account all these features. In this chapter we shall only be concerned with the mathematical treatment, and it is emphasized that this, while it elevates to a science what was formerly an art, is only part of the general problem of determining stock levels. It may assist the reader if an outline is given of some general characteristics of situations involving the need to operate a stock holding. Firstly the need itself arises because of a mis-match between the supply of and demand for the commodity under discussion. The mis-match may be due to various causes. One example is the seasonal production of some agricultural product, say wheat, and the demand for this taken over the whole year. Another is the high demand over a short period of a commodity, for example Christmas toys, which it is necessary to produce at a fairly uniform rate. Other types of mis-match arise where batch-production is necessary, or where buying is in lots because of the operation of a quantity discount. In all of these examples stock holdings arise spontaneously and not because of any uncertainty about supply and demand. If there is uncertainty, and there is in most practical situations, then it will be desirable to hold stock at some augmented level to reduce the risk of not being able to meet a demand. The main mathematical contribution is at this point, namely the link between stock levels and uncertainty.

2. Some elementary problems of optimization

In this section four problems are solved. They only involve simple situations and will prepare the reader for the complications of later sections. The first problem deals with the simplest case of optimization of a stock level and leads to the classical square-root formula for the economical lot-size. The second problem, which introduces uncertainty in almost the simplest manner, concerns the owner of a fleet of N wagons, who experiences a fluctuating demand and who is obliged to hire wagons when the demand exceeds N. The question is to determine the value of N which leads to the lowest rate of operating costs, remembering that ownership of a wagon ties up capital and, on the other hand, there is a cost to hire a wagon, when necessary. The third problem is like the second but involves a slight extension. The owner of a newspaper shop can buy a paper at a price a, sell a paper at a price b, and return an unsold paper to the publisher and obtain a refund c, where $c < a < b$. If the probabilities of selling 1, 2, 3, ... newspapers are known, how many papers should be bought in order to maximize profit? The fourth problem deals with a commodity available in continuous amounts, and subject to a highly variable demand.

(i) *The Economical Lot Size.* Consider a situation where a merchant sells some commodity, and suppose, for simplicity, that there is a uniform rate of demand. The merchant buys the commodity in lots, of size Q, and tries to arrange that a replacement arrives at the time when the previous lot becomes exhausted. The time between the procurement of a lot and the exhaustion of the lot will be called a *cycle*. Repeated buying over a long period of time, involving a large number of cycles, carries a certain total expense, depending inversely on Q, and the holding of the stock involves a carrying charge which depends linearly on Q. The

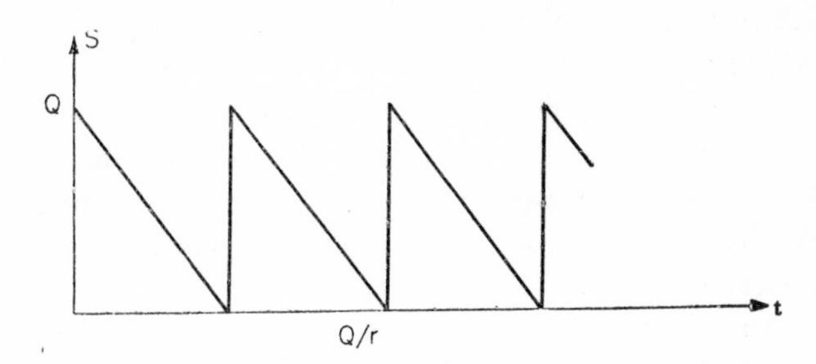

FIG. 1.

problem is to find the value of Q, say Q_0, which minimizes the sum of these two costs. This value, Q_0, is called the *economical lot size*. The method is as follows.

Let Q = the lot size,
a = the cost to place an order (independent of Q),
c = cost of holding unit stock for unit time,
r = rate of demand, assumed uniform.

In Fig. 1 the amount of stock, S, is graphed against time, t. It is clear that the cycle time is Q/r. The holding cost for a cycle is $\frac{1}{2}Q \cdot (Q/r) \cdot c$, that is $\frac{1}{2}cQ^2/r$, and the cost of an order is a. Hence the total cost of operating the system per unit time is C where

$$C = r\{a + \tfrac{1}{2}cQ^2/r\}/Q = ar/Q + \tfrac{1}{2}cQ.$$

Now C is a minimum when $\mathrm{d}C/\mathrm{d}Q = 0$, that is when

$$Q = Q_0 = \sqrt{(2ar/c)}.$$

This is the classical square-root formula for the optimal lot size. It has undergone many extensions (see (8) and (10)), and has been used extensively in industry. However, its limitations should be appreciated, and the reader is referred to a recent paper by Duckworth (3) for a critical discussion.

(ii) *The Optimal Size of a Wagon Fleet.* In this problem the owner of a fleet of wagons finds that on some days not all the wagons are in use, while on other days it is necessary to augment the fleet by hiring extra wagons. If the size, N, of the fleet is large then wagon utilization will be low; if N is small it will be necessary to hire wagons rather frequently. To determine the optimal value, N_0, of N we minimize the expected cost of operation per day. Let the cost of owning a wagon be one unit per day, and let p_n be the chance that n wagons are required on any one day, where $n = 1, 2, 3, \ldots$, and let k be the cost of hiring a wagon for one day, where, clearly, $k > 1$. The chance of having to hire S wagons is p_{N+S}, so that the expected cost of hiring on any one day is $k(p_{N+1} + 2p_{N+2} + \ldots)$. Thus the total cost is C_N where

$$C_N = N + k(p_{N+1} + 2p_{N+2} + \ldots)$$

It is, of course, not possible to use differentiation to find the value N_0 of N for which C_N is a minimum since N is an integral variable. But, if C_{N_0}, is a minimum then

$$C_{N_0} \leqslant C_{N_0+1} \text{ and also } C_{N_0} \leqslant C_{N_0-1}.$$

From these two inequalities it is easy to show that N_0 is the value of N for which

$$p_N + p_{N+1} + \ldots \geqslant 1/k \geqslant p_{N+1} + p_{N+2} + \ldots.$$

This result will yield the value of N_0 in any actual case where the p_n $(n = 1, 2, 3, ...)$ are given numerically. It is worth noticing that since $p_{N+1} + p_{N+2} + ...$ is the chance that the demand on any day exceeds N, the optimal value of N is such that it is necessary to hire wagons on the average about once in every k days.

(iii) *The Newspaper Problem.* In this problem papers are bought at a cost a per paper, sold at a price b per paper, and unsold papers are returned to the publisher at a refund c per paper, where $c < a < b$. Let p_n $(n = 1, 2, 3, ...)$ be the probability of a demand for n newspapers. How many newspapers should be bought in order to maximize the expected profit? If N is the number of papers bought then the income is Nb when the demand exceeds N, and nb when the demand is n, where $n \leqslant N$. Thus the expected income from sales is $b(p_1 + 2p_2 + ... + Np_N) + Nb(p_{N+1} + p_{N+2} + + ...)$. When the demand is n, where $n \leqslant N$, there are $N - n$ unsold papers and on return to the publisher the refund is $(N - n)c$. The probability of this event is p_n. Hence the expected refund is $c\{(N-1)p_1 + (N-2)p_2 + ... + p_{N-i}\}$. Since the cost of buying N papers is Na, the expected profit is P_N where

$$P_N = b\sum_{s=1}^{N} sp_s + Nb\sum_{s=N+1}^{\infty} p_s + c\sum_{s=1}^{N-i} (N-s)\,p_s - Na.$$

The maximum expected profit occurs for the value of N satisfying

$$P_{N-1} \leqslant P_N, \quad P_{N+1} \leqslant P_N,$$

and these inequalities reduce to

$$b(p_N + p_{N+1} + ...) + c(p_{N-1} + p_{N-2} + ... + p_1) \geqslant a,$$

$$b(p_{N+1} + p_{N+2} + ...) + c(p_N + p_{N-1} + ... + p_1) \leqslant a,$$

In a given numerical case it is an easy matter to solve the inequalities for N.

(iv) *A Problem of Supplying a Highly Variable Demand.* The following problem is unusual but is discussed for two reasons. Firstly it will assist the reader in appreciating the widely differing types of stock problems which arise. Secondly it provides a good illustration of a feature well-known in operational research, namely that optimization and sub-optimization may be markedly different problems, and it by no means follows that the problem of optimization is the more difficult, either to formulate or to solve, merely because it is set in a wider context.

In the manufacture of steel great quantities of oxygen are required and it is necessary to install a tonnage oxygen plant. This plant supplies most of the requirements, but when demand exceeds the capacity of the plant it is necessary to take a supplementary supply from cylinders of oxygen, at a greater cost per unit than the cost of gas taken from the plant. When the rate of demand is less than the capacity of the plant, which produces at capacity whenever it is operating, the excess oxygen is lost to the atmosphere. Given the pattern of demand, the problem is to determine the most economical size of the plant, that is to determine the size so that the total cost of supplying both from the plant and from cylinders shall be a minimum.

The problem of sub-optimization is to minimize the cost of the excess oxygen supplied by the plant (when the demand is less than capacity) and the cost of the supply from the cylinders. For an outline of this problem, in its original context, the reader may consult a paper by Jones, Lee and Steer (7).

An abstract mathematical formulation of the problem may be set up as follows. Suppose that a commodity C may be supplied by each of two methods, (i) at a constant rate ϑ from a source S which supplies the commodity whether it is needed or not, (ii) from a source T at a rate which may be varied at will. In case (i) it is supposed that there are no storage facilities and that when the demand is less than ϑ, the excess production from S is wasted. The costs of a unit of C from the sources S and T are $a(\vartheta)$ and b respectively, where b is a constant and $a(\vartheta)$ a known function of ϑ, with $a(\vartheta) < b$ for all ϑ. By taking a to be a function of ϑ recognition is given to the fact that the cost of supplying from S depends on the size of S, that is, S supplies at capacity at the rate ϑ, and the greater ϑ the greater will be the size of S.

The rate of demand, $v(t)$, for C is a quantity highly variable with the time t, with a considerable number of peaks and troughs over a long period P of time. During this period $v(t)$ may display a number of discontinuities, and a typical practical case is illustrated in Fig. 2, where the average rate of demand in each of 100 units of time is graphed.

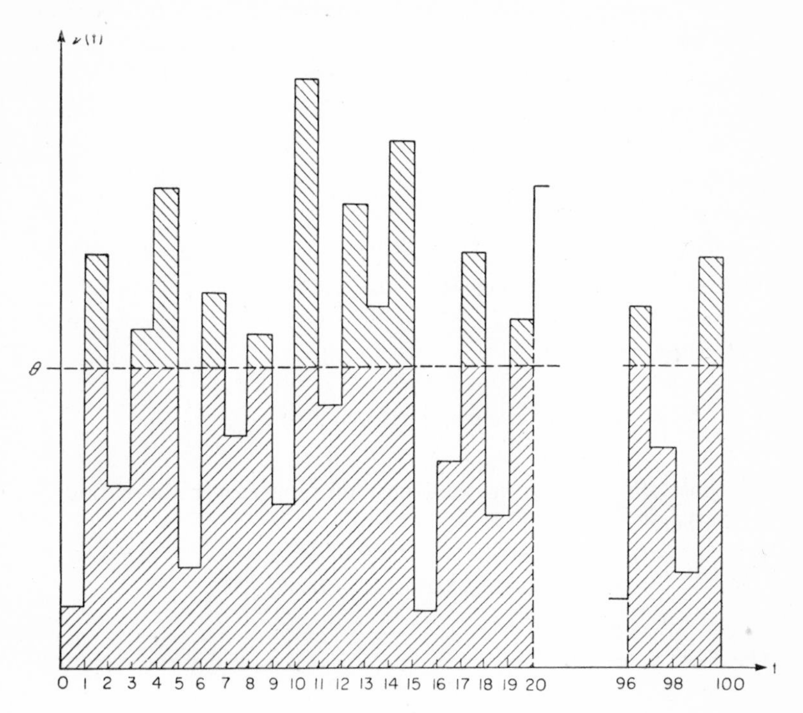

FIG. 2.

Regarding the method of operation, since $a(\vartheta) < b$ it is always cheaper to supply from the source S and not T, if possible. Suppose S is designed to operate at a rate ϑ_0, to be determined. Then, if at any particular time, t', it happens that $v(t') \leqslant \vartheta_0$, we supply from S, and waste the excess supply at the rate $\vartheta_0 - v(t')$. But if $v(t') > \vartheta_0$, we supply from S at the rate ϑ_0, and from T at the rate $v(t') - \vartheta_0$.

We can now state the

Problem of Optimization: given $v(t)$ (usually numerically) find the rate ϑ_0 at which the source S should be operated in order that the total cost of operating both sources of supply shall be a minimum.

To solve this problem, note that there are two components of the cost of operating the system. Over a long period P of time the source S, operating at a constant rate ϑ, produces an amount ϑP of C at a cost $\vartheta P\ a(\vartheta)$. In order to obtain the cost of the supply from source T during the period P, we introduce a variable φ and a function $f(\varphi)$ as follows. Let

$$U = \max_{t \varepsilon P} v(t)$$

and let φ have the range $0 \leqslant \varphi \leqslant U$. Define $f(\varphi)$ as the sum of time intervals during which $v(t) > \varphi$, and note that $f(\varphi)$ is defined by the given function $v(t)$. Then the amount of C supplied by T is A where

$$A = \int_{\theta}^{U} f(\varphi)\,\mathrm{d}\varphi,$$

at a cost Ab. Hence the total cost of supply over the period P is K where

$$K = \vartheta a(\vartheta)P + b \int_{\theta}^{U} f(\varphi)\mathrm{d}\varphi.$$

The least value of K, given by $\mathrm{d}K/\mathrm{d}\vartheta = 0$, satisfies the equation

$$f(\vartheta) = P\{a(\vartheta) + \vartheta a'(\vartheta)\}/b,$$

and the source S should be so designed that it supplies C at the rate ϑ_0 where $\vartheta = \vartheta_0$ is the root of this equation. In the particular case where $a(\vartheta)$ is a constant, say a,

$$f(\vartheta) = aP/b.$$

The Problem of Sub-optimization: This is the problem of minimizing the sum of the cost of supplying C from T when $v(t) > \vartheta$ and the cost of the excess of C supplied by S when $v(t) \leqslant \vartheta$. These costs are, respectively,

$$b \int_{\vartheta}^{U} f(\varphi)\mathrm{d}\varphi, \quad a(\vartheta) \int_{0}^{\vartheta} \{P - f(\varphi)\}\mathrm{d}\varphi,$$

so that it is necessary to minimize K where K is the sum of these two costs. By placing $dK/d\vartheta = 0$ we obtain

$$\{a(\vartheta) + b\}f(\vartheta) = \{\vartheta a'(\vartheta) + a(\vartheta)\}P - a'(\vartheta) \int_0^{\vartheta} f(\varphi)d\varphi ,$$

and the root $\vartheta = \vartheta_1$ of this equation is the solution of the problem. It is interesting to note that when $a(\vartheta)$ is constant, the equation becomes

$$f(\vartheta) = aP/(a + b) .$$

Now $f(\vartheta)$ is, by its definition, a monotonically decreasing function of ϑ. Hence the solution $\vartheta = \vartheta_1$ of this last equation is *greater* than the solution $\vartheta = \vartheta_0$ of the equation $f(\vartheta) = aP/b$. Thus, if we sub-optimize, a larger source S is required than in the case of optimization. Finally, it may be noted that Jones, Lee and Steer (7) solve the problem of sub-optimization in the case $a/b = 2/3$.

3. Operating characteristics of a simple stockpile

The following situation frequently occurs in practice. There is an initial stock of some commodity, and demands are made by customers at various times for various amounts of stock. The stock level diminishes until, at some time, a replenishment arrives, which may or may not restore the level to its initial value. Then the process is repeated, that is demands diminish the stock level until the next replenishment arrives. It is supposed that the process is repeated indefinitely, and then various questions arise such as the following:

(a) what is the probability that the stock level will reach zero between successive replenishments?

(b) what is the average amount of stock held per unit time?

(c) given the cost of stockholding per unit time and the cost (a penalty cost) of not being able to meet a demand (when the stock is exhausted) what is the optimum initial stock which minimizes operating costs?

We can answer such questions, under fairly general conditions, once the situation is formulated mathematically.

To proceed to the formulation let the commodity be measured in terms of some unit, and suppose the initial stock consists of N units. Let

$n_i =$ the ith demand ($i = 1, 2, \ldots$),
$t_i =$ the time interval between the $(i-1)$th and ith demands,
$\tau_i =$ the time interval between the $(i-1)$th and ith replenishment.

It may assist the reader to refer to Fig. 3, which shows a graph of the stock level S against the time, t.

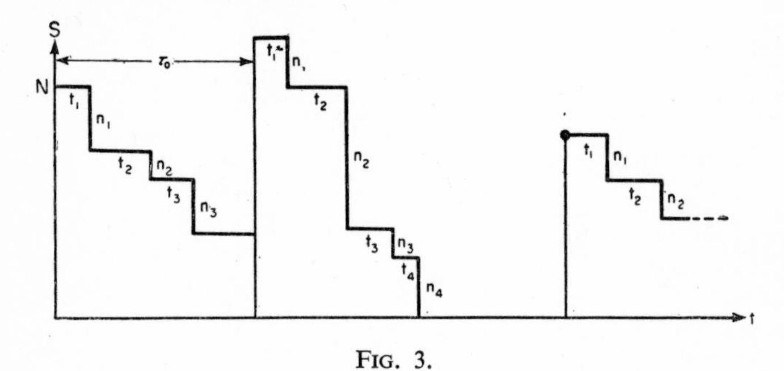

FIG. 3.

It is supposed that

(i) the n_i are independent discrete random variables and that

$$P(n_i = j) = p_j \quad (j = 1, 2, \ldots),$$

(ii) The probability of a demand in an interval dt is $\lambda\, dt$, so that the instants of demand follow a Poisson distribution of parameter λ and the t_i are independent variables with an exponential distribution given by

$$P(t_i \leqslant t) = 1 - e^{-\lambda t} \quad (0 < t < \infty),$$

(iii) The τ_i are independent variables with a given distribution function $K(\tau)$, that is

$$P(\tau_i \leqslant \tau) = K(\tau).$$

Further it is supposed that the n_i, t_i and τ_i are all independent of each other, so that, for example, the size of a demand is not only independent of other demands but also of the time at which it is made, and the time τ between successive replenishments does not depend upon the number or sizes of demands made during this time. These restrictions are satisfied, at least approximately, in many practical situations.† It is now possible to proceed to the problem of the next section.

4. The problem of Hammersley

In an interesting paper (5) Hammersley discussed the situation where

(i) at each replenishment the stock level is raised to the initial level, N;

(ii) the demands, n_i, follow a continuous distribution.

His problem was to find the probability that the stock level becomes zero between successive replenishments. The expression found for the probability is somewhat complicated from the point of view of practical usage (it involves the limit of an integral), and a simpler result may be obtained, using the method of probability generating functions, by allowing the demands to have a discrete rather than a continuous distribution.

Suppose that a demand, when it occurs, is for one or more units, so that $P(n_i = 0) = 0$, and let

$$P(n_i = r) = p_r \qquad (r = 1, 2, 3, ...).$$

We write, for the probability generating function,

$$G(x) = \sum_{r=0}^{\infty} p_r \, x^r,$$

where $p_0 = P(n_i = 0) = 0$. Now suppose that in the interval τ between replenishments there are m demands where $m = 0, 1, 2, ...$. Note that since the demands follow a Poisson distribution, the chance of m demands in τ is $e^{-\lambda\tau}(\lambda\tau)^m/m!$, so that the case $m = 0$ does occur, and with the chance $e^{-\lambda\tau}$. If $p_r^{(m)}$ is the chance that in the m demands the total demand is τ, then

(i) when $m = 0$,

$$p_0^{(0)} = 1, \quad p_r^{(0)} = 0 \text{ for } r > 1,$$

---

† They would not however be satisfied in a case where customers had information about the likely demands of other customers and fear of a general shortage led to demands not being placed at random.

so that

$$\sum_{r=0}^{\infty} p_r^{(0)} x^r = 1,$$

(ii) when $m > 0$, by the convolution theorem,

$$\sum_{r=0}^{\infty} p_r^{(m)} x^r = \{G(x)\}^m.$$

We can now build up the probability P_r of a total demand r in the period between two successive replenishments. Firstly, given τ, the chance that there are m demands in this interval and that the sum of the demands is r is $q_{m,r}$ where

$$q_{m,r} = e^{-\lambda\tau}(\lambda\tau)^m p_r^m/m!$$

Then, since the cases $m = 0, 1, 2, \ldots$ are mutually exclusive, the chance that the sum of the demands in time τ is r is $\sum_{m=0}^{\infty} q_{m,r}$. But τ has the distribution function $K(\tau)$, so that, finally,

$$P_r = \int_0^{\infty} \sum_{m=0}^{\infty} q_{m,r} dk(\tau) = \int_0^{\infty} e^{-\lambda\tau} \sum_{m=0}^{\infty} (1/m!)\,(\lambda\tau)^m p_r^{(m)} dK(\tau).$$

The generating function for this sequence of probabilities is $\sum_{r=0}^{\infty} P_r x^r$ where

$$\sum_{r=0}^{\infty} P_r x^r = \int_0^{\infty} e^{-\lambda\tau} \sum_{m=0}^{\infty} (1/m!)\,(\lambda\tau)^m \left(\sum_{r=0}^{\infty} p_r^{(m)} x^r\right) dK(\tau)$$

$$= \int_0^{\infty} e^{-\lambda\tau} \sum_{m=0}^{\infty} \frac{\{\lambda\tau G(x)\}^m}{m!} dK(\tau)$$

$$= \int_0^{\infty} \exp\{-\lambda\tau[1 - G(x)]\} dK(\tau).$$

If $\varphi(x)$ is the Laplace Transform of $K(\tau)$, that is,

$$\varphi(x) = \int_0^{\infty} e^{-\tau x} dK(\tau),$$

then

$$\sum_{r=0}^{\infty} P_r x^r = \varphi[\lambda(1 - G(x))] .$$

The problem of Hammersley is to find the chance Q_N that the stock level becomes zero between successive replenishments, if the stock is N immediately after a replenishment. It is clear that $Q_N = \sum_{r=N}^{\infty} P_r$, and the generating function for the $Q_N (N = 0, 1, 2, ...)$ may be found by using the following:

LEMMA: Let

$$A(x) = \sum_{n=0}^{\infty} a_n x^n, \qquad C(x) = \sum_{n=0}^{\infty} c_n x^n,$$

where,

$$A(1) = 1, \qquad c_n = \sum_{i=n}^{\infty} a_i .$$

Then

$$C(x) = \{1 - xA(x)\}/(1 - x) .$$

The proof follows by comparing coefficients in the series $(1 - x)$. $C(x)$ and $1 - xA(x)$.
From this lemma it follows at once that

$$\sum_{r=0}^{\infty} Q_r x^r = [1 - x\varphi\{\lambda(1 - G(x))\}]/(1 - x) .$$

Examples: Explicit expressions for Q_r are sometimes obtainable and the reader may care to work out the detail in the following cases:

(i) If each demand is for one unit, then $G(x) = x$ and

$$\sum_{r=0}^{\infty} Q_r x^r = \frac{1}{1 - x} - \frac{x}{1 - x} \varphi\{\lambda(1 - x)\} .$$

If τ follows the Erlangian distribution, E_k, that is if

$$\frac{dK(\tau)}{d\tau} = \frac{(\mu k)^k \tau^{k-1}}{(k-1)!} e^{-\mu k \tau},$$

where $k = 1, 2, 3, \ldots$, and the mean is $1/\mu$, then

$$\varphi(x) = \left(\frac{\mu k}{x + \mu k}\right)^k,$$

and
$$\sum_{r=0}^{\infty} Q_r x^r = \frac{1}{1-x}\left[1 - x\left(\frac{\mu k}{\lambda + \mu k}\right)^k (1 - \varrho k)^{-k}\right],$$

where $\varrho = \lambda/(\lambda + \mu k)$. In this case it is found that

$$Q_0 = 1, \quad Q_1 = 1 - \left(\frac{\mu k}{\lambda + \mu k}\right)^k,$$

and

$$Q_{r+1} = 1 - \left(\frac{\mu k}{\lambda + \mu k}\right)^k \left[1 + \binom{k}{1}\varrho + \ldots + \binom{k+r-1}{r}\varrho^r\right],$$

for
$$r = 1, 2, 3, \ldots .$$

The two cases, $k = 1$ and $k = \infty$, deserve special mention. When $k = 1$, the time τ between replenishments follows the exponential density distribution, $\mu e^{-\mu x}$. Then it is found that

$$Q_r = \varrho^r = \{\lambda/(\lambda + \mu)\}^r \quad (r = 0, 1, 2, \ldots).$$

When $k \to \infty$, τ becomes constant, namely

$$\tau = 1/\mu = L,$$

say. Then $\varphi(x) = e^{-xL}$ and

$$\sum_{r=0}^{\infty} Q_r x^r = [1 - x e^{-\lambda L} e^{\lambda L x}]/(1 - x).$$

It follows that

$$Q_r = \frac{\lambda^r L^r}{r!} e^{-\lambda L}\left\{1 + \frac{\lambda L}{r+1} + \frac{\lambda^2 L^2}{(r+1)(r+2)} + \ldots\right\},$$

a result which could be obtained independently, since, in the case of unit demand, Q_r is the chance of r or more demands (from a Poisson distribution) in time L.

(ii) If the demand follows a geometric distribution, that is,

p_r = chance of a demand $r = (1-a)\,a^{r-1}$ $(r = 1, 2, \ldots)$,
it is easy to show that

$$G(x) = (1-a)\,x/(1-ax)\,.$$

If, in addition, τ has the exponential distribution, $\mu\,\mathrm{e}^{-\mu\tau}$, then $\varphi(x) = \mu/(\mu + x)$.
Thus

$$\varphi\{\lambda(1 - G(x)\} = \frac{\mu(1-ax)}{\lambda + \mu - (\lambda + a\mu)x},$$

and it is found that

$$\sum_{r=0}^{\infty} \mathrm{Q}_r x^r = \frac{1}{1-x}\left[1 - \frac{\mu x(1-ax)}{(\lambda+\mu)(1-vx)}\right],$$

where $v = (\lambda + \mu a)/(\lambda + \mu)$. Upon expansion and comparing coefficients it is found that

$$\mathrm{Q}_r = \frac{\varrho}{1+\varrho}\left(\frac{a+\varrho}{1+\varrho}\right)^{r-1} \qquad (r = 1, 2, \ldots)$$

where $\varrho = \lambda/\mu$. Thus the Q_r follow a geometric distribution, (although, of course, $\sum_{r=0}^{\infty}\mathrm{Q}_r \neq 1$).

5. The problem of Finch

In the model to be studied in this section discrete demands are made upon the stock, whose initial size is N, at various times until the stock level becomes zero or negative. This is as in the Hammersley model. But it differs from the latter in that, as soon as an order is received for a demand which reduces the stock level to zero or a negative level there is an immediate replenishment to the original level N. Then the process is repeated, and an infinite sequence of cycles is obtained. This model was considered by Jackson (6), who, in the case where the demands follow a Poisson distribution, computed the cost of stock holding per unit time. But the first serious mathematical treatment, covering a more general situation where the sizes of the demands and the instants at which they are made are arbitrary, was given by Finch (4). In this case a formula was obtained for the cost of stock holding per unit time, averaged over an infinite number of cycles. In the present section we shall derive the result of Finch by using a more natural method and at the same time some further results will follow from our method.

As in § 3, consider discrete demands from an initial stock of N units and let

n_i = the ith demand $(i = 1, 2, \ldots)$,

t_i = the time interval between the $(i-1)$th and ith demands,

$p_j = P(n_i = j) \quad (j = 1, 2, \ldots)$.

Further, let the t_i be independent random variables with a common distribution function and with a mean $E(t)$. As before let $G(x)$ be the generating function for the (p_j), that is

$$G(x) = \sum_{r=0}^{\infty} p_r x^r \quad (p_0 = 0).$$

The stock level, S, as a function of time is shown in Fig. 4 for a few cycles.

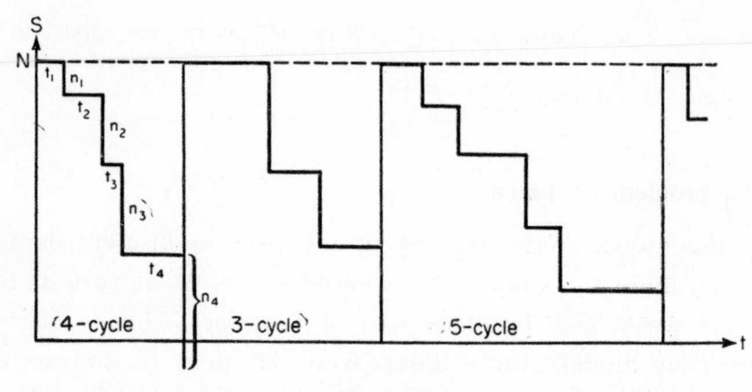

FIG. 4.

Suppose that in some cycle the mth demand exhausts the stock but the $(m-1)$th demand does not, that is

$$n_1 + \ldots + n_{m-1} < N, \quad n_1 + \ldots + n_m \geqslant N.$$

Then we call this an m-cycle. It should be noticed that in the evaluation of the cost of stockholding it is immaterial whether the customer is willing or not to accept $N - (n_1 + ... + n_{m-1})$ units instead of his order for n_m units. For as soon as his order is placed a replenishment is made irrespective of whether the order is satisfied or not.

Let $P_m(N)$ be the probability of an m-cycle, that is

$$P_m(N) = P(S_{m-1} < N \leqslant S_m)\,,$$

where

$$S_m = \sum_{i=1}^{m} n_i\,, \quad S_0 = 0\,.$$

Since a demand is for one or more units, m ranges over the values $1, 2, ..., N$; and N itself ranges over the values $1, 2, ..., \infty$. Also let $E[m(N)]$ be the mean length of a cycle, that is

$$E[m(N)] = \sum_{m=1}^{\infty} m\, P_m(N)\,,$$

where, for $m > N$, we place $P_m(N) = 0$. Then the following theorems will be proved on the generating functions for $P_m(r)$ and $E[m(N)]$:

THEOREM 1:

$$H(x, y) \equiv \sum_{r=1}^{\infty} \sum_{m=1}^{\infty} P_m(r)\, x^r y^m = \frac{xy[1 - G(x)]}{(1 - x)[1 - yG(x)]}\,.$$

THEOREM 2:

$$\sum_{r=1}^{\infty} E[m(r)] x^r = \frac{x}{(1 - x)\,[1 - G(x)]}\,.$$

Theorem 2 is due to Finch (4); here we obtain it as a corollary of Theorem 1.

In the proof of Theorem 1 use will be made of the following result. Considering the sums S_{m-1} and S_m of $m - 1$ and m demands respectively, it is clear that if $S_m \geqslant N$ then either $S_m \geqslant N > S_{m-1}$ or $S_{m-1} \geqslant N$, and conversely. Hence

$$P(S_m \geqslant N) = P(S_m \geqslant N > S_{m-1}) + P(S_{m-1} \geqslant N)\,,$$

and we have the

LEMMA:

$$P_m(N) = P(S_{m-1} < N \leqslant S_m) = P(N \leqslant S_m) - P(N \leqslant S_{m-1})\,.$$

Now, let the chance that the sum of m demands is r be $p_r^{(m)}$, that is

$$p_r^{(m)} = P(S_m = r),$$

and write

$$q_r^{(m)} = P(S_m \geqslant r) = \sum_{i=r}^{\infty} p_i^{(m)}.$$

Then, by the convolution theorem, we have

$$\sum_{r=1}^{\infty} p_r^{(m)} x^r = \{G(x)\}^m,$$

and by the Lemma of § 4,

$$\sum_{r=1}^{\infty} q_r^{(m)} x^r = \frac{1 - x\{G(x)\}^m}{1 - x}.$$

Next, by the Lemma of the present section,

$$P_m(r) = q_r^{(m)} - q_r^{(m-1)},$$

so that

$$\sum_{r=1}^{\infty} P_m(r) x^r = \frac{1 - x\{G(x)\}^m}{1 - x} - \frac{1 - x\{G(x)\}^{m-1}}{1 - x}$$

$$= \frac{x}{1 - x} [1 - G(x)] \{G(x)\}^{m-1}.$$

It follows that

$$H(x, y) \equiv \sum_{r=1}^{\infty} \sum_{m=1}^{\infty} P_m(r) x^r y^m = \frac{x}{1 - x} [1 - G(x)] \sum_{m=1}^{\infty} y^m \{G(x)\}^{m-1}$$

$$= \frac{xy[1 - G(x)]}{(1 - x)[1 - yG(x)]}.$$

This is Theorem 1. To derive Theorem 2 observe that, since

$$E[m(r)] = \sum_{m=1}^{\infty} m P_m(r),$$

we have

$$\sum_{r=1}^{\infty} E[m(r)] x^r = \left(\frac{\partial H}{\partial y}\right)_{y=1} = \left(\frac{x[1 - G(x)]}{(1 - x)[1 - yG(x)]^2}\right)_{y=1}$$

$$= \frac{x}{(1 - x)[1 - G(x)]}.$$

The average cost of stock-holding. In an m-cycle, where the demands are $n_1, n_2, ..., n_m$ it is clear (see Fig. 5) that a stock N is held for a time t_1, a stock $N - n_1$ for a time t_2, ..., and a stock $N - n_1 - n_2 - ... - n_{m-1}$ for a time t_m. Let c be the cost of holding a unit stock for unit time. Then the total cost of stock holding during the m-cycle is $C(N)$ where

$$C(N) = c[Nt_1 + (N - n_1)\, t_2 + ... + (N - n_1 - n_2 - ... - n_{m-1})\, t_m]\,.$$

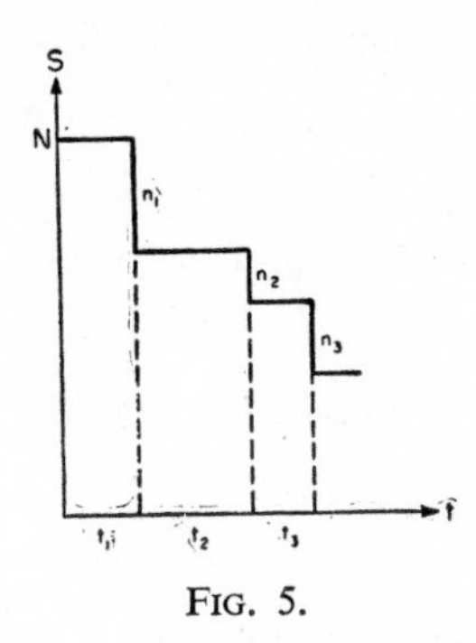

FIG. 5.

We shall find the average $E[C(N)]$ taken over an infinite sequence of cycles. It is necessary to remember that the average is carried out over the three random variables, n, t and m, where $m = 1, 2, ..., N$.

Let, for any random variable z related to the cycle, $E_m(z)$ be the mean value of z subject to the cycle being of length m, that is involving m demands before replenishment occurs, so that, for example, $E_m(n)$ is the mean demand in an m-cycle. Since the times t_i are independent of m it follows that $E_m(t) = E(t)$. Thus

$$E_m[C(N)] = cE(t)\, [N + (N - E_m(n)) + ... + \{N - (m - 1)\, E_m(n)\}]$$
$$= cE(t)\, [Nm - \tfrac{1}{2}\, m\, (m - 1)\, E_m(n)]\,. \qquad (1)$$

Before proceeding it is necessary to find $E_m(n)$. Let $p_r'(cm)$ be the probability of a demand for r units, given that the demand occurs in an m-cycle, that is

$$p_r'(m) = P(n = r) \mid S_{m-1} < N \leqslant S_m)\,.$$

Then

$$E_m(n) = \sum_{r=1}^{\infty} r\, p'_r(m) \tag{2}$$

The value of $p'_r(m)$ is given by

THEOREM 3:

$$p'_r(m) = p_r \frac{P_{m-1}(N-r)}{P_m(N)}.$$

This follows by an application of the formula

$$P(AB) = P(A|B)\,P(B) = P(B|A)\,P(A),$$

proved in Chapter I, p. 13. For, let A be the event $n = r$, that is, that a demand is for r units, and B the event that a cycle is of length m, that is, that $S_{m-1} < N \leqslant S_m$. Then we have

$$\begin{aligned} P(n = r\,;\quad S_{m-1} < N \leqslant S_m) &= P(n = r)\,P(S_{m-1} < N \leqslant S_m |\, n = r) \\ &= P(S_{m-1} < N \leqslant S_m)\,P(n = r|\, S_{m-1} < N \leqslant S_m), \end{aligned}$$

that is

$$p_r P(S_{m-1} < N \leqslant S_m \mid n = r) = P_m(N)\,p'_r(m).$$

Now, $P(S_{m-1} < N \leqslant S_m| \, n = r)$, being the probability of an m-cycle, given that one demand is of size r from a stock initially of N units, is the probability of an $(m-1)$-cycle given an initial stock of $N - r$ units, that is, $P_{m-1}(N-r)$. Hence

$$p_r\, P_{m-1}(N-r) = P_m(N)\,p'_r(m),$$

which is the result of the theorem.

It now follows from (2) that

$$E_m(n)\,P_m(N) = \sum_{r=1}^{\infty} r p_r\, P_{m-1}(N-r),$$

and hence (1) becomes

$$E_m[C(N)] =$$

$$= cE(t)\left[Nm - \frac{1}{2P_m(N)} \sum_{r=1}^{\infty} r p_r \cdot m(m-1)\; P_{m-1}(N-r)\right].$$

The final average $E[C(N)]$ may now be found. It is given by

$$E[C(N)] = \sum_{m=1}^{\infty} E_m [C(N)] P_m (N)$$

$$= cE(t) [N \sum_{m=1}^{\infty} mP_m(N) - \tfrac{1}{2} \sum_{m=1}^{\infty} \sum_{r=1}^{\infty} a_r b_{N-r}]$$

where

$$a_r = rp_r, \quad b_{N-r} = m(m-1)P_{m-1}(N-r).$$

A generating function for $E[C(N)]$ may be derived as follows. Using the standard result on the product of two power series,

$$(\sum_{r=1}^{\infty} a_r x^r)(\sum_{r=1}^{\infty} b_r x^r) = \sum_{N=1}^{\infty} (\sum_{r=1}^{\infty} a_r b_{N-r}) x^N,$$

where $b_{N-r} = 0$ for $r \geqslant N$, and the fact that $E[m(N)] = \sum_{m=1}^{\infty} mP_m(N)$, we have

$$\sum_{N=1}^{\infty} E[C(N)]x^N = cE(t) [\sum_{N=1}^{\infty} NE [m(N)]x^N -$$

$$- \tfrac{1}{2} \sum_{m=1}^{\infty} \{\sum_{N=1}^{\infty} (\sum_{r=1}^{\infty} a_r b_{N-r}) x^N\}] = cE(t) [\sum_{N=1}^{\infty} NE[m(N)] x^N -$$

$$- \tfrac{1}{2} (\sum_{r=1}^{\infty} a_r x^r)(\sum_{m=1}^{\infty} \sum_{N=1}^{\infty} b_N x^N)].$$

But, from Theorem 2,

$$\sum_{N=1}^{\infty} NE[m(N)]x^N = x \frac{d}{dx} \left\{ \frac{x}{(1 - x[1 - G(x)]} \right\}$$

$$= \frac{x}{(1-x)^2 [1 - G(x)]} + \frac{x^2 G'(x)}{(1-x)[1 - G(x)]^2}.$$

Also,

$$\sum_{r=1}^{\infty} a_r x^r = \sum_{r=1}^{\infty} r p_r x^r = xG'(x),$$

and, from Theorem 1,

$$\sum_{m=1}^{\infty} \sum_{N=1}^{\infty} b_N \, x^N = \sum_{m=1}^{\infty} \sum_{N=1}^{\infty} m(m-1) \, P_{m-1}(N) \, x^N$$

$$= \left(\frac{\partial^2 (yH)}{\partial y^2} \right)_{y=1} = \frac{2x}{(1-x)\,[1-G(x)]^2}.$$

These values lead to

Theorem 4: The generating function for $E[C(N)]$ is given by

$$\sum_{N=1}^{\infty} E[C(N)] \, x^N = cE(t) \cdot \frac{x}{(1-x)^2 \, [1-G(x)]}.$$

On comparing the generating functions for $E[m(N)]$ and $E[C(N)]$ given in Theorems 2 and 4 respectively it is an easy matter to derive $E[C(N)]$ in terms of $E[m(r)]$ for $r = 1, 2, ..., N$. We use the result that if

$$A(x) = \sum_{r=1}^{\infty} a_r \, x^r, \quad B(x) = \sum_{r=1}^{\infty} b_r \, x^r,$$

where

$$b_{ij} = \sum_{s=1}^{j} a_s,$$

then

$$B(x) = A(x)/(1-x).$$

By taking

$$A(x) = \frac{x}{(1-x)\,[1-G(x)]}, \qquad a_r = E[m(r)],$$

it follows from Theorems 2 and 4 that

$$E[C(N)] = cE(t) \, \{E[m(1)] + E[m(2)] + ... + E[m(N)]\},$$

a result due to Finch (4). However, in a particular case, where $G(x)$ is given explicitly it may be an easier matter to compute $E[C(N)]$ directly by using Theorem 4 rather than by using this last formula.

Example. In the case of the geometric distribution, where

$$p_r = (1 - a)\, a^{r-1} \quad (r = 1, 2, \ldots)$$

we have

$$G(x) = (1 - a)x/(1 - ax)\,.$$

Then

$$\sum_{N=1}^{\infty} E[C(N)]\, x^N = \frac{cE(t)\, x(1 - ax)}{(1 - x)^3}$$

so that $E[C(N)]$ is the coefficient of x^{N-1} in

$$cE(t)\,[(1 - x)^{-3} - ax(1 - x)^{-3}]\,.$$

It is found that

$$E[C(N)] = cNE(t)\,[1 + \tfrac{1}{2}(1 - a)(N - 1)]\,,$$

a result also given by Finch (4).

6. Types of replenishment policies

In the operation of a simple stockpile, as outlined at the beginning of § 5, there is a wide variety of replenishment policies which may be used. In this section several of these will be discussed. The reader who desires a more extensive account is referred to the book by Whitin (11).

In the classical system of stock control, an (s, S) policy of replenishment is used. In this a stock of initial size S is run down until the first demand which reduces the stock level to $s(< S)$ or less occurs. An order is then placed for an amount $S - s$, which arrives after some time τ, which may be a constant (including zero) or a random variable. During this time the stock level may or may not reach zero, and if it does reach zero a further order for an amount s is placed. It is clear that with this type of policy the stock level immediately after replenishment may be S or less than S but it cannot be greater than S. Partly for this reason the mathematical analysis of this type of policy is difficult and incomplete. However, the policy may be modified in a way which permits a deeper mathematical investigation. Suppose that when an order for replenishment is placed the size of the order is *unspecified*, and that after a time τ, when the replenishment may be effected, the stock level is restored to its initial value S. The system is then at a critical point in time. The future stock level is determined only by the fact that the level at that time is S and by the future pattern of demand; it is independent of the past history of the stock level. Such a point of time is called a point of *regeneration*, and when a system possesses points of regeneration, an extensive mathematical theory (the so-called renewal theory) is available for its analysis. This theory is, however, too advanced for this book and we shall confine our attention to some general remarks. For the interested reader who possesses the mathematical equipment necessary for an understanding of renewal theory reference may be made to the important paper, published in 1951, by Arrow, Harris and Marschak (1). In this paper, which is concerned with finding optimal values for s and S, it is shown that the expected cost of operating an (s, S) policy satisfies a renewal equation, which is actually solved. For the application generally of renewal theory to stock problems the reader is referred to the recent book by Arrow, Karlin and Scarf (2).

A variant of the (s, S) policy occurs when, given an initial stock S, a series of levels $s_1, s_2, ..., s_m$ are taken, where

$$S > s_1 > s_2 > ... > s_m > 0,$$

with the rule that as soon as demand reduces the level to a value below s_j an amount $s_{j-1} - s_j$ is ordered for replenishment of the stock. This may be called an $(S, s_1, s_2, ..., s_m)$ policy and the particular case of an $(S, S - M, S - 2M, ...)$ policy will be discussed.

Note that in the latter case replenishment orders are placed for equal amounts, M, at irregular times. In contrast to this a policy may be considered where an irregular amount is ordered at regular intervals of time, called the ordering cycle, and in this case the policy is referred to as an Ordering Cycle policy. At the end of each cycle the amount ordered equals the total demand during the cycle.

In a pioneering paper of 1946, Pitt (9) compares the (S, $S - M$, $S - 2M$, ...) policy with the Ordering Cycle policy. In each case delivery is supposed to occur at a fixed time T after ordering. An outline of Pitt's results will be given. Let policy A be the (S, $S - M$, $S - 2M$, ...) policy, and policy B the Ordering Cycle policy, where the cycle is of length M/c, c being the mean rate of demand. Then in both cases the mean size of a replenishment order is M and the mean interval between orders is M/c. It is supposed that the total demand follows a Poisson distribution with the parameter c, that is, that the chance that the demand is n in an interval of time t is $e^{-ct}(ct)^n/n!$. Pitt then proves that, if $f_n(t)$ is the probability that the stock level is n at time t, we have, for policy A,

$$f_n \equiv \lim_{t\to\infty} f_n(t) = \frac{1}{M}\sum_{i=0}^{M-1} g_{S-n-i},$$

where $g_n = e^{-cT}(cT)^n/n!$ if $n \geqslant 0$, $\quad g_n = 0$ if $n < 0$.

And, for policy B, where $f_n(t)$ itself does not tend to a limit as $t \to \infty$, it is proved that

$$f_n \equiv \lim_{\tau\to\infty} \frac{1}{\tau}\int_0^{\tau} f_n(t)dt = \sum_{i=0}^{\infty} Q_i g_{S-n-i},$$

where

$$Q_i = \frac{1}{M\, i!}\int_0^M e^{-y}y^i dy.$$

Now consider the two functions, $S^+(N)$ and $S^-(N)$, of N defined thus:

$S^+(N) =$ mean of the positive values of the stock level,
$S^-(N) = -$ mean of the negative values of the stock level.

It is clear that $S^+(N)$ increases and $S^-(N)$ decreases with increasing N. Also from the point of view of cost, the greater $S^+(N)$ the greater will be the cost of stock holding while the greater $S^-(N)$ the greater will be the loss of business (or goodwill), due to the inability to supply customers' demands.

A given replenishment policy may be represented graphically in the following way. Let P_N be the point whose coordinates are $[S^+(N), S^-(N)]$. Draw a smooth curve through the points $P_1, P_2, ..., P_N, ...$ as shown in Fig. 6

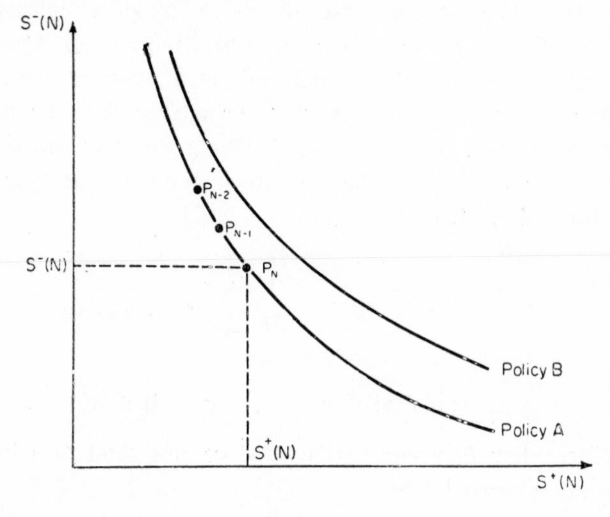

FIG. 6.

Since $S^+(N)$ increases and $S^-(N)$ decreases with increasing N, the curve is concave upwards as shown, that is $S^-(N)$ as a function of $S^+(N)$ is decreasing. It is this function, and hence the graph, which represents the replenishment policy. Now consider a second policy and its representative graph. If this graph lies above that of the first for all values of N, then we shall say that the first policy is the better of the two. Pitt shows that, in this sense, policy A

is better than policy B. The values of $S^+(N)$ and $S^-(N)$ may easily be derived. For, since f_n is the probability that the stock level is n, it follows that, for policy A,

$$S^+(N) \equiv S_A^+(N) = \sum_{n=0}^{\infty} n f_n = \frac{1}{M} \sum_{i=0}^{M-1} \sum_{n=0}^{\infty} n g_{S-n-i},$$

$$S^-(N) \equiv S_A^-(N) = -\sum_{n=-\infty}^{0} n f_n = \frac{1}{M} \sum_{i=0}^{M-1} \sum_{n=0}^{\infty} n g_{S+n-i}.$$

Also, for policy B, we have

$$S_B^+(N) = \sum_{i=0}^{\infty} Q_i \sum_{n=0}^{\infty} n g_{S-n-i},$$

$$S_B^-(N) = \sum_{i=0}^{\infty} Q_i \sum_{n=0}^{\infty} n g_{S+n-i}.$$

With these values Pitt shows that the point

$[S_B^+(N), S_B^-(N)]$ is above the point $[S_A^+(N), S_A^-(N)]$

in the sense that, for every integer N,

$$S_B^+(N) \geqslant \tfrac{1}{2}[S_A^+(N-1) + S_A^+(N)],$$

$$S_B^-(N) \geqslant \tfrac{1}{2}[S_A^-(N-1) + S_A^-(N)].$$

Thus the curve representing policy B lies above that representing policy A, so that the latter is the better policy. Expressed otherwise, this means that it is better to replenish in fixed amounts at irregular intervals rather than in irregular amounts at constant intervals.

7. A variant of the problem of Hammersley

In this section we consider a model which incorporates most of the features of both Finch's model (discussed in § 5) and Hammersley's model (discussed in § 4). It is a system with an $(s, s+S)$ type of replenishment policy, and as in the problem of Hammersley we consider the problem of finding the probability of exhausting the stock between succesive replenishments. This is not by any means the only problem, or even the main problem that would arise in a practical case, but we consider it because it is a natural extension of the problem of § 4.

Suppose that a stock of initial size, $s + S$, is run down as in the Finch model, by demands n_i, at the end of time intervals t_i ($i = 1, 2, \ldots$), these intervals having an exponential distribution of parameter λ, but that instead of replenishment immediately upon the stock level becoming zero, an order for replenishment is placed as soon as the stock level first reaches s or less. The replenishment arrives after a time τ, which is a random variable, and the amount of the replenishment is such as to restore the stock level to the initial size, $s + S$. The variation of the stock during a typical cycle is shown in Fig. 7. It is clear that such a cycle, where the mth demand is the first to reduce the stock level to $s - r$, where $r \geqslant 0$, is a Finch m-cycle, with an initial stock of size S, followed by a Hammersley cycle with an initial stock of size $s - r$.

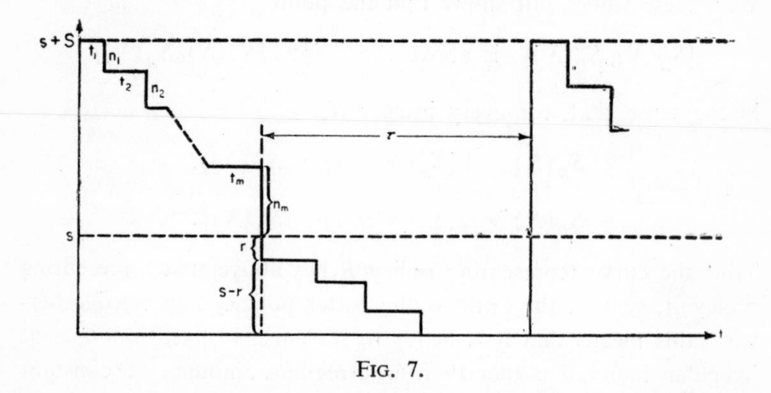

FIG. 7.

The problem we shall solve is that of finding the probability of running out of stock before a replenishment arrives. There are two stages. Firstly, we find a generating function for the probability, $P(r, m, S)$, that starting from a stock S, the cumulative demand reaches the value $S + r (r = 0, 1, 2, \ldots)$ in m but not $m - 1$ demands; that is

$$P(r, m, S) = P(S_m = S + r\,; \quad S_{m-1} < S)\,,$$

where

$$S_m = n_1' + n_2' + \dots + n_m .$$

This is Stage 1. Then, using Hammersley's result for an initial stock $s - r$, for $r = 0, 1, 2, \dots,$ we find a generating function for $Q(s, S)$, the probability of running out of stock before a replenishment arrives, given an initial stock $s + S$ and the policy of ordering a replenishment as soon as the level reaches s or less. This is Stage 2.

STAGE 1. The probability $P(r, m, S)$ satisfies a recurrence relation obtainable by noting that in the first trial demand may be for any number of units from 1 to $S - m + 1$ (if it is for $S - m + 1$ then the succeeding demands must be for 1 unit each). But it cannot be for more than $S - m + 1$ demands since there are definitely m demands. Also, if the first demand is for i units, this is followed by $m - 1$ demands starting from a stock of size $S - i$. Thus

$$P(r, m, S) = p_1 P(r, m - 1, S - 1) + p_2 P(r, m - 1, S - 2) + \dots + p_{S-m+1} P(r, m - 1, m - 1) .$$

Now, in forming a generating function for $P(r, m, S)$ we shall make use of the standard result,

$$\left(\sum_{r=1}^{\infty} a_r x^r\right)\left(\sum_{r=1}^{\infty} b_r x^r\right) = \sum_{S=1}^{\infty}\left(\sum_{r=1}^{S-1} a_r b_{S-r}\right)x^S ,$$

where $b_0 = 0$. For this purpose we must extend the recurrence relation for $P(r, m, S)$ to one of $S - 1$ terms, and this is an easy matter since, clearly, $P(r, m, S) = 0$ if $m > S$. Thus

$$P(r, m, S) = p_1 P(r, m - 1, S - 1) + \dots + p_{S-1} P(r, m - 1, 1) ,$$

and from this it follows that if

$$h_1(r, m, x) = \sum_{S=1}^{\infty} P(r, m, S) x^S ,$$

then
$$h_1(r, m, x) = \left(\sum_{i=1}^{\infty} p_i x^i\right)\left(\sum_{S=1}^{\infty} P(r, m - 1, S) x^S\right)$$
$$= G(x) h_1(r_1 \, m - 1, x) .$$

From this it is apparent that

$$h_1(r, m, x) = [G(x)]^{m-1} h_1(r, 1, x) .$$

To evaluate $h_1(r, 1, x)$ notice that

$$h_1(r, 1, x) = \sum_{S=1}^{\infty} P(r, 1, S) x^S ,$$

and $P(r, 1, S)$ being the probability of a demand $S + r$ in 1 trial is p_{S+r}. Hence

$$h_{.}(r, 1, x) = \frac{1}{x^r} \sum_{n=r+1}^{\infty} p_n x^n ,$$

and we have

$$h_1(r, m, x) = [G(x)]^{m-1} \left(\frac{1}{x^r} \sum_{n=r+1}^{\infty} p_n x^n \right) .$$

Now, writing

$$h_2(r, m, y) = \sum_{m=1}^{\infty} h_1(r, m, x) y^m = \sum_{m=1}^{\infty} \sum_{S=1}^{\infty} P(r, m, S) x^S y^m ,$$

it is easily found that

$$h_2(r, m, y) = \left(\frac{1}{x^r} \sum_{n=r+1}^{\infty} p_n x^n \right) \frac{y}{1 - yG(x)} .$$

Finally, putting

$$H(x, y, z) = \sum_{r=0}^{\infty} \sum_{m=1}^{\infty} \sum_{S=1}^{\infty} P(r, m, S) x^S y^m z^r ,$$

we have

$$H(x, y, z) = \frac{y}{1 - yG(x)} \sum_{r=0}^{\infty} \left(\sum_{n=r+1}^{\infty} p_n x^n \right) \left(\frac{z}{x} \right)^r .$$

If we now use the result

$$\sum_{r=0}^{\infty} \left(\sum_{n=r+1}^{\infty} q_n \right) t^r = \left(\sum_{n=1}^{\infty} q_n - \sum_{n=1}^{\infty} q_n t^n \right) / (1 - t) ,$$

it follows with $q_n = p_n x^n$ and $t = z/x$, that the generating function for $P(r, m, S)$ is given by

$$H(x, y, z) = \frac{xy}{1 - yG(x)} \cdot \frac{G(x) - G(z)}{x - z}.$$

STAGE 2. From the definition of $P(r, m, S)$ it follows that if $\Pi_r(S)$ is the probability that the demand, when it exceeds S, does so by an amount r (where $r = 0, 1, 2, \ldots$), then

$$\Pi_r(S) = \sum_{m=1}^{\infty} P(r, m, S).$$

The generating function for $\Pi_r(S)$ is now given by

$$\sum_{r=0}^{\infty} \sum_{s=1}^{\infty} \Pi_r(S)\, x^s z^r = H(x, 1, z) = \frac{x}{1 - G(x)} \cdot \frac{G(x) - G(z)}{x - z}.$$

To proceed, if (as in the Hammersley model of § 4) Q_{s-r} is the probability that, starting with a stock $s - r$, the level becomes zero before replenishment, the order for replenishment having been placed when the stock was $s - r$, and if $Q(s, S)$ is the probability that the stock level, initially $S + s$ with a re-order being placed when the level first falls to s or below, becomes zero before replenishment, then

$$Q(s, S) = \sum_{r=0}^{s} \Pi_r(S)\, Q_{s-r}.$$

Hence

$$\sum_{s=0}^{\infty} Q(s, S)\, z^s = \sum_{r=0}^{\infty} \Pi_r(S)\, z^r \sum_{s=0}^{\infty} Q_s z^s,$$

and it follows that the generating function for $Q(s, S)$ is given by

$$\begin{aligned} K(x, z) &= \sum_{S=1}^{\infty} \sum_{s=0}^{\infty} Q(s,S)\, z^s x^S \\ &= \sum_{s=0}^{\infty} Q_s z^s \sum_{S=1}^{\infty} \sum_{r=0}^{\infty} \Pi_r(S)\, z^r x^S \\ &= \frac{1}{1 - z}[1 - z\,\varphi\{\lambda(1 - G(z))\}] \cdot \frac{x[G(x) - G(z)]}{[1 - G(x)]\,(x - z)}. \end{aligned}$$

Example: In the case where the size of a demand follows a geometric distribution, $G(x) = (1 - a)\, x/(1 - ax)$, and if the time τ has an exponential distribution, $1 - e^{-\mu\tau}$, then $\varphi(z) = \mu/(\mu + z)$. It is easily found that

$$K(x, z) = \frac{(1-a)\, x(1-kz)}{(1-x)\,(1-az)(1-lz)} = \frac{x}{1-x}\left[\frac{1}{1-lz} - \frac{a}{1-az}\right],$$

where $k = \mu a/(\lambda + \mu)$, $l = (\lambda + \mu a)/(\lambda + \mu)$. Now $Q(s, S)$, being the coefficient of $z^s x^S$, has the value

$$Q(s, S) = l^s - a^{s+1} = \left(\frac{\varrho + a}{\varrho + 1}\right)^s - a^{s+1}.$$

8. Problems involving a lead time

In the practical operation of a stock holding it seldom happens that a replenishment may be ordered for immediate, or almost immediate, delivery. In fact, if the delivery is immediate, no useful purpose is served by holding stock, even when there is uncertainty about the demand, unless the cost of ordering is comparable with the cost of holding, when the lot-size formula of § 1, or one of its variants, is applicable. In the great majority of cases there is a time lag between the instant of placing an order and the instant of delivery. This lag, denoted by τ, is called the *lead time*, and while it may have a constant value in some cases, it is a random variable in many important practical situations. In fact τ may be a highly variable quantity such as, for example, where a raw material for stock has to be shipped overseas and is subject to transit delays not only on the sea but also between the production centre and the loading port and between the unloading port and the final destination. Moreover, in a case such as the one just cited, a great penalty may be incurred involving the cessation of production (of a finished material from the raw material) if the stock of raw material becomes exhausted through an unusual delay in delivery. The importance, then, of a realistic determination of adequate levels of stocks, particularly protective stocks, will be appreciated. In practice most levels are determined by trial and error, having regard to experience gained over a period of time. But there is no doubt that many stock piles are operated at levels in excess of those required for a reasonable protection against a run-out. The size of stocks held by industry is perhaps not very widely appreciated. A recent estimate (3) for the United Kingdom, gives a figure of £ 4×10^9, and it has been suggested that this could be safely reduced by about £ 10^9 "if the problems were tackled vigorously and scientifically". The reader who requires a critical practical appraisal of the situation may consult the paper by Duckworth (3). Here attention will be confined to a few problems where some specific questions may be answered by mathematical analysis; for it is our aim to demonstrate mathematical method. However the practical details surrounding any particular case must be taken into account when assessing a realistic stock level.

9. Problem 1

Suppose that a stock, of initial size S, is subject to a demand at a uniform rate r, and that when the level reaches a value s, to be determined, a replenishment order is placed for the initial amount S. The replenishment arrives after a lead time τ, which has the distribution function $F(t)$, and the stock level at the time of arrival of the replenishment is y_1, where clearly $s \geqslant y_1 \geqslant 0$. The stock level immediately after replenishment is $S + y_1$ and then

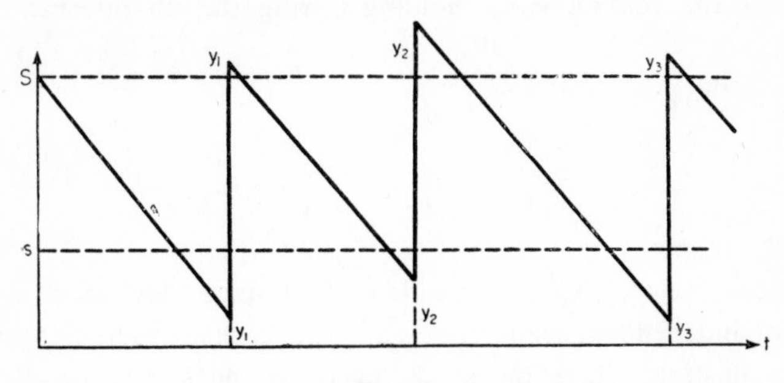

FIG. 8.

the stock is run down, as before, to the level s, when a second replenishment order is placed. The operation is continued, as before, and in Fig. 8 there is shown a graph of the stock level against time for the first few replenishments.

It is clear that the policy outlined is not of the type mentioned in § 6, where renewal theory may be applied, since the stock level immediately after replenishment is not constant but varies through the sequence $S, S+y_1, S+y_2, \dots$. On the other hand, since $y_i \leqslant s$, the stock level is never greater than $S+s$.

Let s be the stock level at which a replenishment should be placed, in order that the probability of exhausting the stock during the lead time τ, before the replenishment arrives shall have some prescribed value, ε. Since the rate r of demand is uniform the chance of exhausting the stock from the level s, before the replenishment arrives, is $P(\tau \geqslant s/r)$, that is, $1 - F(s/r)$. Hence s is determined by the equation

$$F(s/r) = 1 - \varepsilon.$$

We now consider the cost of stock holding. Let the time between the replenishment to level $S + y_{i-1}$ and level $S + y_i$ be called the ith interval ($i = 1, 2, 3, \dots$, and $y_0 = 0$). Then, since a uniform rate of demand is assumed,

(i) the average stock during the ith interval is $\frac{1}{2}(S + y_{i-1} + y_i)$,

(ii) the duration of the ith interval is $(S + y_{i-1} - y_i)/r$. Hence if c is the cost of holding unit stock for unit time, and C_i, is the cost of stock holding during the ith interval, then

$$C_i = \frac{c}{2r}(S + y_{i-1} + y_i)(S + y_{i-1} - y_i)$$

$$= \frac{c}{2r}(S^2 + 2Sy_{i-1} + y_{i-1}^2 - y_i^2).$$

Now the levels $y_1, y_2, \dots$ are independent since they occur at the ends of independent lead times $\tau_1, \tau_2, \dots$, each measured from an instant of time where the stock level has the constant value, s. Hence, on averaging the last expression, we have for the average cost $E(C)$ taken over an infinite number of intervals,

$$E(C) = (c/2r)(S^2 + 2SE(y)),$$

where $E(y)$ is the average stock level immediately before a replenishment arrives.

The value of $E(y)$ follows on observing that

$$y = s - r\tau \text{ for } \tau \leqslant s/r \text{ and } y = 0 \text{ for } \tau > s/r.$$

Then

$$E(y) = \int_0^{s/r} y\, dF(\tau) = \int_0^{s/r} (s - r\tau)\, dF(\tau) = sF(s/r) - r\int_0^{s/r} \tau\, dF(\tau).$$

But $F(s/r) = 1 - \varepsilon$ and

$$\int_0^{s/r} \tau\, dF(\tau) = E(\tau) - \int_{s/r}^{\infty} \tau\, dF(\tau).$$

Hence

$$E(y) = s - rE(\tau) + \left(r\int_{s/r}^{\infty} \tau\, dF(\tau) - s\varepsilon\right).$$

For $\varepsilon \ll 1$, $s/r \gg 1$ and hence the term in the bracket is very small. Hence we have

$$E(y) \approx s - rE(\tau),$$

or, in words, $E(y)$ is approximately the difference between s and the run-down of stock in the mean lead time.

We can now compare the cost of stock holding when τ is fixed with the cost when τ is a random variable. Let R be the ratio of the latter to the former, where, in the case of τ constant, the level s is fixed at $s = r\tau$, that is, at a level such that the stock is exhausted just at the moment of arrival of a replenishment. In this case the levels $y_1, y_2, \ldots$ are all zero and $E(C) = c\, S^2/2r$. Thus

$$R = \{S^2 + 2SE(y)\}/S^2 = 1 + (2/S)\, E(y) \approx 1 + (2/S)\,[s - rE(\tau)].$$

The factor $2[s - rE(\tau)]/S$ may be regarded as a measure of the extra cost involved in stockholding incurred by a desire to protect oneself against a run-out of stock at the level ε. In other words, if one stipulates that the probability of a run out shall be as low as ε, then the extra proportional cost to ensure this probability is $2[s - rE(\tau)]/S$.

Example: In the case where τ has the exponential distribution, $F(t) = 1 - e^{-\lambda t}$, the level s is given by $e^{-\lambda s/r} = \varepsilon$, that is, $s = (r/\lambda) \log (1/\varepsilon)$.

Let $\varepsilon = e^{-p}$, so that $s = pr/\lambda$. Now $E(\tau) = 1/\lambda$, so

$$R \approx 1 + (2/S)\,(pr/\lambda - r/\lambda) = 1 + 2r(p - 1)/\lambda S.$$

To take a numerical example, let $S = 100$ and suppose the rate of demand is 5 units per day, that is $r = 5$. Then the stock would become exhausted in about 3 weeks. If $\lambda = \frac{1}{2}$, so that the mean lead time is 2 days, then $s = 10p$ and $R = 1 + (p-1)/5$. If $p = 3$, then $R = 1{\cdot}4$ and $\varepsilon \approx 0{\cdot}05$, that is, there is, on average, a run out of stock about once in 20 periods of 3 weeks each. Thus to avoid running out of stock *on average* not more than about once in fifteen months the cost of stock holding is about 40% greater than in the case of a fixed lead time. If $p = 4$ the result obtained is that an increase of about 60% in the cost is required if a run out is to occur on average about once in three years. Note that $s = 30$ when $p = 3$ and $s = 40$ when $p = 4$.

10. Problem 2

We shall discuss now a problem of optimization where there is a fixed lead time and where the replenishment policy is to place an order every time a demand occurs, the size of the order being equal to the size of the demand. This problem was discussed by Whitin and Youngs (12), and is a good example for illustrating the methods we have developed.

Suppose that demands occur at unit intervals of time, $t = 1, 2, 3, \ldots$, the demand at time r being n_r. Let a replenishment order for an amount n_r be placed at this time, the amount being delivered at time $r + \tau$ where τ is a fixed integer, so that there is a constant lead time, τ. The variation of the stock level is shown, in a typical case, in Fig. 9, where the initial level is S.

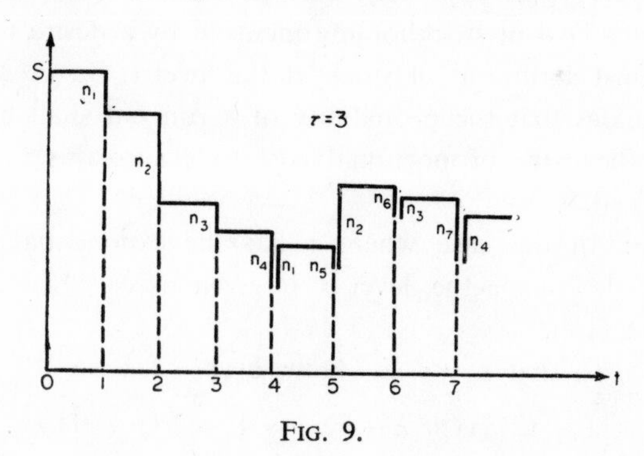

FIG. 9.

It is assumed that the sizes of the demands follow a Poisson distribution of parameter λ, that is

$$P(n_r = j) = \mathrm{e}^{-\lambda} \lambda^j / j! \quad (j = 0, 1, 2, ...).$$

Let

$$\sigma_\tau = n_{t+1} + n_{t+2} + ... + n_{t+\tau}.$$

Since σ_τ is the sum of τ demands from a Poisson distribution, the distribution of σ_τ itself is independent of t and is Poisson, with parameter μ where $\mu = \lambda\tau$, that is

$$P(\sigma_\tau = j) = p_j = \mathrm{e}^{-\mu} \mu^j / j! \quad (j = 0, 1, 2, ...).$$

Let $S(r)$ be the stock level at time r. Then

$$S(r) = S - (n_1 + n_2 + ... + n_r),$$

if $r \leqslant \tau$, while if $r > \tau$,

$$S(r) = S - (n_1 + n_2 + ... + n_r) + (n_1 + n_2 + ... + n_{r-\tau}) = S - \sigma_\tau.$$

It is to be observed that $S(r)$ may take a negative value.

The problem to be solved is this. If, when an actual stock exists, that is $S(r) > 0$, there is a holding cost c per unit per unit time, and if, when there is a negative stock, $S(r) < 0$, there is a penalty cost of being out of stock, equal to π per unit per unit time, find the optimal level, S, for the initial stock, that is the level which, over a long period of time, will minimize operating cost.

It is necessary to introduce two auxiliary random variables, $x(r)$ and $y(r)$, where

$$x(r) = \text{amount of actual stock at time } r$$

$$= \begin{cases} S(r) \text{ if } S(r) \geqslant 0 \\ 0 \quad \text{if } S(r) < 0, \end{cases}$$

$$y(r) = \text{deficit at time } r$$

$$= \begin{cases} 0 \quad \text{if } S(r) > 0 \\ -S(r) \text{ if } S(r) \leqslant 0. \end{cases}$$

The probability distribution functions of $x(r)$ and $y(r)$ are clearly given by

$$
\begin{aligned}
P(x(r)=0) &= P(S-\sigma_\tau \leqslant 0) \\
&= P(\sigma_\tau = S) + P(\sigma_\tau = S+1) + \dots \\
&= p_s + p_{s+1} + \dots \\
P(x(r)=j) &= P(S-\sigma_\tau = j) = \begin{cases} p_{S-j} & \text{if } S \geqslant 1,\ j=1, \dots, S, \\ 0 & \text{if } j > S \geqslant 0, \end{cases} \\
P(y(r)=0) &= P(S-\sigma_\tau \geqslant 0) \\
&= P(\sigma_\tau = 0) + P(\sigma_\tau = 1) + \dots + P(\sigma_\tau = S) \\
&= p_0 + p_1 + \dots + p_S, \\
P(y(r)=j) &= P(S-\sigma_\tau = -j) = p_{S+j}, \text{ if } j = 1, 2, 3, \dots .
\end{aligned}
$$

Now let $C_n(S)$ be the total expected cost of operating the system over n units of time from $t=r$ to $t=r+n$. At time $r+k$ there is a penalty cost $\pi y(r+k)$ and a holding cost $cx(r+k)$, so that if $E\{y(r)\}$ and $E\{x(r)\}$ are the expected values of $y(r)$ and $x(r)$, we have

$$C_n(S) = \pi n E\{y(r)\} + cnE\{x(r)\} .$$

But

$$E\{y(r)\} = \sum_{j=1}^{\infty} j p_{S+j}, \quad E\{x(r)\} = \sum_{j=1}^{S} j p_{S-j},$$

so that $C_n(S) = nC_1(S)$ where

$$C_1(S) = \pi \sum_{j=1}^{\infty} j p_{S+j} + c \sum_{j=1}^{S} j p_{S-j}.$$

In view of the relation $C_n(S) = nC_1(S)$ it is evident that the expected cost of operating over a long period will be minimal for the value of S which makes $C_1(S)$ minimal. Such a value of S satisfies

$$C_1(S) \leqslant C_1(S \pm 1).$$

Now it is easy to show that

$$C_1(S) - C_1(S-1) = c - (\pi + c)(p_s + p_{s+1} + \dots),$$

and that

$$p_s + p_{s+1} + \ldots = \mathrm{e}^{-\mu} \sum_{j=S}^{\infty} \mu^j/j! = 1 - \mathrm{e}^{-\mu} B(S),$$

where $$B(S) = 1 + \mu + \frac{\mu^2}{2!} + \ldots + \frac{\mu^{s-1}}{(S-1)!}.$$

On observing that $B(S)$ increases with S and that

$$C_1(S) - C_1(S-1) = \pi + c)\,\mathrm{e}^{-\mu} B(S) - \pi,$$

it follows that $C_1(S) - C_1(S-1)$ increases with S. Hence either

(i) $C_1(1) - C_1(0) > 0$, that is $\mathrm{e}^{\mu} < 1 + c/\pi$, in which case the optimal S is zero so that it is best to hold no stock, or

(ii) $C_1(1) - C_1(0) \leqslant 0$, that is $\mathrm{e}^{\mu} \geqslant 1 + c/\pi$, in which case the optimal S is determined by

$$C_1(S) \leqslant C_1(S \pm 1).$$

In the latter case it is easy to show that the optimal value of S satisfies

$$\frac{1}{B(S)} \geqslant \frac{1 + c/\pi}{\mathrm{e}^{\mu}} \geqslant \frac{1}{B(S+1)}$$

The value, or values, of S satisfying these inequalities may be found numerically for given values of c, π and μ.

Generalization. An important feature of Problem 2 is that the replenishment policy is such that the stock level at time r is given by

$$S(r) = S - \sigma_\tau,$$

where σ_τ is the *total demand during the lead time*, which extends from $r - \tau$ to r. This leads to the following generalization of the problem, where the lead time τ itself is a random variable and where demands may be made at *any* time.

Let the initial stock level be S and let the previous replenishment policy be followed, namely that whenever a demand is made an order is placed for an amount, equal to the demand, to be delivered after a lead time τ, which may be a random variable. Further let σ be the total demand occurring in the lead time, τ, and let $f(u)$ be the probability density function of σ, that is

$$P(u \leqslant \sigma \leqslant u + \mathrm{d}u) = f(u)\,\mathrm{d}u\,.$$

Then it is clear that the stock level $S(t)$, at time t, is given by

$$S(t) = S - \sigma.$$

If, as before, there is a holding cost c per unit per unit time, when $S(t) > 0$, and a penalty cost π per unit per unit time, when $S(t) < 0$, the optimal value of S may be found as follows. If $S(t)$ has a value between x and $x + \mathrm{d}x$, where $0 < x < S$, the holding cost per unit time is cx. The probability of this is $P(S - x - \mathrm{d}x < \sigma < S - x)$, that is $f(S - x)\,\mathrm{d}x$. If $S(t)$ has a negative value, in the range $(-y, -y - \mathrm{d}y)$ where $0 < y < \infty$, there is a penalty cost πy per unit time. The probability of this is $P(S + y < \sigma < S + y + \mathrm{d}y)$, that is $f(S + y)\,\mathrm{d}y$. Hence the average cost per unit time is φ where

$$\begin{aligned}\varphi &= c\int_0^S f(S - x)\mathrm{d}x + \pi\int_0^\infty y f(S + y)\mathrm{d}y \\ &= c\int_0^S (S - x)f(x)\mathrm{d}x + \pi\int_0^\infty (y - S)f(y)\,\mathrm{d}y\,.\end{aligned}$$

Now

$$\frac{\partial\varphi}{\partial S} = c\int_0^S f(x)\mathrm{d}x - \pi\int_0^\infty f(y)\mathrm{d}y = (c + \pi)\int_0^S f(x)\mathrm{d}x - \pi\,.$$

Thus the optimal value of S is the root of the equation

$$\int_0^S f(x)\,\mathrm{d}x = \frac{\pi}{\pi + c}\,.$$

In the case of the exponential distribution, where $f(x) = \mu e^{-\mu x}$, it is easily found that the optimal value of S is given by

$$\mu S = \log_e(1 + \pi/c)\,,$$

while in the case of the Erlangian distribution, E_2, where $f(x) = (2\mu)^2 x\,e^{-2\mu x}$, it is found that S is the root of the equation

$$e^{2\mu S} = (1 + \pi/c)(1 + 2\mu S).$$

If we use the fact that the equation $e^x = k(1 + x)$ has a solution when $k > 1$, it is seen that the equation for S always has a solution (given, graphically, by the intersection of the curve $y = e^x$ with the line $y = k(1 + x)$, where $k = 1 + \pi/c$ and $x = 2\mu S$).

REFERENCES

1. K. J. ARROW, T. E. HARRIS and J. MARSCHAK, "Optimal inventory policy", *Econometrica*, XIX (1951), 250–72.
2. K. J. ARROW, S. KARLIN and H. SCARF, *Studies in the mathematical theory of inventory and production*, Stanford Univ. Press, 1958.
3. E. DUCKWORTH, "Stock control problems: some fallacies in their current treatment". *Appl. Statist.*, IX (1960), 133–51.
4. P. D. FINCH, "Note on a stock model", *Operat. Res. Quart.*, **9** (1958), 1–8.
5. J. M. HAMMERSLEY, "Storage problems". *Math. Ann.*, **128** (1955), 475–8.
6. R. R. P. JACKSON, "A stock model", *Operat. Res. Quart.*, **7** (1956), 140–2.
7. H. G. JONES, A. M. LEE and D. T. STEER, "Oxygen for steelworks use", *Iron and Coal Rev.*, CLXIX (1954), 613–7.
8. J. F. MAGEE, *Production planning and inventory control*, McGraw-Hill, N. Y., 1958.
9. H. R. PITT, "A theorem on random functions with applications to a theory of provisioning", *J. Lond. Math. Soc.*, XXI (1946), 16–22.
10. M. SASIENI, A. YASPAN and L. FRIEDMAN, *Operations Methods and Problems*, John Wiley, N. Y., 1959, Ch. 4.
11. T. M. WHITIN, *The Theory of Inventory Management*, Princeton Univ. Press (1957).
12. T. M. WHITIN and J. W. T. YOUNGS, "A method for calculating optimal inventory levels and delivery time", *Nav. Res. Logistics Quart. 2* (1955), 157–73.

INDEX